David

GOD'S CHOSEN CRUCIBLE

David

GOD'S CHOSEN CRUCIBLE

A Biblical historical novel

BY JOSEPH GANCI

First, get thee knowledge, and then get thee wisdom, and with all that getting, get thee understanding.
Understanding is the practical application of both wisdom and knowledge.
Where there is much wisdom, there is much sorrow. Where there is knowledge, there is much learning. Where there is much understanding, there is much compassion.

Love is the encouragement of the beloved to seek their highest and best spiritual life, and by doing so, increase your own.

Please save me from the heathen and the evil design.
Please save me from the atheist who knows no God of any kind.
Please save me from the agnostics who can't make up their mind.
But, most of all, save me from the self-righteous who are convinced of their superior connection to the infinite divine.

I believe in God as I believe in the Sun, not because I can see the Sun, but because I can see everything because of the Sun. And so, too, His Son the Holy Messiah, the Prince of Peace, wonderful counselor. The only begotten of the Father, my savior, my redeemer, my friend, Jesus the Christ.

TABLE OF CONTENTS

Table of Contents

PROLOGUE

David, God's Chosen Crucible

A Biblical historical novel

This book covers First Samuel 23:26 through Second Samuel 12:31. The story picks up where *Gideon, the Sound and the Glory* leaves off. This work and my subsequent novels came about when a dear friend asked me, "What happens next? After reading part five of Gideon: The Sound and The Glory."

As a novelist, I take full advantage of poetic license to depict events using details consistent with the human mind, will, and emotions. As practically as possible, I lay out the geography, local customs, rumors, legends, and the ever-dark spin of power politics. In King Solomon's immortal words, "There is nothing new under the sun."

The beginnings and the endings remain consistent with the Biblical narrative. This work and all my works are for the sole purpose of glorifying God. I hope that the reader will confirm my understandings for themselves, by searching out the scriptures, and so delve deeper into the mind of God while developing an underlying appreciation for Biblical history.

David means "beloved." He was the great-grandson of Ruth the Moabite and Boaz the Ephrathite. David was the seventh and youngest son of Jesse the Bethlehemite. He was the child most often called upon to perform chores left undone or shunned by his older brothers. Farming and sheep ranching were this young man's lot. He lived only a half-day's journey south from the bustling city of Jebus, or Jerusalem. Early on, King Saul lost favor with God, and his punishment was a long time coming. God had bided his time waiting for His chosen successor. It finally happened years later in Jebus. Samuel declared that Saul's kingdom and his dynasty would be lost forever and claimed by another and the least likely of men.

God commanded Samuel the prophet to journey to Jesse the Bethlehemite's house, and there he would separate and then anoint the next king of Israel.

The rod of Samuel knocked, echoing against Jesse's cottage door. The prophet announced his intentions to all present, and then he had the sons of Jesse parade ritually before him.

Then Jesse called Eliab (meaning "God is the father." He was also known as Elihu, meaning "My God is He"), his first and oldest son, and made him pass before Samuel. When Samuel, the prophet, looked on Eliab and saw that he was tall and muscular, he said, "Surely, the Lord's anointed is before me."

But the LORD said unto Samuel, "Look not on his countenance, or the height of his stature; because I have refused him:

for the LORD seeth not as man seeth; for man looketh on the outward appearance, but the LORD looketh on the heart."

After Eliab, Abinadab, the second son, passed, so they moved in turn and in that order: Shimea, the third son, Nethanel, the fourth son, Raddai, the fifth son, and then Ozem, the sixth son. Eliab was downcast from not being chosen. He moved quickly around in the shadows and passed again before Samuel's aging eyes. Eliab's desperate ploy went unnoticed in the dim light of the shepherd's windowless hut, but it confirmed, once again, that Eliab, the oldest son, was not to be the chosen one. All he had accomplished was a mounting resentment against David, his baby brother, and falsely increased the numbers of sons that are counted righteous in the house of Jesse.

"The LORD hath not chosen these." Samuel said unto Jesse, "Are here all thy children?"

Jesse answered, "There remaineth yet the youngest, but he is out keeping the sheep."

And Samuel said, "Send and fetch him: for we will not sit down till he comes hither."

Jesse sent for him and brought him in. Now he was ruddy and withal of a beautiful countenance, goodly and handsome. The LORD said unto Samuel, "Arise, anoint him: for this is he."

Then Samuel took the horn of oil and anointed him amid all his brethren: and the Spirit of the LORD came upon David from that day forward. So, Samuel arose and went to Ramah.

And so, David's destiny became the stuff of legend.

David's youthful exploits as a giant killer and a warrior prince of Israel strengthened his reputation. But, on the other hand, some saw him as a cunning and clever usurper of King Saul's crumbling dynasty. On numerous occasions, David narrowly evaded Saul's trackers through the Ziph Forrest. Finally, by God's grace, David escaped to the barren Maon wilderness and then to the lush oasis of Engedi in the eastern desert of Judah, the western slopes of the Dead Sea.

Here is where our saga continues.

CHAPTER ONE

A Trackless Wilderness

David was looking down at the lush green thicket from the heights of a crescent ridge. His eyes combed the wooded floor below, watching for signs of life and pondering his next move. He was thankful for his brief reprieve from the maddening and murderous pursuit of King Saul. But rapidly, the thick, brushy wilderness of Ziph, once overflowing with wild game, had become scarce from overhunting. The once-secure haven for the warrior prince and his six hundred roaming warriors could now quickly become a death trap if they lingered there any longer.

"Abiathar, bring forth Gideon's Golden Ephod. I need to voice my petition to God," David thundered.

"Coming, my prince," replied the everobedient priest. "I have been lugging this weighty vestment longer than I care to mention. The linen Ephod is much lighter, and it serves the same purpose. I don't know why you would use this generations-old relic, passed down through my fathers at the Tabernacle at Nob, and displayed beside the oil cloth-wrapped sword of Goliath.

You know that it has been a bane and a curse to anyone who has possessed it. But, honestly, it is time to pass it through the fire. We need the gold and the gemstones that Adorn the breastplate of judgment necessary to feed and supply our men to thrive and fight another day."

Abiathar's timely counsel echoed David's nagging thoughts. "I agree it is time to reduce that burdensome icon to ensure our continued survival. But, for now, give me the claimed holy channel to God."

After donning the heavy chest-piece and harness, David gritted his teeth and dropped to his knees; this was his practice in such weighty matters.

Sharp pebbles dug deep into his bare skin, but he was determined to maintain his humble position in the hopes of currying favor with God until his needed answers were forthcoming.

He knelt in silence for what seemed like a time without end in the unforgiving sun.

Rivulets of sweat dripped from David's forehead. His knees ached from his lengthy stay on unforgiving rocky ground. David reasoned that a prayer of deliverance was ever more powerful when heightened by pain and suffering.

"Oh, Lord God Adonai, your anointed King Saul hunts me like a ravenous dog. I can find no peace. My men hunger and are faint. The Ziphites who people this land threaten our very existence and have already turned against us and seek my destruction. My path is unclear, and I hunger for compassion. Lord God, send me a sign directing my course, and deliver me from my oncoming enemies. Provide the meat needed to sustain the army of God that we may do Your will more perfectly with an eye single to Your glory. Hear my prayer, Master of All Creation, that I may know Thy will in all that I must do and where I must go to fulfill my destiny witnessed by your prophet Samuel's holy anointing oil of separation. Amen."

David's "amen" was still ringing in his ears when an outpost guard shouted, "A man approaches from out of the north," rousing the whole of the sleepy encampment.

David lifted himself and bolted a span to acquire a choice view, attempting to get a closer look at the speedily advancing intruder. Slowly, the outsider's face came into focus, the familiar likeness of a secretive go-between, Malek, the messenger. David exhaled with a sense of relief that his petition was about to be answered.

As usual, Jonathan's trusted servant would impart Saul's lethal intentions, allowing David to keep one step ahead of Saul, his relentless mortal enemy.

"Malek!" David shouted. "How is it that you always seem to find my hiding place?"

"It is not I, as it is Prince Jonathan and his multitude of household spies who report back to him on all his father's evil plans and designs. Because of his love for you, he watches his father's every move. The Ziphites came to Gibeah, telling Saul that you hide in their wooded strongholds, even on the hill of Hachilah, even to the south of Jeshimon. They have invited Saul to come down, and they will do their part to assist in your extinction. King Saul is on the move and headed this way, confident in your capture. I fear I am late in my warning of the coming rout."

A long shofar blast rocked the camp. An alert outpost guard signaled the near approach of Saul and the army of Israel.

3

"Well, Malek, it appears that Saul has also used you to help to ferret out my exact whereabouts. We cannot fight here in the Ziph. We must seek higher ground that we can better defend. What say you, Malek?"

"Please forgive me, Prince. I was in such a rush I neglected to cover my tracks and failed to keep a wary eye to my back and carelessly marked my trail."

"Never mind about that. We need to resolve our immediate problem rather than waste time second-guessing fate's unpredictable nature. So let us flee straight away. But where?"

Malek advised, "The only high ground within reach is the wilderness summit of Maon. It is roughly five miles from here, and you will pass through the rich fields of Carmel before reaching the rocky heights of the Acrabbim precipice. But, unluckily, with Saul closing in, we have no other choice. The wilderness of Maon is rocky and barren. Perhaps it might throw the Ziphites off our scent and give us some breathing room before going to the oasis of Engedi for shelter and rest. However, to go to Engedi from here leaves you vulnerable and too long exposed in the open."

"Maon? Malek, that is undoubtedly the last place I would have considered; it is an uninviting and lifeless desert. Yet, do not forget for a moment that it is a stark and barren wilderness. There is no game there, only serpents and bats."

"Exactly. Saul will have his army needing feeding, and so for him, it is also the last place that he would wish to engage in a siege. You need to travel fast and light, but bring what meat you can carry. Scorch the land as you pass through, forcing all remaining prey to scatter. If Saul has no food, it will force him to go back to his pomegranate court at Gibeah."

"There is no time to consider any other options, Noble Prince, as it might already be too late to evade Saul's onslaught. But, most importantly, bring as much water as you can manage. The elevation is hot and arid, and finding fresh drinking water will be a challenge."

"Like it or not, it sounds like you are coming with us, Malek."

"Yes, I shall, for I have no choice in the matter. I am a dead man. If I return to Saul, I will be labeled a traitor. The king will dispatch me to my grave, even before Jonathan could make a plea for my life."

"You are better with us than beheaded—that is, if you prefer my company to the company of maggots and worms."

David smiled and rallied his army for the perilous journey. Having been rousted many times in the previous month, they were ready in short order. At last, Abiathar, the Priest, and David's three older brothers, Eliab, Abinadab, and Shammah, assembled for final orders.

David sounded: "My brothers, now the Ziphites have turned against us and have joined forces with Saul to help rid themselves of our presence. Saul, and his entire army, are swiftly approaching to trap us and ensure our ruin. As he has sought my destruction over the mountain pass and desert coast, his desire to murder me has only increased. So, we need to run and push our people to the wilderness in the desert of Maon. We will carry what little food we have and as much water as we can carry."

All four men looked dumbfounded at the proposal. Then, finally, Eliab spoke up, "You must be joking, right? Maon? It is nothing but a barren rock occupied by snakes and scorpions, and littered with boulders. Even the jackals and vultures give it a wide berth."

David remained steadfast and said, "There is nowhere else that is close enough and affords us a measure of protection. Its hostile nature and elevation are suddenly to our benefit. It is hard to track over stone, and it would be hard for Saul to support his army for an extended period. So, all we must do is hold out until Saul gets weary of falling rocks and tumbling boulders and he retreats to Gibeah. Then, once again, we are freemen. We need to trust in God to provide for our needs in the wilderness. So let us make haste. There is no time to quarrel or debate. Our very lives hang in the balance."

Eliab dug in as much as he dared. "I think Maon is a foolhardy detour, my brother. I would think that we would first go to the oasis of Engedi. There are wild goats, deep wells of water, and dates by the bucketful. But I will concede and go where you lead, little brother. We have survived so far by following your instincts. But I believe this time you are mistaken, my headstrong sibling."

"Hearken to my words, big brother. If we stay here, we will be fighting both the Ziphites, who know our every hiding place, and Saul's army, with little or no cover. Engedi is too far a trek and leaves us vulnerable to attack. The Ziphites will not hold back in a fight. We have no choice. Saul is hot on our heels and will be here within the hour." David stressed every word to put a fine point to his argument: "We need to avoid a battle that we cannot win."

Eliab relented, surrendering in silence.

David breathed out, "Very well. We depart. Sound the horn. We leave at once."

A triple shofar blast brought the army of misfits, debtors, and adventurers quickly to the ready. "Men, friends, and brothers in arms. We must leave straight away at the double-quick or face destruction. The king's army will be here within the hour. We are but a few miles from Carmel—and, from there, we must endure a grueling climb to the stony peaks of Maon. The rocky ground will make it near impossible to track, and it is the least likely guess of our hiding place."

Finally, one man from the ranks yelled out, "David, you are our fearless captain and the anointed king of Israel. We will follow you to Hell's hearth and perdition's flame. So, lead the way, and we will follow." All cheered and began their life-and-death dash, with David spurring on his faithful men.

The march became a fast-paced sprint. David's army was soon in the lush hills of Carmel. David's brothers paused only slightly to ignite fields afire, but the grass was too green to burn entirely and only accomplished a cloaking smokescreen. Still, the climb to the peak was a strenuous ordeal. Saul and the warriors of Israel were hot on their heels and were delayed only briefly by the acrid fog of smoldering greenery.

The final climb was three miles of sharp, sandal-shredding rocks to the summit. Once David and his men reached the top, they prepared for battle by piling stones and loosening boulders. However, Maon was not as bleak as first expected. Instead, there were signs of life from the sparse shrub needed for small campfires, and a freshwater spring bubbled up in a hidden gulley.

The sun was about to set without a sign of Ziphite trackers or Saul and his vengeful army. David remarked to Eliab, "Well, it seems that we have eluded our pursuers. The smokescreen must have slowed Saul down just long enough, and the hard ground left no telltale markings."

Dawn of the first day ended, and the last of the meager rations echoed in the empty bellies of David's men. David summoned Abiathar. "Priest, it is time to put Gideon's Golden Ephod through the fire. God will provide, but first, we turn to Him and ask, and then He will see to our needs. So, burn the damned thing, and let us trust in God and Him alone."

Suddenly, an eagle-eyed sentry rang out, "Saul and the army of Israel approach. They cover the hills below and are more numerous than a plague of locusts."

David, steadfast and determined, drew his sword, his words echoing off the chasm walls: "Men, our time has come to prove our faith in God. Prepare for battle. Let the fall of stones and dislodged boulders do their crushing dirty work."

CHAPTER TWO
Escape and the Dead-Sea Ambush

Saul hoisted his spear as if piercing the heavens. He cried out mightily, unable to contain his jubilation, and shouted, "Who is this David that has eluded me through dense forests and mountain passes? I have him now—completely and surrounded. All I need to do is to tighten my fist on this, my phantom nemesis. Then, once again, my dynasty will be secure, forever; Praised be the Name of our Lord and our God, Adonai. All that prevents me is the Sela-hammahlekoth or the Rock of Separation, but not for long." The thinly-veiled obstacle was not much more than a steep boulder-laden ravine.

David's last refuge in the wilderness of Maon was now entirely encircled. Saul filled his lungs to give the final command and shuffled his feet in a victory dance. He savored the sweetness of his long-anticipated victory, licking his lips.

Then an unexpected and fast-approaching messenger, waving and yelling, broke Saul's outcry and upset the moment of his relished vengeance.

Malaki, the messenger, was both swift and alert. He knelt at Saul's feet while gulping hard for air and breath. His lungs were burning hot from his breakneck pace, and he barked, "Your Majesty, Israel is under threat of invasion. The Philistines were alerted to your far-flung expedition to capture the renegade son of Jesse. Even now, their armies have crossed over our borders and are in full battle array. The heathen threatens Israeli settlements, and if you do not come straight away, it will be too late. Your kingdom and Israel, my king, will be pillaged and sacked."

Malaki gulped in another lungful. "Axle, the Philistine general, leads the marauding invaders. They are raiding and burning villages and towns without pity or mercy. They advance north and east with their goal to capture Gibeah, your home and capital. But, Your Majesty, the distance is fifty miles over uneven ground. You and your army must travel—both day and by night and without rest or sleep to have even the slightest chance of repelling the enemy offensive. Your march must be at a double-quick pace; it is your only hope to delay the intruders' cunning invasion. I fear, sire, that we might be already too late."

Saul's nostrils flared as he pointed the tip of his spear at the rocky rift and thought that he could hear David's mocking laughter carried on the wind. He cocked back his arm and relived the exact moment when he narrowly missed David with his spear at his festive banquet table.

Saul growled, "Almost—but foiled again, and by less than a hair's breadth." Saul's frustration sprouted the all-too-familiar wings of anger and despair.

Saul, stunned by this bitter summons, rallied his captains of hundreds and three captains of thousands. Saul spiked his spear into the ground, causing the tip to spark on the exposed bedrock, and he thundered, "Israel is in dire peril, and our absence has left our watchtowers empty and vulnerable to the Philistine horde. We must make haste to return and repel the merciless pagans at our gate. The lives of our women and children depend on our rapid response. So, too, the salvation of all Israel."

Malaki, putting decorum aside, called out, "Your Majesty, please pardon my interruption."

Saul impatiently barked, "Speak on, and speak up; we have no time for idle chatter."

But Malaki persisted. "I made all haste to return and report. I found empty grain barges and sailed down the Yam HaMelah (Salt Sea); it eliminates two full days from an overland trek. Before leaving Israel, I had heard of several boats that carry on a steady trade between Moab and Canaan. I took a chance, trusted in God, and ran like the wind the fifteen miles to the salten pier. I was duly rewarded and found several barges that had just unloaded their full-grain cargo. They were coming about, attempting to return to the Far Eastern shore. I hailed them and tempted the vessel captains with the bribe of gold and the promise of favor in the name of King Saul. Most agreed to sail to the southern shallows on a rescue mission to save Israel. We now have enough ships but only enough room to carry about one thousand men at arms. They wait upon your boarding and orders."

Saul tried to maintain his composure but was puzzled and stood motionless and silent.

Finally, breaking the stillness of Saul's awkward uncertainty, Malaki forced down his fear and said, "We wait on your command, sire."

Saul shook his head, stepped up onto a nearby rock, and roared, "Malaki, you take too much upon yourself, for this adventure of yours will cost me your weight in gold."

Changing his tone, he smiled broadly and continued, "Well done, young Captain of One Hundred—your promotion is valid immediately, as you might have just saved the nation of Israel. I am reluctant to dismiss my sure capture of the runt of the house of Jesse, but Israel's protection is my duty and divine mandate. We will use your tactic to our full advantage. We will cram as many men as possible aboard the waiting barges. There remain fifteen miles between us and your waiting barges; we must make all possible haste, and there are no moments to squander." Saul called out and commanded, "We will separate our fighters. The oldest and most experienced soldiers will board the ships. The remaining younger men that are light of foot will navigate the hills and the valleys. I do not doubt that they will be hard-pressed to keep pace with General Abner's stamina, for there are none that can match Abner's speed and endurance once he puts his mind to the task of impending combat. Abner's young men will leave immediately, and before the rest of us, old men have made our trek to the Salten Sea scows. We depart with all speed to the beach of the Dead Sea. With a bit of luck, the flatboats will accommodate the needed number of men. My loyal Abner, you will take the remainder of two thousand young men who are able and fit and follow hard upon the fastest possible route to my center place in Gibeah. I will bring as many as we can stow on the waiting makeshift ferries. We will get far ahead of the advancing Philistine army and then hold them at bay. You, Abner, and your troop will come up from the south and be at their backs. The enemy will never expect a fresh army, and just at the most opportune moment, we will tighten our grip like a vise. Abner, when you approach my skirmish lines, launch three fire arrows. I will return a matching signal when I am ready to begin a full-scale frontal assault—allowing you ample time to position your men to attack the Philistine center. We will squeeze the Philistine mongrels between two Israeli armies.

"Our ploy will take the Philistines utterly by surprise. They will not expect a new legion to attack their rear and flanks simultaneously without pause or reprieve. They will be overwhelmed—and they will run back to Philistia, or we will quickly destroy them. Are there any questions? Now is the time to ask."

A cheer went up, acknowledging confidence in a plan that seemed to promise a sure-fire success.

Upon reaching the beach, the barges appeared as promised. Malaki took a deep sigh of relief once the mastheads peeked over the crest of the hill. Captains started shouting orders, and the assembly split into regiments as if cut with a knife. One thousand experienced veterans were indeed all that could board the ship safely. The sea captains welcomed Saul and his men with all due respect. Saul took the captains aside and said, "You barge captains are the saviors of all Israel and my kingdom. A fortune in gold and my undying respect will confirm my gratitude."

A leathery and battered-looking skipper took a step out of the crowd. "I am Captain Chobel." He and all about him bowed low. The captain, in a deep monotone, voiced, "The barges ride high above the waterline this far south more so than in the northern reaches of the Dead Sea; the salt is so thick here you can almost walk from shore to shore without getting your feet wet. We can stack your men in like stalks of wheat; these ships, after all, are grain haulers, so they will have to stand tall. They will have to sleep in shifts; most will have to hold fast for the journey. The wind favors us, but the current is against us. We will have to row to make up the difference, for this will be an oversized load. We need to depart, just as soon as you can, sire. Have your men board immediately, for time and tide, and the ebb and flow of creation is solely by the will of God."

Saul commanded his men to board quickly. Abner's army was already off on the run, kicking up clouds of dust and disappearing into the distance. The barges were not accustomed to such weight and sank to just inches above the gunwales. The gross weight had to be evenly divided to avoid capsizing. Some men pressed uncomfortably hard against the railings. The barges were now a moving mass of tightly packed humanity.

Melach, the leading barge's master, remarked to Saul that the wind could pick up with a bit of luck, and they could make their landing the next day at eventide. The closest and best disembarking point would be at the most northern beach on the Dead Sea, and from there, it would be a fifteen-mile overland trek to the city of Jebus (that is, Jerusalem). Saul prayed that speed would get him between Gibeah, his capital, and the approaching Philistine army, rapidly approaching from the south and west.

The first waves tossed the tightly packed crafts, causing the morning's undigested breakfast to rise and spew out of gagging mouths. Many quickly discovered the windward and leeward meanings as their vomit splattered back into their startled faces. The wind was with them, but the current was against them. The sails began to billow. The conflict between wave and wind made a miserable rolling and bounding. Saul was now second-guessing himself as to his decision. The men soon grew accustomed to the harsh conditions. Food and fresh water were scarce, forcing a fast lasting the entire voyage. Reluctantly, Saul announced in a loud and booming voice to all within earshot from the height of the prow of the leading craft, "Men of Israel, take heart, and make no mistake these vessels were God-sent. A moment's misery will only help to ensure our triumphant victory. How so, you might ask? The depth of the descent will be equal to the height of the rise. We will, men of Israel, rise above and conquer our enemies. We will return once again to the capture of the renegade son of Jesse." A muted cheer quickly vanished on a stiffening breeze. Israel was both on the march and the sea to a hopeful but uncertain victory.

CHAPTER THREE

Abner, the Kin of Kings

Abner, the youngest son of Ner, was born unexpectedly late by the grace of God in Ner's declining years. Abner was the baby brother of Kish, the father of Saul. Saul grew from humble obscurity to become the power-hungry mad king of Israel. Abner grew to maturity at the same pace as Saul, eye to eye with his nephew, playmate, and closest friend.

Abner's cohort of two thousand youthful warriors was itching for a fight; each man pressed hard to match the swift strides of Abner. Abner was surprisingly light on his feet for a man of such girth and weight. Cautiously, Abner held back his steps to avoid outdistancing some of the younger men who struggled to keep up with the general's blistering pace.

Malaki, Saul's messenger who had found favor with a field promotion to captain of one hundred, could match Abner stride for stride. The two could effortlessly speak without the slightest loss of step or breath. "General," Malaki interrupted Abner's concentration and huffed, "with such a late start, we are soon to lose daylight. Running in the dark will only ensure injury from potholes and cracks on this uneven ground."

"True enough, Malaki," Abner breathed out his agreement. "I feel light as a feather, strong as a lion, and eager as a bridegroom when pounding the ground." Abner grinned, giving a knowing wink.

"I could smoothly run or make love till the break of day, as I have done so many times both as a warrior and a lover." Abner continued to the following hilly rise only to catch the last glorious rays of a dying sun. Abner's spear poked at the twilight of heaven, signaling a halt to their double-time parade. He filled his lungs to be heard over the heavy breathing, panting, and sputtering of his advancing army. Abner bellowed, "We will camp here for the night, men. Captain Malaki, deploy your sentries; build your fires, but eat sparingly from your rations. Food will be scarce, and we are moving too fast to live off the land."

Most men were fast asleep as soon as they took their weight off their blistering feet and lay their heads upon the hard, unforgiving ground. Abner gained a little reprieve from sleep and often rested in meditation and conversation. He was always alert and found vitality with the rising of the sun.

Maliki moved closer to Abner, gathering warmth from the flickering campfire and his commander's endless strength. "General, please excuse my ignorance, but my recent and unexpected rise in the ranks has left me in the dark as to many things, and if it is not tiresome or unfitting, I would like to know more about my commander, on whom my life will soon depend."

Abner, an already imposing figure, stretched, boasting his full length and stature. His shadow grew threatening against the dying rays of sundown. Sweat and caked dust dotted his mantle.

"So, you would have me speak of myself so that you might decide the likelihood of your survival under my command in our coming life-and-death battle?"

Malaki looked up and met his commander's eyes and uttered, "True enough, my general, but I would like to get to know you on a deeper level. People speak of you as legendary, the very man who now stands before me. My ears itch to hear of your adventures, and your heroic deeds spoke firsthand. The scratch of your daring feats can only heighten my admiration for King Saul's ever-loyal right-hand man."

Abner was pleased with the request, evidenced by an unfamiliar broad grin of satisfaction. "You appeal to my vanity."

Malaki stoked the fire to ward off the approaching night chill.

"I will spin you a tale of how childish dreams become the sterner stuff of men. I am Saul's uncle; most think we are cousins because we were born on the same day. We grew up eye to eye in Gibeah, the promised portion of Benjamin. Our land is sparse and not suited for farming; we learned the art of war even as small children. The howling wolves were often our midnight lullaby. Often we hunted all day for fresh meat in the unexplored regions of the forest. We were not concerned about finding shelter in caves or under outcroppings. We were content sleeping under the stars with a roaring campfire; it became second nature to us. Saul and I were much more substantial and taller than most of the other children in our village. We both had a robust and weighty stature, and this invited many toughs to challenge us; it seemed as if one of us was constantly fighting to help the other get out of trouble.

"One night when the moon had lost its glow, the fog engulfed us in a soaking drizzle. Our spark would not ignite the wet wood. Try as we might, neither twig nor grass was dry enough to kindle. We were in the open, without fire or shelter. On that fateful night, a pack of greedy wolves, desperate and hungry, caught the scent of our sweat from our many vain attempts at fire-starting. The wolves were dark shadows slowly circling, looking for an opening, their eyes red with fury. A colossal figure, evidently the pack's leader, showed his stark white fangs as big as daggers—dripping saliva in anticipation of his coming feast.

"Saul immediately swung around, and back to back, we faced the wolf pack, our spears projecting deadly menace. We growled, first me, then Saul, and then together at the looming danger. The pack quickly surrounded us, their circle ever-tightening, snarling, and snapping. They became more daring with each pass. I told Saul, 'Our best chance is to kill the leader, but he will be the last to attack. He will only come in for the kill when he feels safe, just like most kings. That brute will be the first to eat, which is why he is so big. If I see an opening, or if you do, nephew, take it—it might be the only chance we get. So, break ranks and lunge, for our life and breath will depend upon us surpassing the ferocity of our adversaries. One brute took a running start from out of the dark and leaped full out; I was able to catch him mid-flight on the point of my spear. In the time it took me to dislodge my weapon, another two snarling beasts knocked me off my feet and were upon me. I drew my dagger and gutted the one and then dispatched another. Saul made quick work of the second killer. We were back standing, spinning and jabbing; the rest of the pack was now wary. They were holding back their attack from our sharpened and determined fury. The leader either had to rally his troops with a show of strength or tuck his tail and scurry back into the cold, wet underbrush with wounded pride and empty bellies. The leader's blood was up; he was not retreating. Two wolves, one on each side of him, came first. The larger of the two chomped down on Saul's leg. The lesser wolf tried to knock him down; I braced Saul against the weight of both. The leader then came full-on after Saul. I spun my spear around and jabbed; it caught him in the throat, and he went down with gurgling and whimpering. The remainder of the pack shrank back into the gloom. I used my tattered shirt to wrap Saul's gaping wound, and we held fast through the night. The pile of dead wolves gave us a little warmth, and we had some raw wolf meat for our supper.

"Dawn broke clear and bright. Nature's majestic living sketch always seems sharper after a narrow escape from death's dark door. We made a promise that morning that we would always be loyal to each other, come Hell's pit or riptide's high water.

"So, young Malaki, you can now see that the story of Abner is also the story of Saul, for we are more than kin and greater than brothers. Our lives remain forever yoked by fate and blood. And so now it is time to rest. We race to meet another pack of predators ready and snarling for the fight."

"Yes, General, and thank you for your inspiring tale. I will dream of snarling wolves and iron-clad Philistine chariots.

Goodnight, my general, for my confidence now waxes certain of our upcoming victory."

The cock's vain challenge to the sun could not compete with the shofar's hot horn blast in raising young men from the dead sleep of fatigue. The pangs of morning hunger then pushed aside their fleeting dreams. Reluctantly the young men rolled out their meager rations of unleavened bread and salted meat; these had to sustain both body and soul until effective scavenging could fill empty bellies.

Abner paced and bellowed, "Form ranks, each man to his place, and be quick about it. We are burning daylight! Drink sparingly, men. Our next water is seven leagues over the dry and dusty ground. Squeeze your water skins for every drop as we go. If your lips start to crack, put pebbles in your mouth. Breath as much as you can through your nose, and so, no idle chatter."

The breakneck pace quickened; each man became of one mind and one stride. Abner's legs were a blur of determination. Pauses were few and far between. Only when men started coughing and hacking up dissent did Abner order a short rest.

And yet, as they rested, Abner's voice rang out, "Our urgency, men, could very well mean the life or death of Israel. Saul's force is sailing on the water; they will reach Jebus, or Jerusalem, well before us, and he will start his maneuver of a defend, delay, and retreat strategy. Saul will lure them in, starting with his defense of the ruins of Nob. He will then draw the Philistines north and

21

up to the heights of Gibeah. We will, in time, come up from behind the Philistine marauders. We will attack them violently when they are halfway up the steep embankments. As you can imagine, our success or failure depends on the swiftness of our travel."

Abner called for silence, and he knelt upon the rocky ground. His voice echoing to the hearing of all the young men, he prayed, "Brave warriors, fate will find us in the coming struggle to repel heathen invaders from our nation's holy borders. Our cause is just, and our task is from God. I pray that our eyes be single to His glory, that we obey His commandments, and follow all His statutes. May our resolve never fade or falter. We will be triumphant, and our victory is certain for our marvelous God goes before us. Adonai, our God, Your will be done."

Darkness finally came, and the army halted for the evening. The full moon reached its pinnacle, and all the bright stars sparkled in the sky. The army gathered strength from Abner's prayer and a much-needed rest that was both just and vital.

CHAPTER FOUR
Through Small Acts, Great Things Come to Pass

David could not believe his eyes. He was more shocked than surprised and shook his head, utterly confounded. He looked down from the rocky heights, only to see Saul and the army of Israel departing in a rush for unknown parts. No rock, spear, or arrow had crossed over in anger. There were no massive boulders dislodged to deter or discourage—an overwhelming attack that never happened and, by all reasoning, a disaster in the making. The grievous battle had mysteriously halted even before it had begun. But, why?

The last flaxen threads from Gideon's golden ephod melted down into Abiathar's brimming melting pot. All twelve gemstones were pried loose from their breastplate settings. The cursed artifact, created with the best intentions, had brought death and woe to all that possessed it, spanning generations. The Baal-Berith, or the Lord of the Covenant, was now reduced to bullion for food, wine, and weapons.

Abiathar called out to David, "Gideon's ephod is no more."

The last of the vestment vanished in the fiery crucible, and at that very moment, Saul's overwhelming force began a hasty departure.

David joyfully confessed, "I don't believe in accidents. I see God's hand always working behind the scenes, His wonders to perform—if I do not get in His way by exercising my will or challenging the commandments. All things work for good for those who love Adonai, the one true God."

David called forth his family for counsel: his three brothers Eliab, Abinadab, Shammah, and his three nephews Abishai, Joab, and Asahel. Abiathar, the Priest, also came along.

Raising his hands to the heavens, David began, "We have witnessed a divine intervention. God has saved us from certain destruction. Even now, praise and gratitude are necessary steppingstones ensuring the success of our next adventure. There is no time to linger. We must, with all due haste, plan our departure and next destination."

Eliab shook his head and curiously questioned the prince. "I thought that we had already decided on Engedi [or the fountain of the kid], my brother. There are seven waterfalls, two natural freshwater springs, and year-round wild ibex goat herds, guaranteeing a plentiful supply of meat and milk. In addition, there grows an oasis of date palms ripe with sweet goodness. There are sheepcote caverns that seem to go on forever, some large enough to shelter our 600 vagabond warriors. We will also be close to Hebron, where we can trade gold and gems for wine, weapons, and needed supplies."

David sheepishly smiled and said, "Yes, older brother, it was all but decided that Engedi was the obvious choice. If it is so predictable, then Saul probably will, in time, come to the same conclusion. I fear that he is determined and will not give up the chase until one of us is dead. Besides, we do not know what grave pressing matter interrupted his long-sought-after capture or how long it will be before he resumes the hunt, if ever. So let us trust in fate and seek refuge and rest under the wings of our almighty God. Unless someone here has a better idea, let us prepare to eat fresh meat, rest, and take a refreshing bath."

Asahel quipped, "A bath, uncle? It seems that spring has come early this year." A subdued chuckle made it around the circle.

The distance to Engedi was just over the next horizon. The trek, although short, was deliberate and grueling. Trying to achieve the fastest route over broken ground was fraught with rocky crags and steep-sided ravines. As a result, the forward scouts came across many dead-end trails that led into box canyons.

The 600 followed a labyrinth of trails and dried riverbeds until they finally crested the last wilderness ridge. The army, as one man, acquired the welcome view of the long-awaited oasis sanctuary. The faint and thirsty men then broke ranks, ripping off their filthy rags and dashing headlong to the inviting spring-fed pool. The onslaught scattered a herd of startled ibex. David dismissed all decorum; he stripped down and joined the frolic, splashing in the life-giving water. His three brothers, as well as his loyal nephews, sheepishly looked at each other. Then, with a smile and a shrug, they disrobed and dove right in, washing away rank and Maon's choking dust. The men romped and played, half-submerged in the sweet water spring of salvation. Then, after a reviving soak, and when all had had their fill, every man's attention turned to the demanding growl of empty bellies.

25

David, sensing the distress of his men and suffering from pangs of hunger himself, began organizing the encampment. He put his dusty clothes back on and said to the gathered men:

"Joab, take forty of your best hunters and bring us meat. The ibex herd we had startled has gone to ground, but would not stray very far from this, their water source. I believe that many ibex kids remain scattered in the underbrush. Their tender sweetmeat will be a succulent feast, perfect for roasting. Gather up all you can kill or capture, as we have 600 starving souls to manage. Asahel and Abiathar, take sixty men and fan out. I need you to forage for dates, nuts, and berries. Gather up palm leaves for carrying and for cover if the caverns prove uninviting. Abishai and I will take ten men to search the caves and hollows. The army needs shelter from the bitter cold, searing heat, and frequent dust storms. Abinadab, take twenty men, circle the refuge from here to the edge of the Dead Sea, and report back all that you witness. Keep a wary eye for intruders, particularly Ziphite trackers and anything you deem as hostile or unusual. Finally, Shammah and Eliab—organize the remaining men to hone their axes, gather wood, and start warming campfires while creating a secure boundary for our first night at rest. Are there any concerns or questions?"

The matter hung in an uneasy silence, until one soldier yelled, "When do we eat?"

David reacted by saying, "No man here is hungrier than I. We will feast when our borders are secure and there is fresh meat on the spit. So put your back to the task at hand, and forget the weak inner man. Our survival depends on our shared will to overcome and thrive against all odds."

Names and commands at once rang out, dampened only by the rumbling waterfall. Soon every man was in motion, bringing food, fire, and order to confusion.

David, Abishai, and their twenty-man scouting party sparked their moss-wrapped torches and went searching for protection against the harsh desert climate. They diligently searched every hollow that dotted the forward slope, but all were too narrow and shallow, suitable for only a few dozen men at best. Finally, after many hours, the scouting party was slowed to a crawl by hunger, fatigue, and the approaching sundown. Just before turning back, a lone scout cried out, "A widemouthed chamber." David and Abishai rushed over, and turning a corner, David began, "There it is—a sizable tunnel hopefully leading to a secure hollow. Perhaps there is also a deep recess where all the men can rest protected from the weather. A large cavern is what I was hoping for, a place big enough to provide an inner sanctuary. Let us explore further."

Entering the fracture, the smell of ancient mold was potent and inescapable. The temperature drop was immediately noticeable while the dimming outside light thickened the dark inner shadows. David and Abishai's torches produced a fiery glow that danced against the inner walls. The sandy floor had some bird, bat, and rat skeletons scattered all about. On closer inspection, a second darker opening presented itself, protected by a gray-bearded desert tarantula. Abishai instinctively picked up a hefty stone to smash the creature to bits. He cocked back his arm, threatening destruction. The spider, sensing danger, reared up on its back legs in a defensive posture. David caught his nephew by the wrist and commanded, "Drop the rock." Abishai looked puzzled but did as ordered. David scowled at his sister Zeruiah's oldest son and began a scolding, "Why are you so quick to kill one of God's lowly creatures that mean you no harm? Besides, it is we who have invaded the spider's domain. We are guests in his house, and you would repay his hospitality with a violent death? Let our host go free and remain nimble and fill the measure of its creation as God intended."

"Alright, uncle, as you wish. Spiders are such creepy and alien insects. It seems unsettling just knowing that we share the same ground, but I will adhere to your wise counsel."

The tarantula, no longer threatened, dropped down and slowly crawled off, disappearing into a nearby crevice.

The scouting party headed down the connecting corridor, torches blazing, stirring bats and rats unaccustomed to a human invasion. The company trekked through a winding passageway until the cave majestically opened to a grand domed cavern. It had a small opening in the upper layer, giving a view of the night sky.

David was delighted and exclaimed, "Perfect—there is enough room for a herd of sheep and all 600 men. We can build fires here, and water, meat, and sweet dates are all within reach. We will have access to the Dead Sea and its salt in abundance. Hebron is close enough to buy weapons, bread, and wine. It is God's will that we are here at this time so that we can rest in His hands and regain our strength."

CHAPTER FIVE
The Blind, the Lame, the Deaf, and the Dumb

Saul's salt-encrusted barges made their landfall; the wind and the tide had favored Israel's timing. Some of the aged soldiers were green from the constant rolling and churning seasickness.

Saul cried out, unable to hide a touch of a smirk. "We have conquered our first wave of challenges, men. Now it is only two days' march to Gibeah." The steady land under their feet gave natural strength to quivering legs and knocking knees. Jerusalem would be in sight within a few hours.

Saul called forth his captains for final instruction. The king first addressed Acaph, his most loyal and senior captain. "Gather all your men in ranks; the sun is setting, and our timing is more than perfect. We could not have wished for a better position. We will approach the city at dusk, blinding the Philistine spies and their searching eyes. The Jebusite fortress [Jerusalem] will afford us bread, wine, and sweetmeats. We will rest this night on hay-filled couches. The house of Jebus and the tribe of Benjamin and Judah have a long-standing and beneficial treaty; we occupy a full city quarter and have access to merchants, gates, wine, and water. It is an open city as long as all groups remain peaceable and act within Jebusite law and conventions. My compound is a mile from the main gate. The stables and the stars will afford comfort and rest so that we may gain the needed strength. The food will be plentiful. We will roast the fatted calf but will ration the wine sparingly. We have a man's work before the cock crows."

A low rumble of disappointment was quickly overpowered by the slap of leather on metal and by the slap of marching sandals.

Soon the king's army was through the high gates of Jerusalem and was shuffling through its narrow streets and alleyways. The gates of Saul's villa swung open, saluting his approach. Saul's chief advisors stood anxiously in attendance. They had nervously gathered, hoping that their urgent life-and-death message signaled that an invasion was in progress and that the warning was timely. They were praying that Saul and the army of Israel would make all possible haste to repel the Philistine marauders from Israeli borders before the kingdom of Jacob was lost forever.

Saul's chieftains greeted the king and his weary army with raised spears, drums, and shofar horns. Chief Maher embraced the king and took a knee in homage. "Your Majesty, we are amazed as to the speed of your arrival. Surely God has put wings on your feet. If I might speak, sire?"

Saul nodded and said, "By all means, but keep it short—my men and I starve."

"Where is chief captain Abner and the rest of the army?"

Saul winked as he said, "I have a revealed strategy that I believe to be a winning combination," and then he raised his voice, breaking a long silence. "All my chieftains and captains are invited to my banquet table. But only after all our men have been fed and bedded. The two things I miss most when on these extended campaigns are my wife Ahinoam's down-filled bed and the privacy of my cool, marble-slab summer parlor. But, speaking of nature's call, that is now demanding my undivided attention. So I had put off my relief until this very last moment, knowing full well that I would soon reach my personal and private chamber. It is the only place where I can take a breath and collect my thoughts undisturbed."

He wanted to make an impression on the seriousness of his orders, so Saul stretched to his full height and stature. "Make sure all the men are supplied with rations and water aplenty. We depart before sunrise. Let us organize now, and before we take our rest, reducing the fumbling delays of darkness long before our pre-dawn departure."

Chiefs, servants, and captains began shouting orders and commands, and fires were hastily stoked to cook and ward off the night's bone-chilling gusts. Finally, the cadre was left to feast with the men and ensure that only the smallest ration of wine would be allowed, the generous portion set aside for rank and privilege. Every last-minute detail was made secure, and every needful thing remained within reach even for a blind man when groping in the dark.

Saul's banquet table overflowed with delicious meats, dark red wine, and nervous conversation. All of Saul's captains and chieftains entered in ones and twos until the great hall filled. Ushers quickly found each man his chair. The closest seats to the king were a sign of rank and importance in descending order.

Then the king banged the iron end of his spear on the polished stone floor, bringing the chatter and clatter of the anxious gathering to order. Saul paused in the silence until every eye was upon him. He tilted his spear to the horizon, creating a deadly and demanding pointer. "Men, you are this day the hope of Israel and the strong right arm of Adonai, the one true God. We are here on God's errand. Let us pause in remembrance of our fallen comrades—Let us pray to You, Adonai, for this excellent food and drink that You have generously provided through Your endless bounty, which will nourish our minds and strengthen our bodies. May You defend our homeland that You had bestowed upon the twelve sons of Jacob, also known as Israel, through and with Your perfect wisdom and endless mercy, rescue Israel from the heathen Philistine invaders. Bless our campaign with rapid success, and know that all glory in battle is Yours, forever and ever, the one true God, Yahweh."

The hungry men then swallowed down succulent flesh and splashed fresh wine in their cups. The conversation was marked by grunts and burps and with the clatter of swords and daggers. Soon, some loud laughter trickled in as the wine made cowards heroes and heroes into gods, with legendary tales to tell.

Again, Saul brought the noisy commotion to order with the blunt end of his ceremonial spear.

"I have good news," Saul bellowed, and the hall fell silent. "My spies and scouts have confirmed that the Philistine army is approaching from the west and south of Jebus. We will leave before daylight and brace for our first encounter north at the ruins of Nob, and then we will stage a calculated retreat to the hills of Gibeah. We will then defend against the invaders' offensive, all the while withdrawing to the very heights. Then, from the same peaks, we will make our final stand. This strategy should prevail by God's will and grace. Abner and the bulk of the army are now marching at a forceful stride, all trying to keep up with Abner's renowned breakneck pace. If our strategy is correct, we will give his army enough time to flank the Philistines from the sides and rear.

"Men," Saul paused—in a dramatic reflection until every ear was at the ready. "We will then charge our adversary, using the downward slope like an overpowering falling boulder, gaining speed and force. We are determined to drive the enemy back into Abner's pointed spears and his young, strong warriors. Are there any questions? Now is the time to voice them."

A dead silence prevailed, and there was not a word, cough, or errant sneeze; then a spontaneous banging on the wooden table ensued until reaching a deafening crescendo of approval.

"Very well," Saul continued, "we will toast to our victory; see it in your minds and your hearts as vivid as these cups of wine. So, you orderlies, fill the cups of these thirsty warriors for one last round before we rest to regain our strength." Saul raised his cup, and before it touched his lips, he lowered his wine and uttered, in a loud voice, "We praise the God of our fathers for our victory over all the enemies of Israel." Every cup was hoisted and drained to the dregs. Everyone followed when Saul took back his seat.

A newly made captain named Elias stood up on his chair to be recognized. He had to shout to be heard over the din and distance. "Your Majesty, I understand that you know Torah scripture and ancient history."

Saul nodded and acknowledged the inquiry with a personal sense of accomplishment. "What is it, Elias? I learn best when teaching and preaching God's law."

Immediately the room went still. "Your Majesty, upon entering the marketplace and the city center, there is a statue prominently placed for all to witness. It was of two men on a single pedestal. One man was blind, for his eye sockets were deep hollows. The other man was lame and seemed to have a withered hip. The lame man rode on the back of the blind man and held his hand directing their travel. Their mouths appeared forever opened, as if speaking of something both dire and important that needed proclamation. In the dark, I could barely make out a brazen plaque installed at the base of the idols, but I could not make out so many words, for we were passing by so quickly and in the dim torchlight. It appeared to be written both in the Amorite language, as well as in our holy tongue of Hebrew."

Saul renewed his memory from the question; he was well versed in the subject and was more than happy to take center stage in a packed room of captains and chieftains. So, the king stood up and braced himself for his performance, and he motioned for all to remain seated.

"Thank you for the question, my young captain," Saul said, then he paused for effect. "While I answer, I shall allow the wine to continue to flow if done quietly. One last story before we take our rest."

There were smiles throughout the great hall as the king took a long, deep breath and began. "It all started with our father Abraham and his needful purchase of the cave of Machpelah for Mother Sarah when she died. Father Abraham needed a place where she could find peace and rest. An angel of the Lord had earlier whispered in Abraham's ear. The cave of Machpelah was the place where our first parents, even Father Adam and Mother Eve, lay sleeping until judgment. That cave was the gateway to heaven. Abraham, in a vision, entered the cave, where he found Father Adam and Mother Eve upon their beds as if asleep. Father Abraham knew that he must obtain the refuge for Sarah's and his resting place, whatever the cost. Abraham approached the sons of Heth, who were the sons of Canaan, the sons of Ham, the son of Noah.

"Abraham spoke gently of his need to secure a plot for his wife, the love of his life, even Sarah, to be her final resting place with room enough for himself and his posterity. All the sons of Heth were compassionate to his request. The sons of Heth offered the cave without cost or price to the stranger in their midst. His plea touched their hearts.

"Father Abraham was both learned and wise, for the finger of God had touched him many times. Father Abraham thanked the brothers for their kindness, 'My heart enlarges with your generosity and compassion, but I can only accept your offering with a value of consideration of my own, to you, the sons of Heth. Would you please receive my 400 pieces of silver to bind this agreement and seal my good claim for all time and eternity?' This matter includes Ephron's field, which the son of Zohar the Hittite had found in Hebron.

"Like most things dealing with property, there was another claimant, which was the house of Jebus. The Jebusites insisted it was their land, which is why Heth's sons offered it for free. The Jebusites took pity on the patriarch and required no money. Still, they refused to relinquish their claim until Abraham had sworn an oath that, when his descendants conquered the land of Canaan, they would spare the city of Jebus [Jerusalem] from capture by force of arms. Jebusites realized that Abraham's posterity would one day become a powerful and great nation. Abraham had no choice in the matter, and so he agreed and took their oath, saying, 'I Abraham, ben Terah, Ur of the Chaldeans, bring to bear my sacred covenant and oath that my future posterity will not by force of arms capture Jerusalem or the ancient city of Jebus. With this pledge and promise, the Jebusites release all rights and claims to me and my future generations, securing the cave of Machpelah forever.' The Jebusite scribes recorded the promise in detail.

"Abraham secured his purchase of the cave of Machpelah by a formal deed also signed by four witnesses: Amigal, son of Abishua the Hittite; Elihoreph, son of Ashunah the Hivite; Iddon, son of Ahira the Gardite; Aḵdul, son of Abudish the Zidonite.

"In addition to Father Abraham, Isaac, Rebecca, Jacob, and Leah also found their resting place within the cave in due course. After Jacob's burial, and to this very day, it is called The Cave of the 'Double Tombs,' or 'The Tomb of the Patriarchs.' After Jacob's burial, the Jebusites decided to inscribe Abraham's oath on a brazen idol as a permanent reminder that Father Abraham's pledge would remain through the ages. Firstly, Isaac was Abraham's anointed son, and he went blind before he died; then Jacob, also known as Israel, and Abraham's grandson, was lame after wrestling with an angel and forever limped on his hip. The brazen idol is now prominently displayed in the marketplace to attest to Father Abraham's vow that there will be no attempts at a forced invasion of Jebus by the future generations of Abraham, forever."

Saul sat down, indicating he had completed his story. Elias was the first to stand up and heartily pound his approval on the table. The rest of the company eagerly followed. Then Saul rose and gave the slightest bow, relishing his well-deserved applause. The king was quite pleased with himself and then quieted the room with a few modest taps of his spear.

Saul began, "Thank you for acknowledging my grasp of our ancient history. Now, there is a connecting tale that you might find of equal interest." Saul's eyes glistened as he continued. "Jacob desired to make peace with his warlike brother, Esau. Jacob gathered all the riches he had inherited from their father, Isaac. With help from his mother, Rachel, Jacob had tricked the old, blind Isaac into blessing him as his heir. Through this action, Jacob received the blessing of the priesthood and all of Isaac's worldly goods. Now, Esau had already traded away his birthright for a bowl of lentils, never considering the consequences of his childish actions. Jacob, even decades later, became fearful of his deception and constantly worried about his brother's vengeance. Jacob sent a message to Esau, agreeing to meet him to mend fences. Jacob brought the total amount he'd inherited with his deception, hoping that Esau would forgive his life-changing trickery. Jacob split his caravan three times, and even at that, an angel had to wrestle with him all night for him to continue and move forward.

"Jacob met Esau in the agreed-upon location and found his brother Esau to be open to reconciliation. Jacob kissed Esau with a holy kiss and brought forth the bounty of all his inheritance. On the third night of their reunion, Jacob approached Esau with a proposition.

"'It is good to have my brother back," Jacob said, "for our voices and words come from one tongue. My dear brother, it gives me solace to be in your presence. Esau,' Jacob continued, 'I wish to purchase from you and for a hefty price of 400 pieces of silver, for the off chance that I might find rest with father and grandfather in the cave of Machpelah. Who can tell when their time may come, even if I am still in Canaan, Egypt, or perhaps in some other distant realm? Likely I shall be eaten by wild beasts or drowned in a river and washed out to sea, for who knows our destiny? So, brother, you see, that this request is more for my peace of mind than for something that may never come to pass.'

"Esau nodded. It made perfect sense, and so he agreed to Jacob's timely and convenient proposition. 'I have 400 men in arms to pay and to feed. Your offer of 400 pieces of silver could not have come at a more opportune moment.

"Jacob's reply was restrained jubilation. 'Well done, my brother. I have a scribe to scribble down our arrangement, if it is agreeable to you, my loving brother. This formality will avoid any future confusion.' And so, the bargain was struck, signed, and witnessed.

"Jacob lived in the land of Egypt for seventeen years after Joseph rose to prominence in the house of Pharoah, and the days of Jacob and the years of his life were 147 years. Before his death, Jacob had Joseph and his other sons swear that his body would lie forever in the cave of Machpelah in Hebron. There was great sadness and grievous mourning at his death, and all his sons set out for the cave carrying Jacob's anointed funeral bier.

"Esau heard the news, for he lived in Mount Seir, and he came down with his sons and all his people and all his household, a people exceedingly pious, and they came to mourn and weep over Jacob. So, Joseph and his brothers brought their father Jacob from Egypt, and they went to Hebron to bury Jacob in the cave by his fathers.

"The procession came unto Kireath-arba to the cave, and as they came, Esau stood with his sons against Joseph and his brothers and blocked the entrance, saying, 'Jacob shall not find rest therein, for it belongs to our father and us.' And Joseph and his brethren heard Esau's sons' stern words, and they were furious. Joseph approached Esau, saying, 'What is this thing which you have spoken? Admittedly, my father, Jacob, bought it from you for great riches after Isaac's death. Five and twenty years ago, he purchased it from you and your sons, and their seed after them, all rights and privileges.' Joseph looked Esau in the eye and challenged his uncle: 'Jacob bought it for his sons and his seed after him for an inheritance forever, and why do you speak these things this day?'

"Esau responded, 'You speak falsely and utter lies, for I did not sell anything belonging to me in all this land. Neither did my brother Jacob buy anything from me in Canaan.' Esau, building on an old man's fury, shouted, 'You were not there. Do you have proof of these hearsay accusations?' Joseph looked puzzled at his uncle's remarks. 'I have seen such a document, Esau. My father had made plain these things with you in the record of the purchase. Besides, the very said agreement was testified by witnesses, for it was with us in Egypt.'

"Esau continued his desperate bluff and answered, 'Bring up this phantom document, and prove all your fantastic claims.'

"Joseph called upon Naphtali, his brother, and said, 'Go quickly as the wind to Egypt. Bring back all the records. I need the cave purchase records, both the sealed and the unsealed files. I also need all the proof of Jacobs's birthright. Make haste!'

"When Esau saw that Naphtali had gone to fetch the records, he knew soon enough that his bluff would be made hollow. So then, Esau and his sons increased their resistance against the procession. Violently, Esau and all his people revolted against Joseph and his brothers and began to battle.

"Chushim, the son of Dan, was with Jacob's sons, but he was about 100 cubits distant from the place of battle. Chushim remained with Jacob's bier to guard it. Chushim was deaf and dumb—but he fully understood the violence of fierce contention among fighting men. With hand gestures and facial expressions, he inquired, 'Why do you not bury the dead, and what is this great commotion?'

"They enacted Esau's words, and Chushim ran directly to Esau during the battle, where he slew Esau with a sword. Chushim took a mighty swipe and cut off Esau's head. The head rolled down a steep embankment into the mouth of the disputed cave. When Chushim did this thing, Jacob's sons prevailed over the sons of Esau, and the sons of Jacob buried their father Jacob by force and by might in the cave of Machpelah. The sons of Esau witnessed the funeral and were bitterly confounded. Chushim, then, buried Esau's head where it stopped rolling just inside the entrance to the cave."

Saul took a deep breath. "You see, men, the history of Israel began with the deaf and the dumb, the blind and the lame."

A chuckle whispered through the chamber. The king was exhausted but glad for his acquired knowledge. Then, sensing the lateness of the hour and knowing that his men needed their rest, Saul rallied. "Men, we have a man's work in a few hours. Finish your cups, and then lie down and get some needed sleep. We have a powerful enemy to conquer on the morrow. We, and by God's will and His favor, must prevail, for the fate of all Israel depends on us scaling the heights and tipping the balance of power. Shalom and good night."

CHAPTER SIX
Defend, Withdraw, and Attack

As ordered, Saul, a heavy sleeper by nature, was roused from his down-filled couch by his faithful bodyguard Shamar in the middle of the fourth watch. The king was aware that the army and its leadership were awaiting his presence in the adjoining courtyard. Two burly guards hefting spark-spitting torches escorted him through the dark passageway. The three emerged to witness the army of God standing at attention and ready for the coming fight. Saul was in his full armor, including breastplate and helmet. Saul had, in his hand, a deadly and accurate spear. On his girdle hung a double-bladed sword of justice.

Saul was an imposing figure. He towered head and shoulders over the standing ranks of Israeli soldiers. Even Abner, his closest kin, was not quite as imposing, being slightly shorter.

Acaph, the head captain of thousands, called the company to order. Saul walked up and down the ranks, making eye contact and addressing some of the men by their familiar names.

Saul paused, standing still in front of the staunch columns. He lifted his spear and spread wide his massive arm broadening his silhouette. He filled his lungs and commanded, "Esteemed chieftains, loyal captains, and brothers in arms: times such as these will prove the mettle of a man. Keep your eye on the task at hand. See our victory over our sworn enemy, the Philistine heathen. We are on the Lord's errand, and our plan is bold and daring. Adonai will give us victory over our foe and all glory to Him forever, the one true God and master of all creation.

"Men, listen up, The Devil may be in the cracks and the crevices, but God is certainly in the details.

"We will pass through the corridor provided by the upper north side of Jebus—that is, Jerusalem. My chieftains have revealed that the Philistines are south and west of the city walls. Our archers can easily defend and repel from the rubble and the ruin of Nob, three miles from the city. When we can no longer hold our position, we can withdraw up to the rocky heights of Gibeah, less than three miles from Nob. We will then lure the enemy, like a fish, and net them at our chosen location. Our advantage is the surprise of Abner and his army. By God's will and God's perfect timing, their force will miraculously appear below them at the base of the hills. Our soldiers' spikes are like porcupine quills aimed down and confusing our enemy. Abner and his army will then emerge below the Philistine rear by God's grace and divine timing, making any attempt at a retreat both dangerous and costly for our adversaries. The shock of a phantom army appearing as if out of thin air will unnerve them. Once Abner is in place, we will charge straight at them, gaining speed and strength in our descent.

"Men, we must now travel through the city of Jebus to the far western gate. Torches are blazing, which will make our presence and intentions glaring to any Philistine collaborators. Our direction, once exposed to the Philistine generals, will serve as tasty bait in our trap. If we go unnoticed, our deception and Israel's fate will be forfeit to the pagans of Canaan."

The army's departure was as lively as one thousand men, captains, and chieftains could muster. Every man stepped lively; the slap of leather sandals echoed off the ancient battlements. Men were singing and chanting, and their torches stood out against the last of the night sky.

Dawn broke brilliant, and Jebus' outer walls were still prominent as Saul's defiant army approached the Mount of Olives. The steep rise gave a sweeping view of the walled-in city's imposing towers. In the distance, a thick gray cloud of kicked-up dust was a sure sign of a large army on a forced march. Saul confided in Acaph, his trusted second, "The Philistines must have been alerted to yesterday's entrance into our Jebus compound, and now the horde is charging headlong to trap us behind the city walls. Men!" Saul rang out and lifted his spear that halted the columns in midstride. "The enemy is closing in and threatening us with destruction. We need to double or even triple our strides. Nob will be in sight within a short time, two and a half miles as the crow flies." Saul took the lead. He was fleet of foot, a family trait, and this despite his bulk and weight.

Sheer necessity accomplished the desired results. The ruins of Nob soon appeared before their panting mouths and wind-stung eyes. Saul sensed the need for rest, for he, too, needed to catch his breath. He gulped in some fresh air to soothe his burning lungs and faced his captains. "I had an inspiration while running. We need to stall the Philistine advance. Have your men build fires. Space them five cubits apart as many as is necessary at the shortest gap to block the entrance to the forest."

Acaph spoke up. "Sire, this little fire will not stop, or even slow down the Philistine advance, not for a moment. What is your thinking?"

Saul looked down his nose with a slight sense of mocking ridicule. "It is not the fire that will slow down the horde, Acaph, but the blinding smoke from green leaves and dried underbrush, enough to obscure the valley floor in a choking fog. The air is still, and the smoke will thicken and blanket the senses. First, they will have to halt, at least until they can determine our strength and our direction. Next, they will have to organize scouting parties to decide the nature of our deception. Then, after your men create a smokescreen, they can scatter and later meet up with Abner's army coming up and from the south. Lastly, they can fall behind the Philistine invaders. This smokescreen will afford us the time to make the remaining two-mile trek to Gibeah and scale the rocky heights. I know every trail and path like the back of my hand, and that is where we will make our stand, holding tight until Abner and his men are in position."

Acaph nodded in both agreement and wonder at Saul's brilliant strategy. "Sire, I will make it so, and I will call for volunteers, so they can find a perfect hiding place to skirmish and harass the enemy. I will task the rest of the men to build firepits, harvest green leaves, and spark the dry kindling. In short, while thick billows of smoke emerge, the still air will help blanket the field in a dull gray haze."

"Gather the men quickly, Acaph. We must take advantage of every precious moment. It is two miles to Gibeah, and we need the time to deploy to the Migron cliffs, the landslip of the crested heights, and set our place for a final defense."

Padi, the well-seasoned Philistine commander, halted his attack at the narrow path beyond the dense forest. The thick smoke barred his way and masked his vision. Arrows started raining down on his stalled army's position. Padi called out, "Captains, deploy your men, and brace yourself for an ambush." Twenty anxious minutes passed, and there was no attack, only an occasional flight of arrows or a long spear hurled without any accuracy. Scouting parties went into the smoke but could find no enemy. An hour later, the wind picked up, and the smoke dispersed, revealing an empty field strewn about with the dying embers of hundreds of smoking fire pits. Padi had been duped but was growing accustomed to the Israelis' cunning deceptions.

Still, he and his army pressed on. Coming to a rise, he spied Saul and his meager force at a distance and was glad for the count of less than 1,000 enemies. Padi knew he would soon make short work of them and took pride that he would finally exterminate those pesky uninvited immigrant invaders. The Philistines took heart in their superior numbers and pushed forward with a cocksureness of victory.

Saul's plan had worked, and it had done well, better than he had imagined. His small force was now well entrenched in the towering Migron cliffs—and not a moment too soon. Padi and the overwhelming Philistine cohort appeared at the base of the rise.

Saul rang out, "Captains, chieftains, and all my most famil-iar brothers. The enemy is at our feet, and soon they will begin their assault on the high ground. So, hurl rocks, dislodge massive boulders, let them fall upon our waiting enemy's heads. Save your arrows and spears for our downhill descent. They will try to overwhelm us with their weight of numbers. The day spent, and the shadows grown long, the Philistines will have no choice but to camp for the night. It will be foolhardy to climb in the dark. First light will bring about their relentless rise to remove our meager force. We will rest here, every man in his place. Captains, set your watch. We do not want to get murdered in our sleep. Some heathens are adept at creeping about under the blind blanket of night."

The cold, a piercing chill, shivered backbones and chattered teeth. Fires would not kindle in the misty drizzle, and for many, a thin cloak was their only relief. The night's rest was fitful; most of Saul's men caught brief catnaps, barely awake but less than asleep. Rumblings from the Philistine encampment heightened the senses and put every nerve at the ready.

The sun was cracking at Israel's back when Canaan's first wave began their ascent. Rocks, stones, and boulders from the small force caused landslides and crushed many.

The Philistine arrows quickly found their deadly range, and despite all of Israel's best efforts, the enemy was making punish-ing headway.

Acaph, on the eastern ridge, spotted Abner and his 2,000 warriors charging up the ravine but still out of sight of Padi, the chief Philistine general.

Acaph made haste to relay the good news to Saul. "Sire, Abner has come. His army is on the run and will be here and arranged before the sun peaks, praise God." Saul, both relieved and empowered, ordered, "Have this joyful message of redemption voiced to each man, passed along from mouth to ear to his next closest comrade." Israel was fighting back with an unbridled fury like a man possessed with supernatural powers. A flaring arrow streaked below the high plateau, signaling Abner, and his youthful army was ready and waiting for permission to advance.

Saul commanded to spark the oil-wrapped shaft, just as Padi realized that he found his army in the jaws of two well-armed Israeli forces. Several shofars from Saul's men erupted with their shrill bone-chilling trumpet call, echoing off the steep rocky walls and alerting Abner's army far down below. Saul's men picked up their weapons of war and were not long in waiting. A blazing arrow was the attack signal. Saul's men hurled themselves down the steep hill like avenging angels at their frightened and now-fleeing adversaries. The offensive from above and the sharp spikes down below ravaged the Philistine army.

Padi fought alongside his fearsome bodyguards through the fury of the ambush maelstrom. They miraculously emerged safe and unharmed on the downside of the battle. They and other escaping fragments of the once-mighty Philistine command hurried back to the borders of Philistia, dazed and confused. They were followed hotly by Saul and Abner's combined forces in a murderous pursuit until the sun disappeared over the horizon. Then the remaining enemy, cloaked in dark shadows, slipped away into the night.

Saul and Abner overflowed with gratitude and thanksgiving, and with sincere hugs and well-done back-slapping. Abner confided, "Saul, we have done God's work this day, and I am both elated and exhausted. We had hardly rested these last three days since I saw you last in the wilderness of Maon."

Saul agreed. "I am no longer young, but Adonai has renewed my mind and heart to accomplish this incredible triumph. We will return to Jebus and to my villa, where we will regroup, rest, and feast, and then praise our amazing God for this, His victory and endless glory."

CHAPTER SEVEN
Spiderwebs and Sheepcotes

The return to Jebus was a grand affair. Garlands showered down from high above the ramparts. The tribes of Judah and Benjamin came out in full support, for rumor and gossip are winged messengers that fly on the winds of envy and judgment. The good news of total victory had preceded the two-and-a-half-mile trek from Gibeah.

As the celebratory procession entered his villa, Saul spotted a familiar and urgent-looking Ziphite tracker who seemed anxious to reveal some timely information.

"Sire," the dark-hooded spy began, "please excuse the poor timing of my interruption, but I believe this information that I have discovered could be of great interest to Your Majesty."

"Yes, yes, go on." Saul was cross and impatient. "What is so urgent to disturb my victory parade?"

The bearded messenger looked Saul directly in the eyes and spoke with grave emotion: "The son of Jesse and all of his band of renegade men are in the wilderness of Engedi. We, the people of Ziph, remain your loyal and trusted servants. Even as I speak, we are keeping an eye on your archenemy, so you will always know his exact whereabouts. Our devotion will help to ensure his death, or detention, whatever is your wish and your pleasure, sire."

Saul was pleased with the loyalty of Ziph, and he was now confident in the location of David and his motley crew of followers. "Very well, uh—what is your name? So that I can thank you properly with a hefty purse of gold shekels."

"My name is Mehrahghel" (meaning "watchful spy").

"Very well, Mehrahghel, you will be my guest and my guide. We will leave for the wilderness of Engedi when my men and I have rested from our recent encounter."

"Acaph," Saul commanded, "find Mehrahghel some fitting and comfortable sleeping quarters. And food and wine in abundance; now be off with you both."

Saul then called out above the celebration, "Abner!"

"Yes, sire." Saul's uncle was behind him and came up close to his ear.

"This man has found the location of the son of Jesse. When our warriors are rested and renewed, we will take three thousand chosen men south to the oasis of Engedi."

"Yes, sire." Abner, the son of Ner, bowed slightly in submission and added, "I will make his capture fast and secure, my overly preoccupied nephew." He promptly set about to comply with the king's wishes and put all necessary plans in motion.

Eleven days of good food, dark wine, and manly diversions filled the army of Saul with deep and abiding fellowship. The four-day trek to the rocks of the wild goats was uneventful. Mehrahghel led Saul and his army to the last-sighted location of David and his 600 assorted drifters, debtors, and otherwise would-be malcontent warriors. Mehrahghel cautiously informed Saul that the last confirmed sighting was three days ago, when the spy on watch had his throat neatly cut.

"Well, where is he? Where is the son of Jesse?" Saul demanded.

Mehrahghel gulped hard, knowing that Saul did not take failure lightly. "Sire, he was here, and we can see many of the ibex bones, campfires, tracks, refuse, and items they left behind. Also, remember that a full fifteen days have passed since I gave you the message in Jerusalem, and David is like a shadow. He disappears when the bright light of Your Majesty's glory approaches."

Saul was pleased with the comparison. The king turned to Abner and declared, "We will turn over every rock and search in every crack and crevice in this wilderness for this enemy usurper. We will begin at first light. Make it so, Commander Abner. Encamp here in the oasis's valley, and set guards all about on the rocky heights. I have marked a cave, and I crave to cover my feet (a private place for bodily relief) free from spying eyes, so I require some privacy. I do so miss my cool marble summer chamber. I had it made after the likes of King Eglon of Moab's summer parlor.

"Consequently, the Israeli hero Ehud slaughtered Eglon while sitting on his marble throne, but no matter, it is ancient history. As you recall, there are no spying viewports, and it locks securely from the inside. My standing order this afternoon is not to be disturbed when sitting and my feet are covered. It seems that, anytime I feel a crisp chill like the cold stone marble inside my summer chamber, I immediately feel a stirring to obey nature's timely calling. In any event, I am going directly to the dark and cold provided by that large-mouthed cave and seek my needed comfort. If you find David, blow the shofar four times."

Mehrahghel cautioned Saul: "The opening of the cave you marked looks to be wide enough to hold a sheepcote [or a space large enough to shelter and contain a large herd of sheep]. Sire, if you wish it, I will accompany you."

Saul did not want company and shook his head. "Mehrahghel," the king growled, "You seem to be hard of hearing. You are to stay here; I am going there to have some privacy, which means alone. Before I cover my feet, I will be vigilant; I will carefully explore for any signs of intruders. Besides, I pride myself on being alert and cautiously aware of my immediate surroundings. The son of Jesse will not catch me napping."

In a short while, Saul hurriedly entered the dark, damp cavern with a torch in hand. To his relief, he found a back alcove that afforded him comfort and privacy. But, as was his custom, Saul took his sweet time. Finally, he completed his business with several grunts of satisfaction. The king then covered up his dirt with a pile of sand that he kicked up with his heavy leather sandals.

King Saul spied a darker passage that went deeper inside the hollow as he raised his firestick. The opening stood covered in an extensive, fine-meshed spider's web. The perfectly intact silken threads declared that no one could have passed through without disturbing the delicate weave. *Indeed,* he thought, *it is a sign of an empty black hole beyond that fragile barrier.*

Saul thought there was no need to investigate further; he shook his head, believing the obvious. The king then let out a deep-seated yawn that echoed against the empty cavern walls.

King Saul's eyes felt heavy at the lids. He was feeling weighed down as if carrying a heavy burden. He consoled himself with the idea that his thick mantle and loosely fitting robe would provide a suitable cushion and protection from the cave's damp floor. The king of Israel formed a sand pillow and covered it with a napkin. In short order, his snoring produced the steady rhythm of a late afternoon catnap.

As the snoring deepened, a pair of eyes, then two, opened and looked at him. A third pair joined them, and all eyes peered keenly at the king's large form from behind the glistening and fully formed spider web. David and all his men had found shelter in the innermost part of that very same mountain!

David observed Saul for several minutes, sleeping helpless and alone. He at first considered going forward but thought better of it and motioned for his brothers to retreat with him, silently, out of earshot. David's companions were gleeful at the opportunity they saw for silencing Saul once and for all. Eliab, David's oldest brother, whispered, "Little brother, do you remember the day that the Lord said unto you, 'Behold, I will deliver your enemy into your hand, and you may do to him what you deem good and fitting?'"

"I do, brother. It still rings in my ears, especially when I consider the time that Saul's hands clutched for my throat or when his thrown spear aimed for my head. God is great, and God is good. He has stopped the king of Israel and all his mighty men with the fragile threads of a spider's web. We see that He has used the weak things of this world to confound the mighty and the foolish things to confound the wise."

David pondered only for a moment his righteous course of action. Should he slay his relentless and defenseless father-in-law and, by doing so, mark himself as a conqueror, successor. Only making himself a future assassination target. How would this be perceived by the tribes of Israel, especially by the king's family, his best friend Jonathan, and the tribe of Benjamin? In addition, Saul was the Lord's anointed, as he was, and they both remained protected by divine mandate.

David instructed his brothers to gather the men and their belongings and prepare for battle. Then, he left the others and traveled back upward toward the king's sleeping form, without leave or explanation, for he knew that none of his men would agree with his foolhardy scheme.

Twenty minutes later, David slipped back into the depths of the cavern and addressed his men. "I did it, and alone, for the Lord forbid me to slaughter the Lord's anointed." The men were silent, straining to hear his detailed encounter. "I approached the sleeping king, helpless as a newborn. I sheared the corner border of his skirt with my dagger, the portion that represents his authority. I then retreated into the shadows."

There were gasps all around. "Brother!" Eliab blurted out, visibly confounded. "This is madness and foolishness at best! So, we have him, and God has granted you license to end our fugitive existence. How can you imagine that the Lord has repented of

His license granted to you? If Saul gets the slightest inkling that we, your followers, are back here with little food and a trickle of water, he will set his vengeful army upon us."

David shrugged. "That is all true and correct what you say, but God has given every man the gift of agency, the right to choose the harder path that is fit and proper or to embrace the convenient evil course that leads to perdition."

Consider, brother: At worst, all they have to do outside is to wait us out. We will either die fighting, a few at a time, or surrender and face extinction from the headsman's ax in the mass execution of traitors. Please, my beloved sovereign, weigh my words in the balance."

Six hundred men were now sweating profusely in the damp cave, but they kept silent to hear their prince's words.

"Do you trust in God, Eliab?" David challenged. "If not, then trust in my faith. I am also the Lord's anointed, and He alone directs my thoughts and my actions. All of this means that you will have to trust more, big brother, for I am counting on your support."

David looked around the silent, assembled men, and his searching eyes then turned to his priest.

"Abiathar, you have remained eerily silent. What say you? Speak up now. You are set apart in the Lord's service. Your leadership and direction have served us well up to this very hour."

Abiathar's jaw was firm in his praise. "I say we must trust in God with all of our might, will, and strength. There is no more to be said." All the men nodded in agreement that the will of

God is absolute. All that was left was acceptance, regardless of the outcome.

David then climbed back toward where the king lay; he struck two rocks together to rouse Saul from his unprotected slumber. The echo broke Saul's snore in mid-grunt. The king arose dull from his nap, stretched, and scratched. He gave a loud yawn to help gulp down some needed fresh air. His torch was now gone out, and the only light in the cavern was coming from the outside; the late afternoon sun fell directly into Saul's squinting eyes as he departed. David also stood up from behind the dark, dense shadows. He followed behind by a bowshot's distance as Saul made his clumsy and uncertain exit. Then he cried after Saul, saying, "My Lord, the king!"

Saul was startled and turned sharply to look back behind him, visibly holding back a chill and a shiver from hearing the familiar voice of his usurper and suspected assassin. David stooped with his face to the earth. He bowed himself to honor Saul and to humble himself to the will of his king.

David kept his focus on Saul's feet, keeping his face hidden. He distinctly avoided hostile eye contact,

"Your Majesty," he said, "many men have counseled you in that I am seeking your injury and death. Now this day, you have witnessed the Lord delivering you into my hands. Many invited me to kill you, but I spared you. I declared, 'I will not put forth my hand against my Lord, for he is the Lord's anointed.'"

King Saul remained silent, and David continued.

"Besides, my dear father-in-law, I have the skirt of your robe in my hand. I sheared off this fabric while you were hidden in the shadows of the hollow, enjoying the sleep of a helpless lamb. I could as readily have killed you, ended my misery, and freed myself from your constant and determined chase. Take this as evidence and proof that I have no evil intent or offense in my heart or hand."

The king looked at his robe and saw where the piece was missing. His face turned pale as the blood drained away. David held out the missing piece and continued.

"I have never sinned against you, my king. There is no wickedness in me, neither in word nor deed, that you can lay at my feet. But against all proof to the contrary, you hunt my soul to take it. Let the Lord God judge between you and me, and may the Lord avenge me of you, but my hand will never be against you. The proverb says, 'Wickedness proceedeth from the wicked,' but my hand will never be upon you. To whom does the king of Israel seek? Whom do you pursue, a dead dog? A flea? The Lord God is judge and allows Him to judge between you and me. And, to Him, I plead my cause and pray He delivers me out of your vengeful hand."

David fell silent, still holding Saul's garment, his arm outstretched toward the king.

The renegade prince's plea of innocence slammed into Saul's heart like a dagger, and he lifted his voice. "Is this my son David?"

David nodded and showed his face.

The king cried out and then wept in great sobs.

"David, you are more righteous than I, for you have rewarded me with good, and I have repaid you with evil. This day the Lord had delivered me into your hands, and you did not kill me when you had the chance. When a man finds his enemy vulnerable and alone, does he let him go on his way, knowing full well that a day of reckoning will soon be upon him? So accordingly, the Lord will reward you for withdrawing your hand and allowing me to live and breathe another day. I know now, and with all certainty, that you will be king, and your hands will establish the empire of Israel. Swear now to me, and by the Lord God, that you will not cut off my posterity after me and that you will not destroy my name out of my father's house."

David was glad, for he trusted in God with his life and with the lives of his men. Saul, with all the heartfelt sincerity he could muster, declared, "I do so swear that as I live and breathe and in everything righteous, I will do as you have requested of me."

Saul repented. He left the cave and returned to the army at the waters of Engedi. The king gathered all his men, dismissed his Ziphite spies and trackers, and sent every man to his own house.

David climbed down deep into the cavern to tell the good tidings to his anxious men, proclaiming, "It is done, finished and completed. Saul has dismissed his spies, and his army departs. The spring of Engedi is again empty for our ease and pleasure."

Eliab was the first to run to David's side, and he hugged and kissed his brother. "I still cannot believe you have achieved this miraculous reversal," Eliab said through tears of joy. "I was sure that, on this very day, I was going to meet my Maker. What now, little brother?"

David, with a sad expression, softly confessed, "As I saw Israel departing, a voice whispered in my ear, saying that Saul's repentance is only for a short season; then an evil spirit will rise and control his mind again. Because of this, I think it best to stay clear of this double-minded monarch until his intentions are clear, stable, and trustworthy. Then, of course, we will continue to seek security in our wilderness strongholds. But, for the time being, I think it prudent to maintain a great distance of many miles between Saul and me against the time when he has another sudden change of mind."

CHAPTER EIGHT

The Shearing of the Sheep

David felt saddened, and, so, too, were all of Israel, by the passing of Samuel. Samuel was the holy prophet who had set David apart by God's command and had anointed him to be the future king of Israel.

David took the prophet's death as a sign and departed the wilderness of Engedi for the stronghold of Paran. The gold and the gemstones from Gideon's ephod brought in only a trifle of its actual value. The word was out that anyone caught helping David the renegade would suffer an agonizing death.

The security of David, his brothers, and his army depended on keeping on the move and lingering only briefly at remote wilderness strongholds. Finally, after months of tramping all over creation, David confided in Eliab, "It is wise for us to move on to greener pastures. Besides, Saul's Ziphite spies are constantly on the prowl. They are always eager and ready to curry favor with the king and receive a script of gold shekels in exchange for the knowledge of our most recent whereabouts."

David was alerted by a caravan of wandering merchants, bragging that Nabal's sheep were as thick as fleas that covered the valleys and hills of Carmel.

David, sensing an opportunity, commanded, "Let us proceed to Carmel. It is the time of the annual sheep shearing. We have an army to feed, and as our bellies grow hollow. Perhaps we can provide safety and protection from trespassers, robbers, and brigands and gain favor from a grateful benefactor Nabal, the wealthy landlord."

Nabal, a very great man from the house of Caleb, resided in the city of Maon with his wife, Abigail. She was as beautiful as she was shrewd. Nabal possessed a marriage pension surpassing a king's ransom and had arranged his loveless marriage. Yet he was rough and rude, and he had a streak of evil in all his doings.

Nabal's possessions of 8,000 sheep and 3,000 goats needed sharp shears in Carmel's lush fields for their yearly clipping.

"Eliab," David counseled, "we will go in strength and provide Nabal's servants with the peace of mind that comes from well-armed security. We will post sentries and ward off wolves, hawks, and all two-legged predators. I am sure Nabal will be grateful for the service we provide, and in the meantime, we can remain hidden as wolves among the sheep."

Weeks slowly passed, quiet and uneventful, when Eliab called upon David, "Brother, the men grow stale, and I, too, grow weary of this month-long sheep shearing babysitting. I think the constant bleating is driving me mad. My nights fill with bad dreams of screaming lambs. The work is nearly finished. Let us present our bill to Nabal and receive some needed coins to refresh our much-needed victuals and equipment. I long to quench my thirst with new wine and break a loaf of freshly baked bread, some sweet raisins, and figs, and any other meat, except goat and sheep."

David laughed at his oldest brother's remarks. The prince then called upon his followers: "I need ten men, for the Lord had said that He would 'spare Sodom and Gomorrah' for the sake of ten righteous men. You ten need to go to the summer home of Nabal; it is easy to find. It is the grandest mansion in all of Carmel. When you see him, greet him in my name, for he is overflowing with prosperity, and say to him, 'Peace be both to you and your house, and peace in all your borders. My master David had heard that you have many shearers that needed our protection. Your shepherds were with us, we did not hurt them, and none came up missing. We protected all of them while in Carmel. Just ask your young men who were there if this is not so. For this cause, we pray that we find favor in your eyes. We come on a good day for your bounty great and our efforts honorable. We humbly ask whatever you find fitting and proper to give us by your hand to your servants and a son of Israel, and Judah, David Ben Jesse.'"

The ten men went to Nabal's home and delivered his message. But David's perfect words fell hollow from their lips, and they served only to evoke Nabal's hostility. Nabal rejected David's straightforward proposal, and he responded in the harshest of terms, "Who is David? And who is the son of Jesse? There are many servants nowadays who break away from their masters. Is this not so that the son of Jesse broke away from his master, even the house of Saul? Did not Saul execute the eighty-five priests that wore the linen ephod and slaughtered everything that breathed in Nob that helped this son of perdition, this usurper, beggar, and vagabond? Saul's brutal message was heard loud and clear on all the coasts of Israel. Should I take away my bread, water, and the flesh that I have killed and prepared for my shearers and give it to an uninvited renegade? These are men that I do not know, nor what their intention might be. There is nothing in my hand for outlaws such as these. So be on your way, and good riddance, I say."

David's ten men were sorrowful from the harshness of Nabal's insulting refusal. They turned away and hotly reported back to David the grievous snub, repeating all the hateful words Nabal had spewed in defiance. David flushed crimson with anger from the ridicule. He hotly wished to kick against Nabal's prickly insults, deciding that he would seek the satisfaction of blood against this thorny nemesis.

David then commanded, "We will avenge our honor before nightfall—belt your swords, and prepare for battle. This mockery will not go unanswered." David arose and strapped on the leather casing that held the sword of Goliath, one of the items he had retrieved from the high priest at Nob. The prince's nostrils were flaring; his breath was short and shallow as he ordered, "Four hundred will accompany me. Eliab and Abinadab and their one hundred each will stay behind and guard our baggage. Abiathar, you remain behind as well, my priest, and pray to Adonai that He grants me satisfaction. Nabal's compound will not be a place for the likes of you, holy man, in the certain and all-consuming bloodletting. Shammah, you will join me, brother, as we seek to balance the scales of justice."

Aleksander, one of the young men of Nabal's household, hastily approached Abigail, Nabal's comely wife. "Mistress, please excuse my urgent intrusion, but I have some news that is of great importance."

Abigail was refined and polite and said, "Speak on."

The young man caught his breath and exclaimed, "David sent a messenger from out of the wilderness to greet our master with a humble request for assistance for their necessary and timely service in guarding the sheep and shepherds during the shearing time. Nabal cruelly protested any payment and rudely dismissed them as trespassers. Consider that David's men were very good to us. We were never hurt and always guarded. Nothing was ever taken or stolen, and they were very friendly and conversational when our shearing gangs were in the fields, all doing our master's bidding. They were a wall of protection to us, both by day and night, while we were shearing Nabal's 12,000 beasts.

"Mistress, I overheard one of David's ten after being scorned by the master's refusal. He was sure that David would be enraged by such vengeful words and seek the most direct and violent act to compensate for this undeserved insult. I fear David and his angry army may be soon be at our doorstep. I regret this distress that I have laid at your feet, my lady. Please consider what you will do next, for evil approaches our master and all his household. The master is drunk, angry, and cruel, a true son of Belial when he is in this mood. I fear to speak to him, and yet I fear that our likely doom approaches."

Abigail was as canny and agile as she was proud and beautiful. Abigail knew how to run a large household and had solved her crass husband's disasters before. She said to Aleksander, "Your master is a drunken buffoon, and I say this with all sincerity. Go and fetch all the servants and tell them I need them to meet me at the storehouse as quickly as possible. Then go to the stables and saddle an ass for me, and ten and eight asses with baskets and braces. Make them ready for travel, and be quick about it. Our very lives may hang in the balance."

Abigail made haste, emptied the pantry, and collected even the feed for the gang of shearers from the now-barren cupboards. She took 200 loaves of bread, 2 casks of wine, 5 sheep ready and dressed, 5 measures of parched corn, 100 clusters of raisins, and 200 cakes of figs, along with other delicacies that were available. Then, quickly, she placed the rich bounty upon the backs of ten and eight asses.

Aleksander cried unto Abigail, "Mistress, this amount is worthy of a king's ransom. But if you could add a few shekels, I am sure it will ring true and quell David's vengeful passion."

Abigail nodded in agreement and confessed, "Yes, I do agree, but Nabal wears the key to the treasure chest around his neck. This current theft requires craftiness so as not to arouse his suspicions, not even in the slightest. Nabal would undoubtedly rail against this 'foolish waste,' so I will have to make do with what we have in hand. We will evoke the display of a womanly charm, instead of shekels, to tip the scales toward mercy. We hope that David will forgo justice for kindness and that a full stomach will subside the anger in his heart."

The feast was quickly loaded, and Abigail saw that it was underway and escorted by the prettiest of her maids and servants. Abigail instructed her servants, "Go on before me, and I will be right after you, announcing my standing and stature as a lady and the mistress of all that comes before me." Her departure went unobserved by Nabal, who was busy finding comfort in a skin of dark red wine.

As Abigail and her entourage traveled on the blind side of a steep hill, they rounded a curve and suddenly came upon David and his men charging, coming straight at them. When she saw David, she hastily climbed down off the ass, fell before David on her face, and bowed herself to the ground at his feet.

Gathering up all her courage, she cried out: "Upon me, my Lord! Let this injustice fall on me. I pray that you give an ear to your handmaiden's plea for forgiveness."

David's heart was now deeply smitten for beauty's sake as well as her meek and submissive disposition.

But the prince's blood was up; he still needed to vent his venom for his benefit, as well as for his men's opinions. He complained, "Surely, in vain have I kept safe all of Nabal's possessions in the wilderness, although nothing is lost or missing. I do not relish the loss of face; I have reaped evil for my good works. If I do not seek justice by killing every man in your household, the Lord will bless my enemies with abundance and me with sorrow and regret."

Abigail remained steadfast, though she grew pale at the thought of a bloodbath. "My Lord has no regard for this man Nabal (meaning "foolish"), and folly goes with him. I did not witness the men you had sent. Please, David, as the Lord lives and your soul lives, withhold from shedding blood. Either by your hand or by your command. Let all the enemies that seek evil against you be like Nabal, who is foolish and full of folly. I have brought all that I could collect for a blessing to you and your men. Please accept my meager offering and give it to the men that follow you with my heartfelt gratitude. Please, my Lord, forgive the trespass of your handmaiden. The Lord, our God, will indeed bless your posterity, and your house will stand forever. You alone fight the battle for the Lord thy God. For in all your days, there is no evil found in you.

"A man has risen to pursue you, my Lord, and he seeks your soul—even Saul, son of Kish. The Lord has spoken much good over you. In God's time, you will become the ruler over all of Israel. When you come into your kingdom, you will have no regrets or grief for avenging yourself with the shedding of blood needlessly, and when you come into your glory, remember your handmaiden."

David delighted in Abigail's heartfelt confession. He spoke sincere and kind words over her: "Blessed be the Lord God of Israel, who sent you to me this day. Truly, your advice inspired me to keep me from avenging myself with the shedding of blood. For in this very deed, the Lord God of Israel has held me back from hurting you. If you, Abigail, had not hurriedly come out to meet me by this morning's light, not one man in your hire would have retained the breath of life, including your husband, Nabal. I would have slaughtered him like a flailed-out goat, but only after he had witnessed the utter destruction of his house and home." David took a deep breath and waited until the blood once again settled down from his head, and only then he calmly addressed Abigail: "I accept all that you have brought, and all that you have said, and I take you, for you are wise, spiritual and comely; go back to your house, and peace be with you."

Abigail departed, leading her servants and her train of emptied asses in tow. Sitting upright in her saddle, she turned briefly to take a departing glance at David's beautiful face and imposing figure when an unexpected flutter of feeling arose in her heart. David spied a delicate but telltale backward glance, proving a woman's subtle invitation.

Abigail entered the compound to find Nabal indulging in the festivities of a king. His wine stores were plentiful, but, his private lauder emptied, Nabal's heart was made merry with gluttony and drunkenness. Abigail decided it was not the right time to speak of her adventure, less or more, and explaining that Nabal was a hair's breadth away from extinction.

The morning light glared and made worse Nabal's aching head. The rich man was hung over, and the wine was out of him. Abigail approached Nabal, slumped in his chair. "Husband," she began, "last evening, I halted David and his army from taking their revenge on you and every man in the compound. You, my husband, would have been swiftly executed. I begged David to forgive your disrespect with all the foodstuffs I could muster in such short order. Luckily for you and me, he accepted my offering and my sincere apology. I believe, once the massacre had begun, all males would have been put to the sword to silence any chance of witnesses starting rumors that would have held David and his men accountable for the slaughter. In which, it could very well have turned Judah, if not all of Israel, against him. Besides my husband, he is already a fugitive from the king's justice. David has no additional fear from man's judgment. What turned his heart, and in his mind, was the fear of God's prosecution.

Nabal went pale as Abigail recounted her ordeal; it was like he had seen a ghost. His heart pierced with stone-cold fear.

David was still hot with rage at Nabal's insult, and it haunted his every waking hour. He called upon Eliab for solace and counsel. "Brother, my insult goes unanswered, and Nabal still walks among the living. Let us put him to sleep permanently. I must admit I am smitten with Abigail, his wife, but she remains unattainable by God's law. If something happened to Nabal, my conscience and my vengeance would be satisfied, and the beautiful Abigail will become available to pursue. Abigail would then inherit all Nabal's holdings, for Nabal has no sons."

Eliab pondered, but only for a moment, "The best course of action, my brother, is obvious—that would be to secure the death of Nabal, but it must look to be natural causes, or by some unfortunate incident or accident. I know a woman who knows the herbs of the field, and poisons are her specialty. We can pay her in gold for her service. She could easily get a position as a scullery maid and gain access to the master's cooking pot."

David liked the idea of putting his troubled mind and his nagging complaint to rest. "Make it so, Eliab—I relish my day of cold vengeance."

Eliab contacted Martu in the fields of Carmel and explained the urgency of his request. She negotiated for a heavy purse of gold shekels before she agreed to the murder.

On the eleventh day after her arrangement, Martu returned to Eliab a bit confounded and distraught, fearing the news she had brought back and that Eliab would deny the purse of her hire. "What news, Martu—is the deed done?"

"Well," she admitted, "Nabal is dead, but not by my hand. I had secured the position as you had directed. Yesterday I had prepared a portion of poison mushrooms and was about to coat his bowl with the deadly dust. Suddenly, an alarm sounded. Nabal had died. He fell dead as if struck from above. So I broke the tainted bowl and discarded the shards in the dust. Now, Eliab, I believe I had accomplished my task, and God had stayed my hand from doing evil. I think I am still entitled to my bounty—what say you?"

Eliab brimmed from the glad tidings but sternly warned, "The purse's value is now only to secure your silence; if word of this plot gets out, it will mean your life—of this make no doubt. So sear my words like a dagger to your throat: that there was never a hire, and you were never there. Seal your lips and let us never speak of this again—now go in peace, Martu, and live."

Eliab's burden from the dark shadow of a murder conspiracy had lifted as he flew to David's side with the good news of reprieve. "Brother, Nabal is dead, and not by our undertaking; the assassin was spared her murderous deed by God's timely hand of intervention. God struck down Nabal before the poison could find its mark. Our conscience is clear. Nabal's blood no longer taints us. God intervened, and on your behalf—and once again, little brother, you remain the Lord's anointed."

David repented of his evil intent and that his hands remained clean, restoring his peace of mind. David raised his hands, looked toward heaven, and pronounced a blessing. "Thanks be to Elohim, our God! For God has pleaded my cause for the blame

I held against Nabal, and He has stayed my hand from doing evil. For the Lord has returned the wickedness of Nabal on his head." David was pleased and gave all glory to God: "Nabal had bruised my heel, but the Lord has crushed his head."

David shared with Abigail a few tokens of affection, and she embraced them with deep longing. David summoned Abiathar, saying, "Priest, your mentoring has served me well. Reading and writing that I had previously dismissed as frivolous are now essential to fulfilling my anointing as the future king of Israel. Before taking the throne, I need to resolve a matter of the heart. I wish to take Abigail to be my wife; is there a prescribed waiting period of mourning related to the death of her husband? His sudden and glorious demise was a blessing in disguise."

Abiathar pondered David's strange request. "Let us recount your marital status. Your first wife is Princess Michal, and your second and most recent wife is the pleasant Ahinoam of Jezreel. What perplexes me is that your vengeance was severe enough to injure Abigail and all her household, and now you are concerned with the appearance of propriety. The wealth she brings to your coffers is substantial and much needed. There is an appropriate mourning period of thirty days in the law, and seven days must pass after touching the dead. My advice is to propose a love letter quoting your heartfelt affection. Send it with me, your priest, your three brothers, and a trusted captain of your army to deliver your proposal. Five is the number of love and marriage, and in this way, she will mark you as having honorable intentions. That is my sage reasoning and learned advice, my lord."

David smiled as if Abiathar had read his mind. "Excellent priest, you are as wise as you are pious. I will compose my longings in a letter for you and my chosen five to deliver. Tell my brothers and my fifth captain to be prepared to set out at first light—make it so, Abiathar."

David set about to put his yearnings to enchanting words of love:

Abigail, the comely daughter of Carmel,

When we had parted, my eyes rebelled and would not allow me to look away. You are etched forever in my waking memory. I stare up at passing clouds only to see the outline of your face. I long for sleep, so in the night, you might invade my dreams. So, when I saw that you had turned back ever so slightly to see me standing there, my heart soared in ecstasy. I have been downcast in my imaginings for the desperate need of your company. Yet, my delight resounds with heated passion at the mere thought of your embrace. I vividly recall your stunning beauty, depth of wisdom, and your unconquerable leap of faith. I long to caress you and seek shelter in your arms, Abigail. You spark in me an unquenchable fire, scorching my soul with love's eternal promise. I would be happy to satisfy your every wish, want, and desire. I would place you on a pedestal higher than my anointed throne. Say "yes" to being my wife, and such happiness you have never known will be ours forevermore.

Your David, son of Jesse.

Eliab, Shammah, Abinadab, Abiathar, and the fifth captain were off before the first bit of light. Reaching Nabal's compound, there were no signs of mourning; instead, there was a tangible lightness that dismissed the shadows and eased the burdens of the servants. Abigail was forewarned of their approach and put her household in motion.

The gate opened when Abiathar yelled to the gatekeeper, "We are on an errand for Lord David, son of Jesse. We seek an immediate audience with Lady Abigail." Abigail and her hand-maidens presented themselves. Abiathar stepped up, handed Abigail a note with David's heartfelt tidings, and waited until her eyes passed over the writing. Abigail's fingers had the slight-est hint of a tremble, and her face had the pale pink pinch of a rose of Sharon. Abiathar, familiar with the language of the heart, confidently proclaimed, "Prince David has sent me, his priest, his brothers three, and his trusted captain to implore you, Abigail, to honor David by allowing him to take you for his wife."

Abigail was overwhelmed. She stood up and then humbly bowed herself with her face to the earth. Her actions had to be superior to mere words. Abigail proclaimed, "A witness for all Israel to see, that your handmaiden will humbly submit to the wishes of my lord David by washing the feet of his servants who have carried to me such good news in my ears this day."

The holy task stood joyfully completed, and the visitors' feet were washed, dried, and pampered. Abigail confessed that thirty days of mourning rituals must be adhered to before marriage to a recently widowed woman was honorable. She passed the time in quiet and sincere anticipation of a new, wondrous life. Thirty days had passed when Abigail rode on her ass, and her five handmaidens followed her. They were gaily chatting about the upcoming wedding.

David had previously taken pleasant Ahinoam of the Jezreel for his wife, gaining wealth and much-needed alliances. Word of these marriages soon pricked the ears of King Saul. Saul was none too pleased, as David was gaining wealth and power. The once prickly thorn was now becoming an avenging sword.

Saul, by royal decree, annulled David's marriage to his daughter Michal. David had first won her hand by slaying Goliath of Gath and then fulfilling the king's challenge of acquiring one hundred Philistine foreskins. But David had gone one better than that—he had gotten two hundred heathen foreskins confirming his killings.

Saul then betrothed the princess Michal to Phaltiel, son of Gallium, for a sizable dowry and a much-needed coalition in a deliberate act of revenge.

CHAPTER NINE
The Hill of Faith

The Ziphites were relentless, and being true to their word, they stalked David and his army of rogues, misfits, and malcontents, like birds of prey. Eventually, the head Ziphite, tracker Manoach, took the long trek to Gibeah, to the seat of kingly power, and begged for an audience with King Saul. Immediately, Manoach bowed low in esteem, announcing, "Your Majesty, your nemesis, the son of Jesse, has, once again, found his rest in the wilderness of Ziph. David and his men are now hiding on the hill of Hachilah, just before the Jeshimon [or the desert]."

Saul was gleeful, and he thanked his loyal and dogged informant with a tidy purse of gold and gratitude.

"Abner," Saul shouted.

Abner replied, "I am at your arm, nephew." Then, stepping out of the shadows, he confided, "I heard the good news. First, I will gather up 3,000 men that are well rested and ready for battle. Then, I will make ready for travel. We will depart at first light after the Shabbat."

David had his spies, which gave him a timely warning of Saul's subtle approach, five days hence. David hid in the dense underbrush of the wilderness, where he could keep a wary eye on the comings and goings of his determined opponent. Saul's army approached near dusk and camped on the hill Hachilah or the "Mountain of Faith." David, by his well-practiced craftiness, attempted to invade Saul's open-air shelter. The forced march of Saul's blind obsession had been exhausting. A pile of empty wineskins was evidence that the army had helped to wash down the miles of dust and dirt. The pitch dark and the weighty silence took their toll on many weary soldiers. Even the most disciplined guards were yawning, and soon all had succumbed to the sleep of cats and cradles.

David spied Saul and Abner, the captain of his host, nestled snuggly behind a makeshift barricade. David sensed an opportunity to prove his innocent intentions. He slipped back to his dark encampment. David whispered, "Who will go with me, to where Saul sleeps? He lies unprotected, roofless, and under the stars. Saul is without even so much as a watchful dog to growl at our intrusion. Every watchman and guard—even Abner, his chief captain—has been put under the spell of fatigue. It is an eerie blanket of sleep, the likes of which are foreign to me, for even the moon has lost its shine. Yet, I will not question my good fortune. Who will join me?"

Ahimelech the Hittite and others raised their hands or nodded in the affirmative. But Abishai, David's nephew, said, "I will go down with you, uncle."

The two proceeded with caution, and in the widespread gloom, they carefully placed each footfall. An offending brittle branch snapped—but it did not arouse the sleeping crowd. The two unwelcome visitors quickly slid over to where Saul lay sleeping, and, like a newborn babe, he was defenseless and completely unprotected.

Next to Saul was the spear that doubled as his scepter, a finely turned white-ash staff with a dark, blood-red stain on the shaft. The blot was from the accused eighty-five priests put to death for treason who wore the linen ephod. The spear had a razor-sharp iron blade firmly stuck into the ground. The weapon was embedded next to his head. Saul lay comfortably nestled against a down-filled bolster. Abner and his choicest sentries slept all around the king, unaware of the pending peril. The only sounds were heavy breathing, an occasional grunt, the snore of wood, and the flap from passing gas.

Abishai tugged on David's arm, put his mouth up against the prince's ear, and, in the faintest voice, breathed, "God has delivered your sworn enemy into your hands this day; please honor me with his killing, and his blood will not be on your hands or your conscience, my pious uncle. I will use Saul's favorite deadly weapon. It is only fitting, and it is so eagerly pleading for the deed. All I need is one clean thrust through the heart, and I will not need a second lucky strike!"

David would have none of it and moved his mouth to Abishai's ear. "Do not destroy him," he breathlessly commanded. "Who can put forth their hand against the Lord's anointed and remain guiltless? If I allow the murder, then I, too, would suffer the blood of conspiracy."

David honored Saul's anointing. The Lord then gifted him with a prophetic vision. Again he whispered in his nephew's ear: "As the Lord lives, the Lord will strike him down, but only on His appointed day. Saul shall surely die this way; in that, he shall descend into battle and perish while defending Israel. God forbid that I should take part and slay a king who has been set apart by the Almighty God.

"And so, Abishai, it is better yet that we will take Saul's spear and the flask of water that is next to his face and peeking out from under his pillow."

David gathered up the evidence of his presence, and they hastily departed. No man saw them or knew what they had done, for a deep sleep from the Lord had fallen upon the entire army of Israel.

David now possessed Saul's spear and drinking flask; he set for the next adjacent hilly crest with his nephew. When they were far enough away to make a quick getaway, but close enough that his voice would echo in Saul's ears, David turned about and cried out in a long, throaty yell: "Abner, Son of Ner! Shama, meaning Obedience is Hearing! Listen to my judgment."

At that moment, the entire army roused from its unnatural slumber as if awakened by a crack of thunder.

"Abner, son of Ner!" David shouted again, and all eyes fell upon him. "Do you have a question for me, Abner?"

Abner stood up to his full stature and answered, "Who are you who disturbs the peace of the king?"

David leaned forward and loudly asked, "Are you not a courageous man, and is it not said that there is none like you in all of Israel? Are you not tasked with the safety and protection of the king against all villains and assassins? Why, then, have you not kept the king—your lord—protected when one had come to destroy the king, and you did nothing to shield him from destruction?

"You have broken your oath and your mandate." David's voice grew louder. "As the Lord of Hosts lives—you, Abner, are worthy to die! And this is because you have not kept your master safe. As a result, the Lord's very elect was left unprotected and exposed to certain harm!"

Saul looked to Abner. Abner shrugged. "I'm right here, and you are safe. So what is this man babbling about?"

David persisted. "I have in my hands the king's spear and his flask of water. These articles were at his head and under his pillow." He hoisted these items in the air, and Abner's face turned a shade of bright red.

Saul recognized the items immediately and David's distinctive speech. He interjected in a loud but remorseful voice, "Is this the voice of my son David?"

David replied, "It is, my lord, O king. Why do you pursue me, your loyal servant? What have I done? Or what evil is in my hand? If the Lord thy God has stirred you up against me, then let Him accept an offering to appease His wrath. But if it is the children of men, may they be cursed! For they have driven you out this day, keeping you from the inheritance of the Lord. False counselors say that I serve other gods, and if so, let not my blood fall to the earth before the face of the Lord this day. The king of Israel has come out to seek out a flea."

Saul's heart melted, and this was evident by his words: "I have sinned a great sin. Return, my son David; I shall no longer seek to do you harm, and this is because my soul was precious in your eyes. But regretfully, I have played the fool and have made a grievous error in judgment."

David had heard Saul's heartfelt remorse before but was not convinced of his often-fleeting sincerity and was reluctant to approach the king again.

David discreetly offered, "I have your spear. Send a young man to fetch it. I will keep your flask as a token between you and me so that you will no longer seek my harm. The Lord delivered you into my hands this day, my king, but I could not and would not strike down the Lord's chosen. As I have spared your life, I would pray you spare mine and let the Lord deliver me from all my troubles."

Saul, ashamed and remorseful, concluded, "Bless you, my son, David! You shall do great things, and you will prevail against all your enemies."

David left the spear for Saul's young messenger and departed for greener pastures. Saul gathered his army and returned to Gibeah the following day.

CHAPTER TEN

The Best of Enemies

D avid pondered in his soul how many times Saul had repented of his obsession to seek his destruction. But Saul always returned, like a dog to its vomit, with hate and vengeance in his heart.

David gathered Abiathar, his priest, his two wives, and three brothers, and they held a council in the wilderness. He confided, "Saul is relentless and craves my destruction to protect his house and his dynasty. I do not doubt that he will catch us flat-footed and unawares one day, and he will seal my doom with sword or spear."

Abinadab firmly nodded, and the others agreed, "But, what are we to do?" he exclaimed. "Where can we go to blind his spies and lessen the devotion of his well-paid informants? I mean, little brother, have you considered another place where we can prosper and be safe from Saul's constant stalking?"

"I am considering a daring destination that will blunt Saul's evil ambitions and largely confound his spies," David explained.

"There is nothing better for us to do than to escape into the land of the Philistines. Saul will not invade Philistia, and he will soon despair in his quest, knowing that it would be both fruitless and dangerous to pursue me. We shall thereby escape from his clutches. Our best protection will be to leave the borders and all the coasts of Israel far behind us."

Abiathar, Eliab, Abinadab, and Shammah looked puzzled.

Abinadab spoke up first. "Philistia?? Those idol-worshiping heathens are our sworn enemies! We would certainly be going from the wilderness of doubt into the certain jaws of destruction with this ill-thought and reckless scheme, little brother."

David replied with an air of self-assured confidence, "I have made a sure friend with one of the Philistine princes, Achish of Gath, the son Moach, the king of all the Philistines.

"I had spared his life in a battle—er, well, we saved each other's lives."

Abiathar piped up: "Pray, tell us the account, noble prince. I am never weary of the telling."

Pleased with the praise, David replied, "Very well, if it will ease my brother's misgivings. We were the last two men left standing from a ferocious Philistine encounter. We were fighting to the death on a wilderness outcropping; everyone else was either dead or fled. Neither one of us would withdraw, concede, or give ground. We were both completely spent, and neither one of us could lift their weapon with enough strength for a killing strike. Suffering from exhaustion, thirst, and utter fatigue, we started laughing while struggling to rise from our knees. We were quite a sight to behold! Achish produced a sparking flint, and I gathered kindling for a warming fire. As night fell, we sought a warrior's common understanding. We both kept a wary eye on each other's weapons, just in case there was a sudden change of heart. The night bit down hard with damp, bitter cold. Then, suddenly, we were roused back to our feet by a menacing growl. We looked up into the reflecting yellow firelight eyes of a ravenous she-bear. The smell of fresh blood had drawn her to our position. By working together, we were able to ward off the demon beast and bone-chilling exposure. Finally, after a fierce struggle, she decided it was safer and easier to drag off a rotting corpse and not reckon with her death. In saving each other's lives, we promised and covenanted in surviving that harrowing ordeal that we would help the other on the day of reckoning. I think that today is that day. Let us seek sanctuary with an enemy of our enemy." All remained breathless in amazement at such a story.

David crossed over the frontier to the side of the Philistines. With him were his two wives, Abigail the Carmelitess (Nabal's former wife) and Ahinoam the Jezreelitess; Abiathar, son of Ahimelech, David's priest; and his brothers three, Eliab, Abinadab, and Shammah, the eldest sons of Jesse. Lastly, bringing up the rear, David's 600 sparsely armed vagabond army of God.

The group covered their weapons and made no stops whatsoever as they traveled into enemy territory. Instead, they peaceably sought Prince Achish and the hope of protection.

At first sight, they had the appearance of an undisciplined mob (with camp followers, wives, and a long baggage train of chests, chairs, and bedding) descending upon the heart of the Philistine capital. As they approached a vast, walled city, David stepped forward and cried out. "We seek permission to enter Gath's royal city."

A lone sentry put his head over the ramparts and inquired, "Who goes there, and what is wanted?" David lifted his voice: "I am David, son of Jesse, the Israelite. My people and I have come with an open invitation from the prince himself and seek admission only to serve my lord Achish."

Word quickly spread to the inner sanctum. Prince Achish appeared at the battlement in short order—only to witness David and his whole ragtag army, a wild bunch who had only one thing in common—a lack of social grace and the ability to defend or kill as the situation warranted.

Achish cupped his hands and yelled down, "A day of reckoning, you say? It has come sooner than I had expected! I see that my friend is in distress, and so is an opportunity to honor my pledge of devotion. But know this, son of Jesse: you and all your friends are welcome here. I will meet you inside the gate, and we shall have a feast and toast to our reunion. Tonight, we shall speak of things most pressing, painful, and pleasant for as long as the dark-red wine flows."

The Ziphite tracker Manoach had witnessed David's welcome into the center of the Philistine nation. Making haste, he reported back to his master, King Saul. "Your Majesty, the renegade son of Jesse, has found sanctuary behind the high walls of the royal city of Gath."

Saul's emotions clashed concerning this unforeseen turn of events. Was David recruiting enemy forces to help him overtake his kingdom? Again, Saul considered how best to deal with this potential usurper and his constant disruptions. Although he was almost pleased with David's voluntary exile, he sighed as a heavy weight lifted from off his shoulders. "I will not, or cannot, invade Philistia, and I will no longer seek the life of David beyond the borders of Israel."

Three weeks had passed in idle pagan pursuits of corruption and luxury. David was becoming uneasy; all around them, the Philistine wooden and stone idols dotted the landscape. Even his men, loafers and malcontents, were fighting amongst themselves from the lack of action, discipline, and direction. The longer they stayed in the capital, the more worried he became that one of his men would get drunk and start an inevitable clash of heritage.

During the very next feasts, David toasted his generous host with a plea, "Prince Achish, your abundant generosity only matches your kindness. My lord, if I find favor in your eyes, I will ask for a much-needed reprieve from my inactivity. My men and I languish and have become sluggish here in your royal city. We are warriors who grow fat and lazy, and our swords rust for the lack of combat. Lord, if you have an outpost town where we could ply our mercenary trade and harass our common enemies, we could gather wealth and past-due taxes to pay you back for your gracious generosity."

Achish was impressed with his guest's timely request. "David, once again, you are a step ahead of my very thoughts. I have such a village on the southern borders of Judah. It is called Ziklag. There are many Israel-friendly towns and villages to plunder— that is, if you have the stomach for such an adventure against your people."

David was glad for the gift and boldly responded, "My people have forsaken me; they seek my harm and my life. I am a wanderer and a nomad. I am tracked and hunted like a wild animal. You, Prince Achish, have given me a home and shelter from the storm. Your enemies are my enemies, and I will prove this agreement in the coming days, weeks, and months."

David and his company, wives, priest, and brothers three descended on Ziklag with the royal decree in hand. The first order of business was to dismiss the standing Philistine garrison and have David's inner circle replace all the town officials.

David installed a town council of his inner circle to work out all the finer details. After settling in, David laid out Achish's cunning plan to pillage Judean villages. Then, passionately, Eliab took the floor, "Are we to believe that we are going to make war on our very own people?"

David, with a mischievous smile, shook his head, "Brother, you think so little of me, your little brother. I had invented that ploy to gain access to this Philistine stronghold. We will pillage the Gershurites, the Gezrites, and the Amalekites—who are our sworn and ancient enemies. They perceive us as being long-term alien squatters in Canaan. We will scorch the earth south to the wilderness of Shur even unto the land of Egypt. In our reaping, we will leave no one alive, men, women, or children."

Abiathar was taken aback at that cruel and vicious statement. "Certainly not the children—how could you?"

David was not pleased with his priest's challenge to his authority. David defiantly responded, "Abiathar, my pious friend, what would you have me do? Who would care for a brood of fledgling blood-feud assassins? None can be left alive to carry the news of our deceit to the ears of Achish, our benefactor, less we would feel the heel of a Philistine betrayal and then suffer a savage reprisal."

And so, David and his men scoured clean the land and left no witnesses to tell the tale of his Philistine treachery. Their fires burned so hotly that they could incinerate entire village populations. David's men took away the sheep, oxen, donkeys, asses, and camels from a village. David and his men gathered up gold, silver, furniture, and fine apparel, and nothing was left that had any value.

A horn of plenty deftly gathered when the time came to give up a portion as taxes to David's unwitting benefactor, Prince Achish. Of course, the prince was pleased with his share of the spoils delivered to his treasury. First, however, he felt compelled to inquire about the trails David had taken to obtain his ill-gotten gain, "Where have your raids taken you these days?

David, practiced in his deceit, said casually, "From the southern end of Judah, south of the Jerahmeelites and against the south of the Kenites."

There were none left alive to contradict David's telling. For if so, it would have meant his life and the lives of all his people. Achish believed David's tall tales and was glad of heart, for he thought David's raids had been against his very own countrymen. Israel would now loathe and despise him, and, thus, David would be his servant forever.

CHAPTER ELEVEN
The Rejection of Renegades

The call to arms had gone abroad, to all the coasts of Philistia. The five Philistine princes had counseled together. The time was ripe for an invasion of the Hebrew immigrants. Not only was the strategy favorable, but it also had more than a promising chance of being overwhelmingly decisive. Accordingly, the princes of Ashdod, Ekron, Ashkelon, Gath, and Azzah, joined together in a war council.

King Moach addressed the gathering: "Princes of Philistia, hear me now. We have, for the very first time, put away all our petty jealousies. We now can be of one heart, one mind, and truly united in a common cause to exterminate the prickly Hebrew immigrants. These unwelcome refugees, who reproduce at such an alarming rate, will eventually swallow up all of Canaan if we let them. We will never be as strong again as we are today. Each prince has made some menacing inroads in the past, but nothing has ever become permanent or lasting. Therefore, we, as a people, need to put aside our petty differences and enslave these vagabond nomads before it is too late and we are the ones who find ourselves extinct."

A cheer went up, and the princes banged their wine cups on the banquet table. King Moach stood for a moment, basking in the acclaim, and then raised his hand, signaling for silence.

"Every man who can wield a spike, sword, battle-ax, or shield will gather at Aphek, our most distant and northern fortress. Our esteemed General Padi will be our sole commander, reducing the friction of competing egos. First, we will attack the enemy's weakest point. Then we will drive southward, pillaging and burning as we go."

Moach extended his hand, and, like spokes in a wheel, all the princes, in turn, grabbed hold, the unity forming the hub of agreement.

Prince Achish was pleased and had high confidence in his servant David, the Israelite rogue. Achish comforted David when he stated, "I want you to know that, as I am sure of anything, I am sure of your loyalty. You and your men will accompany me to the decisive coming battle."

David was pleased with the fruits of his deception and replied, "You do know, Prince, and with certainty, what I am capable of accomplishing once I set my will and mind to a task."

Achish smiled and nodded in agreement. "I am most keenly aware of your dedication, skills, and abilities. Therefore, I will make you my bodyguard for now and forever."

The Philistines gathered en masse at Aphek, the farthest and most northern reaches of Philistia, and threatened Israel's borders with a terrible reckoning. The Israelites were made aware of the enemy buildup, and they pitched their tents at the Jezreel spring so that the long shadow of Mount Gilboa shielded them from view.

The Philistine army passed on by hundreds and by thousands, but David and his men passed on in the rearmost ranks of the gathering, dutifully attended by their benefactor, Prince Achish. The king and the other four princes rejoiced in the mighty show of force. When the tail end of the final column approached, the princes' eyes were stung with the vision from an unlikely host of 600 Judean vagabond warriors.

Prince Seranim [meaning "hinge"] was bewildered and inquired of Achish, "Who are these Hebrews who find credible shelter under your banner?"

Achish was expecting such a challenge and confidently replied, "It is David, the renegade servant of Saul, the king of Israel. He has been with me these many days, and I have found no fault in him. David has done my bidding and has ruthlessly harassed Judea for his needs and our benefit. His people despise him, especially among his countrymen—mainly for his many cruel massacres. Besides, he has pledged his undying loyalty and his allegiance to the Philistine nation and me personally. I have seen for myself his word and his deeds, evidenced by the mounting spoils of Judean pillage."

In turn, all the princes voiced their concerns and were, to a man, displeased with Achish and his ill-advised attempt to give the highly suspicious Judean any credible standing.

Seranim spoke for the lot: "Achish, make this fellow return to his place, the place where you have given him. We cannot allow him and his men to go down with us to battle. For what if, in the heat of battle, David reconciles with Saul, his former master? He then turns against us and becomes our entrenched adversary. David and his army would be at our rear, and the army of Israel would be at our front. On the one hand, his killing of Philistines could be the one act that could balance the scales for past harms done, and thus he could make peace with Saul, his king. But, on the other hand, consider: is this not the David of whom the women sang to one another in dances, saying, 'Saul slew his thousands and David his ten thousand'?"

Achish had no choice, for the collective will of the princes was final, and even to his father, the king, there was no appeal. Achish then summoned David and, sorely downcast, uttered, "I have no complaint against you, my friend. On the contrary, as you have taught me of your living God, I can find no fault or evil in you. On the contrary, all your goings and comings have been upright in my eyes. Still, the princes do not find favor in you. For that reason, you are to return to Ziklag and not challenge the high council. But, know this: You and your men escape with your lives intact only by my insistent pleadings."

David's cunning plan to redeem himself in Saul's eyes was abruptly aborted. The Philistine prince Seranim had uncovered the secret workings of his mind. But just the same, he complained about his dismissal to maintain his standing with Achish.

David pleaded, "Have I not, in all this time, proved myself in your eyes? But now, only to be denied fighting against the enemies of my lord Moach, the Philistine king?"

Achish shook his head. "I know you are a good man and a messenger from the gods—with great wisdom and graceful behavior having an endearing openness about you. But, the unconvinced council of princes was angered and steadfast that you should not go up with us into battle. Some declared that you had already killed more Philistines than anyone living. Seranim reminded me that you were loyal only to me and not to Philistia or our cause. Overall, they hinted that it would be most fitting to take your head and be done with any further argument.

"I need you to depart back to Ziklag before first light. You and all your servants need to rise and leave before the quarrel becomes violent with more wine and less restraint and before your death becomes more appealing than my claim for your continued well-being".

Before the cock crowed, David and his army had departed and set out to return home to Ziklag. He thought best not to risk the wrath of the Philistine princes only to fall prey to their murderous intentions.

CHAPTER TWELVE

The Valley of Sorcerers and Warriors

The trek back to Ziklag was brisk until the Aphek stronghold dropped well below the horizon. With the real possibility that Prince Seranim would have a change of heart and a double mind to engage in a hostile act of reprisal, David wisely installed rearguards to avoid surprises. They acted as a timely warning to prevent a blindsided intrusion that could have devastated the entire column. The pace had slowed just slightly when a flanking action became less and less likely to occur.

Abiathar, young and robust with shoulder-length hair, approached David leading at the very head of the procession and began spouting well deserved praises, "Your plan to infiltrate the Philistine ranks was bold, daring, and divinely inspired. By placing your army in the far rear of the battle, all Philistine eyes would have been forward on the enemy defenses. As the reserve force, your men would still have been fresh, while the Philistine army was exhausted and worn out. You could have sliced easily into the battle at the most tender spot and turned the struggle into a rout. This action could have redeemed yourself once and for all in King Saul's judgment and all of Israel, or we all would have met a bloody but glorious end."

David sighed, both in relief and disappointment. "Yes, Priest, it was not God's will, but either life or death, it would have been a legendary ending or a bright new beginning."

Three days passed before bitter smoke smarted the weary soldiers' upturned noses. However, upon reaching the top of a familiar rise, their eyes were stung with surprise and horror. Their whole town had been razed to the ground by fire. David's men broke ranks and ran at full gait to the smoldering wreckage.

A lame beggar hobbled out of the smoke and shadows. "My name is Mishma," he said, "for I have seen, and I have heard those who have caused this firestorm."

David came up, holding back his rage and eagerness to kill. "Who has done this thing, where are all the people, and why are you still among the living?"

The beggar whimpered. "Forgive me, lord; I was gathering wood when I heard a commotion. I then hid and witnessed the carnage from a distance. The few men you left behind put up a valiant struggle but died fighting. Take heart, sire, for none of the women and children lost their lives, neither the great nor the small; all have been taken away as captives. I crawled in as close I dared, and I heard them say that they had spared a Philistine village but made a fiery exception of Ziklag, for it was the place of the renegade David. The Amalekites knew that the town would be undefended; a Ziphite spy had sold them such knowledge for a purse of gold."

The Amalekites had invaded all the south of Judah. They came up for slaves and spoil. But all was set aside when they found their opportunity to quench their pent-up fury of revenge on Ziklag, the son of Jesse's stronghold. The people howled with grief for losing their wives, sons, and daughters. They lamented their charred and ruined homes and the loss of their flocks and herds. Everyone wept until they could weep no more. Some tore their skirts and put ashes on their heads. Even David's two wives, Abigail and Ahinoam had suffered capture. David was distraught, for the people blamed him for this calamity and spoke harshly of stoning him to ease their sorrow. David was afraid of his men's wrath and encouraged himself by trusting in the God of Israel.

David called out to his friend and priest Abiathar, "Bring me my linen Ephod so that I may commune with the God of Israel for comfort and direction." David prayed, "Shall I pursue after this band of marauders? Shall I overtake them?"

The Lord God answered, "Pursue, for you shall surely overtake them, and without fail to recover all."

David was encouraged, and he gathered up his 600 men and prepared to hunt down these brigands.

Unexpectedly, a shofar horn blast shook the Ziklag encampment; the army of Manasseh formed on the crest of the overlook. Adnah, Jozabad, Jediael, Michael, Jozabad, Elihu, and Zilthai, each a captain of a thousand, were all mighty, valiant men. But, as usual, David was uneasy as to the purpose for the approach of this great host. David moved toward the seven captains, and before he could utter a word, they all, in unison, took a knee and bowed their heads. David stopped in his tracks and voiced, "What brings you, great generals, to my burned-out village?"

Adnah, the head captain, spoke for the crowd, "Saul had summoned us to his coming battle, and we gathered our forces.

Then we received word of your attempt to join the Philistine army to oppose Saul. We agreed by this action that you would have carved a courageous path in the great battle, but then you were rejected by the very same princes of the Philistines, fearing a sudden reversal of loyalties. Therefore, we deem it an honor to come and serve you—David, son of Jesse, the Lord's Anointed and future king of Israel."

"That is well," David replied, a shadow of a tear trickling down his cheek, "for the Lord God, Adonai, has sent you in my time of greatest need. We pursue an army of raiders whose numbers are vast, and your courage will weigh as much as your righteousness in the coming conflict."

Two hundred of David's men were exhausted and spent from the long journey home and the emotional toll from being greeted by scorched houses. Abiathar inquired of David, "Lord, there are 200 souls who beg your leave and pardon, and humbly ask you that they not cross over the river Besor. They will gather up the strays, bury the dead, and protect the resurrected memories rescued from the wreckage. They need time to rest and rebuild their courage and their strength. But they will solemnly pray for your success and safekeeping."

David smiled and nodded in agreement. "Abiathar, and all you men who need to be left behind, know this: The Lord our God has told me of my success. So, either with the many or the few; it matters not, if need be, I will go it alone, for the God of our fathers is with me."

The 400 belonging to David and the 7,000 from Manasseh remained encouraged by David's unwavering faith and steadfast determination. The host crossed over the river Besor, leaving their 200 faint comrades guarding the broken nest.

After several days of hot pursuit, the tracks of their prey grew faint. A positive direction for finding the raiders had become more of a guess than a certainty. David prayed for guidance. Then God answered: An outrider came upon an Egyptian fellow in an open field. On a closer look, he appeared to be dying. The scout brought the listless man to David for questioning. David concluded that the man was near death from a lack of water and starvation. He needed to revive him before he could inquire as to the possible whereabouts of the Amalekite marauders. David dripped water in his mouth and then provided bread and wine. Soon the stranger revived and gulped down a cake of figs and two clusters of raisins. The suffering Egyptian gradually regained his senses.

David questioned him. "You have the marking of a slave. To whom do you belong, and who are you?

The thankful man replied, "I am a young man of Egypt, my name is Ubaid, I am a servant to an Amalekite chieftain, Lotan, the plunderer; my master left me because three days ago I fell sick." He gulped down more water and then continued. "My master had learned of a great battle brewing between the Philistines and all the Hebrew tribes. So he considered that the time was ripe to invade towns and villages in the south because all the men fit to fight would be off to war. We then gathered all our forces and made an invasion upon the south of the Cherethites. We struck all the coasts that belong to Judah and the Philistines, even to the south of Caleb. My master burned Ziklag with the hatred of fire. It was a deliberate reprisal against David, the son of Jesse.

The raiders wanted to kill all who breathed in Ziklag, repaying Jesse's son for his many Canaanite massacres. But my master is a man of commerce, and he knew he could sell the women and children in Egypt as slaves for a hefty profit. So even with the spoils from all the towns, he is still greedy."

David held back his angry hand and asked Ubaid the slave, "Do you know where this company of thieves gather?"

Ubaid was grateful to David for saving his life, and he gladly agreed to cooperate. "I will, and I can, but you must promise me, by all that you hold holy, that you will leave me alive and will not return me to my cruel and demanding master. If you so swear, I will take you there as soon as my legs allow my travel."

David so agreed and added, "Some promises are easier said than done, for your master will not escape my vengeance, neither by black magic nor demonic possession. When I lay my eyes upon him, I will take from him the breath of life. As for you, Ubaid, banishment, but alive and free to return to Egypt, to whatever fate awaits you, I do so swear."

Ubaid was true to his word and guided David and his troops, west, and south, following a secret route until he reached a lush, hidden valley. As David looked down from the rim into the middle of a deep, lush, green canyon, they were many, many more men than David had imagined; they covered the broad valley floor like a swarm of locusts. Enemy lookouts were noticeably absent, for they were all were celebrating a great mountain of spoils recently stolen out of the lands of Judah and the surrounding Philistine borders. The raiders were eating, singing and dancing, all the while emptying red-wine barrels with cheerfulness and laughter. Eliab clutched David's arm and spoke urgently in his ear, "David, I believe we have an opportunity here. As of yet, our presence goes undetected, and the sun is about to drop below the horizon. Fortunately, it will be a perfect surprise to attack during the time of the long shadows."

David thoughtfully considered his older brother's observation. "Good point, Eliab. The longer we linger here, the greater the likelihood of being detected, and we will lose the advantage of surprise. The enemy will undoubtedly form battle lines and will seek the cover of makeshift barricades. Our problem is that night battles are shaded with uncertainty, mainly because, in the hours after twilight, friend or foe is hard to know with any degree of confidence."

Eliab, with a sly grin, countered, "I had considered at length the problem of the failing light. How in the dark, wooded night can you know whether to defend or fight? I had spied several bolts of bright white fabric in the baggage train of Manasseh. Each man is to bind a strip of white cloth around his right arm, so in the dark fog of war, a friend will be marked separate from his adversary."

"Brilliant," David exclaimed in a loud voice that was luckily drowned out by the merrymaking far down below. In a calmer tone, he continued, "Tonight, the moon will have a full bright face. I will take this fortunate timing as a sign of God's grace upon us." David gathered his men and his captains of thousands. He gave them their marching orders for a down-and-out attack. "Men of Israel, we are the vanguard of a vast army of God. A new beginning lies before us with our wives and children's recapture, and the accumulated treasure from these raiders will raise every man and set our place forever in Israel. Men, wrap a white scrap tightly around your right arm. This ribbon of separation will help identify friends from foe, even in the heat of battle and in the coming dark shadows."

David and his growing army found courage with white cloth and fierce determination. The army silently swooped down like birds of prey with the last rays of a dying sun. The surprise to the raiders was complete. The Amalekite raiders always felt safe and secure when settled in their secret lair. They had expected to have another week to celebrate and then disappear before being discovered. Instead, the bandits scrambled, women screamed, and men fumbled for their weapons of war.

The white armbands proved to be a bright beacon of recognition, as many raiders killed their own in the gloom and confusion. The hardiest of the scavengers soon regrouped and were putting up a strong resistance. It was man to man, and face to face; sometimes gangs of fours and fives formed only to disappear in deep ravines or the densely wooded underbrush. It was a battle of shouts and shadows until a distant cock crowed against a blazing sun, revealing a sharp vision of blood and carnage that covered the entire valley floor. Battle lines stood, broke, and reformed. Advantage precariously swayed back and forth through the whole of the following bloodletting day. David caught sight of Lotan several times but getting close to him proved costly and nearly impossible. The combat throughout the afternoon was an even match, as each side worked to play off the other's exhaustion. Finally, on the evening of the following day, victory proved close at hand. Most bandits were dead by sunset except for 400 of the craftiest and most resourceful of Lotan's inner circle.

Amalekites were known as sorcerers who could transform themselves into animals at will to avoid capture. This tale proved true as Lotan and his entire band of 400 broke free and ran over a nearby hill. Hard afoot and in pursuit and cresting the ridge, David looked in astonishment at a flock of 200 camels still on their knees. Each man found a needed mount aiding in his escape. Rapidly, the unholy pack lit out, cloaking their departure with the long shadows from the rapidly approaching sundown.

The glory and the victory would have to wait until all the missing loved ones' whereabouts were made known. Then, by chance, an observant scout discovered a secret cave opening covered by tree branches and dense underbrush. He reported it, and David and Eliab were the first to enter, to find it gloriously filled with exquisite loot from the many days (and perhaps years) of Amalekite plunder. Sparking their torches, David and Eliab ventured deep into the vast underground cavern. Their torchlight glinted back from polished gold and silver trinkets. Just then, a relieved voice of recognition echoed just beyond the reach of the firelight. Abigail and Ahinoam and all the hostage women and children were huddled together in the deep, dark shadows, questioning what harsh fate might befall them. Haloed by the torchlight, David and Eliab looked angelic, with their swords drawn, joyously recognized as saviors coming to the rescue.

The pleasant Ahinoam and the beautiful Abigail jumped up with relief and hurried to the feet of their loving husband David and his brother Eliab. Abigail recounted, "We thought never to see you again, for, on the morrow, the slave traders were to take us away to distant shores of heathen Bedouin kings, all the women, and all the children. Our captors saw that the children provided leverage in helping to keep us docile, with the threat of harm or murder of our offspring."

David hugged and kissed each wife in turn and soothed their fears with kind words: "Dear madams, my wives, and the loves of my life, and all is well. We are victorious. Take no thought of harm or injury, for your welfare is assured and gallantly protected. We will soon make a new home, an elegant royal domicile, and these countless treasures will ensure your comfort and our new prosperity, my future queens of Israel." The women wept, partly in gratitude but mostly from relief.

Both small and large found freedom that day, and no one and nothing went wanting or missing. All the hostage women and children remained unharmed. But emotions were raw and unsettling from the wounded's piercing screams and the countless dead bodies strewn about in the blood-soaked ground.

CHAPTER THIRTEEN
Those Who Keep the Watch Earn As Much

The victor retains life's breath, treasure enough, and acclaim that shakes the pillars of heaven.

David delighted in satisfying his vanity and called a champions council. He began, "Esteemed Captains of Manasseh, Brothers three, and my friend Abiathar, the High Priest. Our first challenge is to burn the dead, aid the wounded, and comfort the dying. We have lost too many fearless warriors and the Amalekites twice again as many. Corpses now rot in the sun, and we need to build funeral pyres. Next, we need to divide the spoil fairly by rank and the number of men who have fallen in battle. Lastly, we need to salt the ground and foul the water, so this hideaway never comes back alive to haunt us ever again."

With all in its order, it was time to return home and rebuild Ziklag.

David's mooing herds and noisy flocks of baaing sheep and bleating goats led the parade of captured livestock. What came first was counted as David's property by right of conquest, which was only fit and proper, followed by a continuous parade of assorted animals.

Upon returning to the brook Besor [meaning "good news"], David saluted his 200 men who had been too faint to go with him and did not partake of the killings. "Men, I have good news—as you can see, the sons of Manasseh have increased our strength and numbers. God has given us an overwhelming victory over the invincible Amalekite pirates. It is a glorious homecoming; all our women and children are back with us. The spoil we carry into view speaks to the bounty of our glorious God. His goodwill and favor have carried us through to our victory over the idol-worshiping heathens."

But charity and generosity were quite alien to some of David's hard-hearted and stubborn men. Samael, a strikingly handsome fellow, was both kind and cruel and spoke for such a bunch: "These loafers faltered, and they all but abandoned us to our fate. They feigned weakness to the challenge on the very day of reckoning. They should not and shall not share in the booty of our blood-spilled labors. They should instead be reunited with their wives and children and depart from us, empty-handed."

The men who'd stayed behind were glad for the victory and the return of their wives, children, and sweethearts. They did not feel entitled to the captured bounty but did not want to be banished. They waited with bated breath for David's judgment.

In response, David scrambled upon a high rock and gathered unto himself the whole assembled force. Then, to one and all, he proclaimed, "The One True God has not only delivered us but has given us an exceptional bounty, enough to make every man rich in his own right. You will not deprive these, our brothers, of the gifts that our God has so generously bestowed upon us. He has preserved our very lives and the lives of our women and children. He has delivered a fierce company that came against us and has put them into our hands. None will listen to your greedy plea, Samael. God's will is always about charity and the generosity of the heart."

David then lifted his voice to the heavens and decreed, "It is our fault that we did not leave sufficient guard and fortifications to defend Ziklag while we were gone to battle. They who went down to the battle shall have an equal part with those who remained behind to guard our homes and belongings. God loves a giving soul and blesses the giver with treasures that will not corrupt or be stolen by thieves in the dark."

David's declaration of unity uplifted all. Even Samael, then, hung his head down and never uttered even so much as a grunt. The anointed David, not yet king, made this a statute and an ordinance in Israel forever.

Arriving at Ziklag, the labor of rebuilding commenced in earnest, with the sweat and toil of many hands to make the work lighter. Surprisingly, several of the Manassehites stayed behind to help rebuild the fortress town.

The haul from the Amalekite treasure trove seemed bottomless. Three trains of carts and wagons were not enough to empty the raiders' vaulted caverns. Security remained tight, but Lotan and his band of raiders disappeared, never to be heard of again. David then called forth his three brothers and Abiathar, the high priest, to help him flesh out an idea. Eliab, Abinadab, and Shammah were soon at the door. Abiathar lagged, trying to swig down his second cup of dark wine, choking down smoke-filled air. He finally stepped briskly out of the shadows.

"It is good that you are here, my dedicated priest. But I see you still stand too close to the fire. I was concerned you might have had something more pressing, like a vat of fermented red wine," David joked, and all had a chuckle at Abiathar's expense.

Good-hearted Abiathar laughed as well, and said, "I am here, Lord. What is needed? My ears are open, and my opinions are freely given—for what they are worth! So what is your pleasure, my lord?"

David began outlining his plan. "We have a great wealth of spoil and an opportunity to gain favor and affection with the Elders of Judah." David began to rattle off a long list of names and places. "Judah, Beth-El, and in the south, Ramoth, Jattir, Aroer, Siphmoth, Eshtemoa, Rachal, and to those who are in the cities of the Jerahmeelites, Kenites, and to those in Hormah, Chor-Ashan, Athach, and Hebron, and to all our regular haunts and hangouts. If you would be king, an army of God needs to be at your command, and this will only occur with the goodwill of the elders and princes of these towns and cities. What say you to all of this political tactic?"

All nodded in agreement, and Abiathar spoke: "My lord, the spoil is boundless and available, and your plan to curry favor with the nobility will undoubtedly ensure your kingship upon the throne of Judah. Once the kingdom of Judah and its army are at your command, can Israel be far behind? Saul's sun is setting, and your star, David, is rising. Let us organize the distribution before we all become too fond of our newfound wealth and glittering gold."

CHAPTER FOURTEEN
The Witch Hunt of Death and Destruction

Israel much lamented the passing of Samuel, the wise and noble prophet of God. Saul and his nobles laid the prophet's body to rest in Ramah, Samuel's city of birth. Elkanah was Samuel's father and had been a respected and wealthy Levite. Samuel's mother, Hannah, was a modest and Godly woman. She, too, had been a prophetess of God, and she prophesied with songs of worship and praise. His parents had also found rest in the hallowed ground set aside for the family of Korach.

Saul was downcast at the loss of his holy prophet, a channel to the divine for advice, inspiration, and much-needed direction. Samuel's burial procession was a regal affair, with great shows of mourning, pomp, and circumstance, all to tingle the ears of Israel in mourning and reverence.

Saul counseled with his uncle Abner, his ever-loyal and dutiful chief captain, and his four sons, Jonathan, Abinadab, Malchi-shua. and Ish-bosheth. "So, likewise, my royal family, Israel, looks to us for protection and guidance. I propose to honor our great prophet so that none will lose sight or memory of his devotion and contribution to our holy nation. Samuel had warned me early on to put away all that had familiar spirits or evil specters that could find no rest but found solace in the haunts and in the presence of certain mortals: necromancers or those who commune with the dead.

"With Samuel no longer here to guide us, these spirits will show themselves in much greater numbers. We must cleanse ourselves of all wizards, warlocks, witches, and anyone who practices the dark arts of black magic. We must also include diviners, enchanters, and observers of times, and so astrologers. These wicked practitioners outrage the Lord. We will put them away from Israel, forever and for all times. We will do this for a lasting memory to honor Samuel, our beloved prophet, and a warning to all those who would fight against righteousness."

Saul sent out a royal decree, and the slaughter of the innocent and the guilty quickly proceeded. Criers invaded every village, town, city, and hamlet. A silver coin would reward all informants who pointed the finger for the slightest whisper of wrongdoing. Anyone even slightly suspected lost the benefit of argument or defense. Herbalists, who practiced the healing arts, found themselves in this hated group. Anyone who owned a silver chalice and a black cat also became suspect. The sharp ax of execution visited those viewed prancing about in the forest during the new moon. The purge was as bloody and thorough as it was widespread. Those who could take flight did so before the headsman's blade, the burning stakes of brimstone fire, or the hangman's choking noose could find them. All suspects hastily and quietly departed so that none could track their whereabouts.

They raced headlong for safety far beyond the borders of Israel. Many found shelter in Moab and Aram.

A great battle was brewing; however, divine direction and intervention to avoid utter destruction went wanting. Saul was fearful of the outcome; an evil spirit had invaded his courage. Saul called forth Abner to discuss his experience in the coming conflict. "I am confident in our strategy, my liege."

Abner attempted to put Saul at ease. "I suggest that your worst enemy is your imagination. Other than that, call upon God, and pray for His favor, peace, and protection."

Saul's desperation grew, so he fasted and prayed just the same, but the defeat of Israel's army was looking more and more like a certainty. Saul's prayers came back void, for God withheld his peace because of Saul's earlier defiance. Saul had now lost his vivid dreams where his deep-rooted questions would be manifest with insights into the present and visions of the future. The king attempted to call upon the Urim and Thummim, the seer stones of lights and perfection, but even his wise men and lesser prophets were confounded and stood silent.

Saul never forgot his grievous offense because it had come early on, when the Lord told him, "Now go and smite Amalek, and utterly destroy all that they have, and spare them not; but slay both man and woman, infant and suckling, ox and sheep, camel and ass." Yet Saul had spared Agag, the Amalekite king, to all Israel's future sorrow and dismay. Saul defiantly saved the spotless livestock, and this, too, was willful defiance against God's command. Animalism was an accepted pagan practice, and many of the herds were grossly infected. Numerous Amalekites practiced black magic, and some could change themselves into animals at will. God had ordered, "All beasts slaughtered." And Saul did not obey. And on that day, Saul's destruction became inevitable, and it would come about at its appointed time and place.

All considered God's curse on Saul, just as news of the grand Philistine invasion commenced. The Philistine grand army had gathered and entered Israelite territory. The heathens had started their rampage and had already razed two Hebrew cities. Israelite troops from all the tribes united, with Abner at their head. Saul's sons waited for him to lead the Israelite army in their greatest battle, which would likely take place at Mount Gilboa.

But the king was going into the fray uncomfortably blind; he was receiving neither inspiration, nor divining, nor personal revelation on this epic battle.

Saul was sure that God had shunned him, which made him even more desperate in his search for answers. Saul called upon his most trusted and secretive servant: "Find me a woman who has a familiar spirit, a necromancer of a known reputation. I must go and ask her some urgent questions and that I might obtain some desperate answers."

In the past, one servant had used a woman necromancer's services but would have never divulged her involvement under the current climate of witch extinctions. But sensing the desperate sincerity of the king's plight, Tivona spoke up.

"Your Majesty, I know of such a woman who has all but retired. She no longer practices the dark arts for fear of life and limb. She is well versed, but few know of her existence. She is only spoken of in dark shadows and only in hushed whispers. Yet, the very woman you seek has contact with familiar spirits. She resides in a thatched cottage on the far side of the Endor Forest."

Saul was encouraged and had a sense of relief that comes from hope, no matter how fleeting. He carefully considered a sly approach, "We will don a commoner's attire for our disguise, neither beggar nor nobleman, so as not to alarm the witch as to my person or to give her misgivings and make her act contrary to my wishes."

Saul had his face shaved and then went to his changing room and disrobed. He tried on some plain clothes set out for him in his wardrobe. The commoner's clothes he tried on were not suitable and much too small. But finally, a sizable hooded cape and tall muddy boots provided complete concealment for his oversized form and familiar face.

With two of his now commonly attired and trusted body-guards, Saul set out soon after sundown. The trio traveled unnoticed, the disguised king riding in the back of a haycart. They were unobserved until reaching the hut of the enchantress. Then, a subtle knock, a gentle tap, tap, pause, and a tap, on an old weatherworn oaken door, a familiar signal known only to trusted patrons.

A women's raspy voice challenged, "Who goes there, and what is wanted?"

Saul's bodyguard replied, "We are strangers from a distant land who have come to pay handsomely for your unique services."

The door slowly creaked open on ancient hinges, producing a shrill screech, like a rusted coffin lid.

"Enter at your own risk and peril," voiced the old crone. "I do not recognize you—who sent you to my abode?" A bullfrog croaked, and a raven squawked somewhere back in dark shadows.

Saul replied from under his heavy hood. Only half his face was visible from the wavering light of a lone candle and the crackling fire under a boiling black cauldron. "Tivona has sent me; she has praised your abilities and described your need for life-and-death secrecy."

The witch beckoned, "Enter freely, then, by your own will and choice." Saul crossed over the threshold and was taken aback by a muffled crack, more felt than heard. He knew then he was in a mystical realm. Saul was inviting a cursing, but there would be no turning back—no matter how sinister, the kingdom of Israel was at stake. One guard found some rest on a makeshift bench. The other stood steadfastly to one side and guarded the sole entry.

Saul continued, "I pray you to divine me up a person—I shall name him when you are ready—by using your divining skills to call on familiar spirits that haunt this place."

The sorceress was wary of this troublesome stranger. She questioned, "Do you not know of the king's decree, even Saul, that he has executed all that have familiar spirits, all the wizards, witches, and all the sources of the black arts from the borders of Israel? I believe you have come here to my house to lay a snare and an elaborate trap to cause me to reveal something that would quickly end my life. For it is the king's command."

Saul attempted to put her at ease and voiced a solemn vow, "As the Lord lives, there shall be no punishment that will happen to you for doing my bidding. I so swear."

The witch discerned his word as true and accurate and asked, "Whom shall I bring up from their rest and sleep of the dead?"

Saul blurted out, "Samuel, the prophet who has recently departed—to him I would wish to speak."

"A moment to the dead is longer than a day," the witch declared. She closed her eyes and clutched a dark crystal lying on the table, willing herself into a trance. But when the woman saw Samuel, her mind was fully enlightened, and she knew all that was about to transpire and shrieked in a loud voice, "Why have you deceived me? For you are King Saul himself."

Saul quickly responded as he pulled back his cowl to reveal his face. "Quell your fears, madam, for I have sworn to do you no harm. Tell me what you saw far beyond the veil."

The aged sibyl was beguiled but only for a small while and eerily expressed, "I saw gods rising out of the ground."

Saul was both intrigued and enchanted by this unholy connection and asked, "What form and in what fashion did this spirit present itself?"

Then, with eyes slightly parted, the old woman hissed, "It was an old man who came up, and he was covered in a mantle."

Saul knew that it was Samuel, the prophet of God. Then Saul stooped with his face to the ground and bowed himself.

Samuel was altogether displeased with this unholy disturbance and said so. "Why have you troubled me to bring me back down to the land of the living?" he growled.

Saul had paid a heavy price but could now inquire of his former prophet, compelling him to continue. "I am painfully upset and uncertain. The Philistines have gathered a great army, and they make war against me. God has abandoned me and will not answer me, either by prophets or in my dreams. Therefore, I have called you, Samuel, from your peace and your rest so that I might know what to do next."

Samuel, with powerful words, pointedly bit back at him. "Why do you ask me these things? The Lord has departed from you and has left you to kick against the pricks. He has become your enemy. The Lord is doing to you what I had said would happen. He has wrenched the kingdom from your hands. He has given it to your neighbor, even David, the son of Jesse. All this because you did not obey the voice of the Lord when you refused to execute his fierce anger upon Amalek, and now the Amalekites will be a thorn in Israel's side forever. Your sorrow and your suffering must help to balance the scales of justice. The Lord will also deliver Israel and its host to the Philistines, along with you and your sons. I expect that you and they will be with me tomorrow."

Saul, hearing the prophecy, collapsed and fell straight away to the earth. His worst possible fears now manifested themselves in the coming battle. It was as if Saul's heart had already died, for Samuel's words had pierced his very soul. Saul was faint, and he had not eaten for a day and a night.

The witch took compassion on the troubled monarch. She solicited Saul with the kind words of a servant girl: "I have done your bidding and have obeyed your voice. I have taken my life into my hands and have dutifully attended to your needs and wants. I now ask of you, sire, to regard my request; let me prepare a morsel of bread for you to eat, so you can regain your strength before going on your way."

Saul, his head hung down, sad and discouraged, knowing the day of his coming death, and worst of all, the end of his house. He stubbornly refused her kindness and her offer.

His usually silent bodyguard, known for his tight lips, pealed in with his uplifting opinion.

"Sire, a full belly will always put a smile on your face. I have seen you prevail against greater odds before; take heart, my liege, for nothing is ever certain. For who knows what tomorrow may bring? But know this, sire—being faint on a day of reckoning will only worsen the sorrows and the suffering." The conjurer and Saul's other guard gently prodded Saul until he finally relented and agreed to take nourishment. His body bent up from the earthen floor as he sat on her unmade bed.

The crafty Sybil prepared a fatted goose for the three visitors, along with a loaf of fresh bread. She served it in her best peasant ware and on her rough-hewn wooden bowls. Saul, his men, and the Wiccan also ate supper without speaking. Then, as she took away the greasy plates, the satisfied siren imparted her heart to the monarch: "Sire, you bless my house and me with the breaking of bread and sharing this meal. I'm relieved to know that no one who would righteously bless could then execute death all in the same breath."

Saul handed the glad Endorian hag a bag of thirty silver pieces and a promise of continued life. He and his men secretly departed into the shadows and left the hamlet without arousing suspicion, for the moon had darkened, and it was well past midnight.

《 《 《 》 》 》

On the morrow, the Philistines gathered: it was the most massive army they had ever fielded. All the Philistine princes had put away their petty jealousies, envies, and strife and came together to eradicate their sworn enemy, the deeply rooted Hebrew intruders.

The Philistines encamped in Shunem [or "the place of double supports"]. A small village now overflowed with enemy infantry. It had belonged to the Tribe of Issachar, near the Jezreel Valley and south of Mount Gilboa. Saul gathered up the army of Israel at Mount Gilboa [or "the place of boiling waters"]. Many tribes refused to take part, as they had already flocked to the anointed David's banner. When Saul looked out upon the enemy's vastness massed against his forces, he was sore afraid, and his heart trembled in despair.

Saul called on his uncle and chief captain, Abner, for consolation and sage advice. "I look down upon Shunem, where every blade of grass is hidden. The thick covering by the enemy encampment reaches far beyond the horizon. Yet, because of your skillful planning, we hold the high ground, my capable uncle. We have as good and as many men as the enemy. But I remain unsure and disheartened. Abner, what would you suggest?"

Abner looked at the assembly and the advantage that they commanded, and he responded with the best of his experience: "Lord, I can cover the far-right ridge to avoid a flanking movement, but it is given to you to hold the center. That is the hinge that will sway the outcome of the battle."

Saul looked exhausted from the burden of worry, and he needed the relief that comes from confession. "I have a secret to disclose, uncle, a revelation that I would have taken to my grave. I did not want to reveal this in that it might undermine your resolve in the coming battle. I did not obey the Lord and took it upon myself to know better than Him, and on that day, my destruction was firmly preordained. My worst fears are about to come to pass, which was confirmed yesterday by a witch's unholy vision. I dread that the time of my death is today, and the location is here at Mount Gilboa."

"We are well-entrenched," Abner stated with steadfast conviction, raising Saul's hope in the outcome. Abner demanded, "We can, and we will, win this battle. I can see how we can turn the tide of war. But, take heart, my downcast nephew, I cannot predict fate's fickle finger. I can only put my best foot forward and, as you, trust in God."

Abner paused, standing to his full height and stature, and continued. "I know our glorious history, and I pass on our certain coming success to our soldiers with conviction and purpose. But, if it is today that any will succumb, let it be in this epic conflict— as God and Israel's heroes. Our sacrifice will be part and parcel of the legendary birth of our holy nation." Abner bowed deeply, mounted his horse, and rode to his position on the far ridge.

CHAPTER FIFTEEN
Nailed to the Wall After the Fall

The battle strategy was still being debated as the host of Israel set up camp in the Jezreel by the boiling springs of Mount Gilboa. The Philistines massed at Aphek ["the place of strength"], and the most northern Philistine garrison, located at the head of the Wadi Fik, six miles east of the Sea of Galilee. The enemy's numbers were more than a plague of locusts. The enemy tents covered the western hills to the plain of Esdraelon.

The morning was overcast, and so was Saul. He had tossed and turned in his bed like a broken hinge; his rest was elusive and sleeping impossible. The specter of Samuel haunted his every waking moment. Saul regretted his ill-fated witch hunt and Samuel's declaration of death—not as much for himself, but for his sons and the likely end of his house. His humiliation would be complete and ridiculed worse than death. There was one bright hope that Saul could hold on to like a straw in a whirlwind. His only remaining legitimate son and heir, Ish-bosheth, had taken ill and would not be at this day's coming battle. Ish-bosheth could take on the mantle of king and save the house of Saul and his future dynasty. Saul reflected on every word spoken by Samuel's phantom. Did he not say, "Today, you and your sons will join me?" If Ish-bosheth survived this day, there would be hope enough. Saul summoned his three sons, Jonathan, ["who was God has given"], Abinadab ["always willing"], and Malchi-shua, ["deliverance"].

Saul struggled with racing thoughts. He could not or would not give his sons the words of Samuel, not instill fear on the edge of battle. It could hasten their deaths and lessen their ability to defend conflict in the heat of battle. Perhaps he could dismiss them all, or two, or even one, from the coming struggle. It was certainly worth a try, thus giving himself even the slightest possibility to sidestep Samuel's morbid pronouncement. After all, the Endorian was a witch, and maybe it was all a trick from the devil himself. He is, after all, the biggest liar of them all. *Better safe than sorry,* thought Saul, muttering under his breath.

Saul's three sons entered the royal pavilion. The familiar family faces bypassed challenges from the well-armed and imposing sentries. The brothers came in and met with a sweet-smelling perfume that delighted the senses. Thick, colorful Persian carpets felt plush under their feet and had protected the king from the damp cold and blistering heat. There was a massive royal chair and a long oak table surrounded by polished brass and gold lampstands. The king saluted his offspring with a hug and a holy kiss, fearing that all their lives could end by dawn tomorrow.

Saul sat on his portable throne to make his words sound official. "The battle we are facing looks uncertain. We have never had to face this great of a Philistine horde before.

"To make matters worse, that renegade son of Jesse, your best friend, Jonathan, has had several princes flock to his banner, leaving us shorthanded and ill-defended. Therefore, I feel it is best for all three of you to leave the field—immediately. I fear for your lives, and the need to continue our house takes precedence. Our pride will all but stain the ground with all our blood, and we will be no more."

The three brothers looked to each other and, without a word, straightened up to their full height and stature. Then, Jonathan, who was his father's choice to be the next king, spoke up for the trio of princes. "Father, with all due respect, if the men witness that we tuck tail and run, for the sake of our safety and protection, all of our men will then question your resolve, and morale already low will all but crumble. As for me, sire, and I believe I speak for all three." His brothers grunted and nodded in agreement.

Jonathan steamed, "I would rather die than carry the yellow stain of cowardice in the presence of the enemies of Israel. My men look to me for courage and stability, as I look to you, my father, and my king for direction and guidance."

Saul lamented that his request was in vain and did an about-face and commenced to applaud his sons' collective bravery. "My brave and noble sons, I would not have thought any less of you for your discretion. Here, your unwavering courage heartens me in the coming maelstrom. I have summoned all the lesser captains and chief captain Abner for our final war council to defend the Jezreel Valley, the gateway to Israel—our food basket and the profitable northern trade route with Egypt, further to the south from Philistine occupation."

Abner filed in with all the other captains. There was no time for pomp and ceremony, as every hour was becoming critical. Just then, a scout soaked with sweat and caked with mud burst in, claiming an urgent report: "Go on, man spit it out!"

"Your Majesty and captains of Israel, I have delicate news."

"Proceed in the telling or feel my sting!" Saul stood up and growled.

"The Philistine army assembled at Aphek and traveled 40 miles south of Mount Moreh. They marched in the direction of the Judean ridge. Their heavy infantry, archers, and an endless train of chariots came upon the Carmel Mountain range. I lit out before being discovered to ensure that I could deliver this dispatch."

"Well done, lad," Abner commenced, "The Philistines have three possible routes in the Jezreel valley. We will have to defend against all three—the long, the short, and the hidden. We will conceal ourselves on this ridge. I believe in this position, and we have a distinct advantage. We are in an excellent place to observe the enemy forces and relay orders below to the defended slopes. We have a natural defense to stop chariot attacks and the ability to counter any frontal assault."

Saul was more than pleased with the merits of Abner's plan and gained confidence in a continued-life-and-breath victory. Saul praised Abner for his quick thinking. "Most excellent, my dear uncle and head captain of Israel—make it so! I have one demand, though—and it is not negotiable—that all my sons and I will fight together. There is no appeal to this decision. Other than that, make the army ready for battle. I can avoid arguments and rebellion by including my sons at the forefront of conflict.

Saul dismissed the council and addressed Abner, "I would speak to you in a private moment." Abner lingered as commanded.

Saul sat back in his chair of command and took Abner by the right hand. "This is undoubtedly good news—for our strategy is sound, better than I had expected. But as a precaution, I wish you to take an oath if I should perish with my three sons during this uncertain coming conflict. In that, you will be the lord protector of Ish-bosheth, my last rightful heir, who would be by the right of birth the next king of Israel, upon my death and the death of his brothers. Place this hand under my thigh, and so do swear by my seed and by your seed."

Abner did so swear, for he was confident in Israel's coming victory.

Achish, Seranim, King Moach, and the two other princes accompanied chief captain Padi, the renowned Philistine commander. Before leaving, King Moach climbed up upon the tallest parapet to address all present and within earshot. "Men of Philistia, princes, captains, and noble warriors. We set off on an expedition to punish and reclaim our long-held trade routes from Israeli bandits, mainly including our caravans that were either coming up from the south, even Egypt, and beyond. Also, all the goods that we are sending back are in a trade. Israel has regularly and routinely stolen all our wealth that passed through the Jezreel. These insults and robberies have gone unpunished for much too long. The place of contention is the fertile Jezreel. We will recapture our trade routes, and in doing so, we will annex all the valley's resources and have this precious gem for our own. We will dismiss these pesky immigrants with fire and fury to pull out this cankerous thorn in our side once and for all. Who is with me?"

A resounding cheer of agreement went up and out among the multitude. Bowman, spearman, and infantryman beat their chests.

War and chariot horses reared up, pawing the air, and whinnied with excitement. The Philistine horde found its footing with enthusiasm and proceeded the twenty miles to the Carmel Pass.

The army halted at the entrance to the Carmel Mountains. A decision as to which way to cross over the range became critical. There were three possible routes through the mountains; one of them had to be ideal. The Philistine commander Padi addressed a gathering of princes and captains. "If we take the southern pass, which would be the fastest route across the Plain of Dothan, we will risk ambush because of its nearness to Judea. If we take the northern way, it will take much longer to reach the Jezreel.

"Accordingly, I propose we take the middle way, which provides considerable cover because of the steep hills and dense forests. This path is called the Wadi Ara. This trail leads directly into the coveted valley. We also gain added security because our fortress of Megiddo is close at hand."

The Philistine army quickly passed through the dry Wadi Ara, and the fortress of Megiddo was now far behind them. They moved swiftly without incident, accident, or discovery. The highly organized legion made their way to Shunem, where they camped on the southern slope of Mount Moreh. To Captain Padi's delight, an additional brigade of infantry and spearman joined them from nearby Beth-shean. Padi gave the order, and the Philistines cohort settled into their designated fighting positions.

Saul ordered the army to move along the Judean ridge and take the high ground on Mount Gilboa. Abner reasoned that, if they kept to the peak, the army of Israel would remain invisible, and Saul could counter all of the enemy advances. The slope of the mountain also afforded him protection from the fearsome

Philistine chariots. Saul then placed most of his army at Mount Gilboa, and he purposefully put some warriors forward and along the slope while Israel camped securely by the spring of Harod.

Captain Padi had a shadow of an idea about the whereabouts of the enemy's location; he knew they were close at hand, but the Israelites had not yet revealed their position, resulting in a deadly calm before the storm. The coming battle of swords, spears, and axes turned into a stalemate of patient waiting, filled with nervous anticipation. Both armies held their collective breath and their positions.

At the very heights, an Israeli scout located a unit of Philistines below the northern slopes.

Once the Israelites made this discovery, they quickly sent word to Saul. Saul was in control of most of the army; he decided on a bold move. He ordered his men to show themselves along the exposed crest line in a futile attempt to disrupt the Philistine formation.

Padi quickly judged their position and immediately ordered the heavy infantry to assemble and join the fray. The infantry proceeded with a crushing determination in their well-trained battle formation. They marched directly up the slopes of Mount Gilboa.

Padi's strategy was a three-pronged coordinated attack from the north, east, and west. First, Padi put massive pressure on the Israelite forward lines and kept them engaged long enough for the Philistine archer chariots to be close enough to reach the summit of Mount Gilboa, at least with their arrows. Padi's spies had carefully scouted the area prior and had discovered the best way for their war wagons to reach the summit of Gilboa. Second, he ordered his thunder carriages to go through the village of

Gina. Gina was near the southern slopes of Gilboa and provided a gentle-enough slope to reach the summit.

As the overstretched Philistine formation pushed up the steep incline, Israeli forces struck back in strength. The Israeli reply was what Padi had in mind and was hoping for that exact enemy response. His three-pronged attack was powerful, well-prepared, well-deployed, and above all, fearsome. While the center engaged, Israel's flank—close to Gina—to flee before the advancing Philistines, and many fell dead on the southern slopes of Mount Gilboa. Philistine infantry was protected from behind by deadly accurate archers that picked off the remaining Israeli defenders. The Philistines steadily continued up to the summit.

Once at the top, the Israelite battle lines braced for a collision. With great ferocity, the Philistines smashed into the Israelite formation. Saul discovered, to his shock and dismay, that Israel could not push back the overwhelming Philistine horde. The king realized, too late, that he had no room to maneuver.

Israel was buckling, spilling buckets of blood, desperately holding on to their last slippery footing. They slowly gave way and became entangled with the infantry attack; the Philistine chariots now made swift headway through Gina and onto the rocky ridge unopposed. At the peak, the Philistine chariots struck, ideally situated above and behind the Israeli defenders. There was no chance of retreat. The charioteer archers combined with the infantry were raining down death and destruction against the trapped Israelite army.

Israel's situation had become desperately precarious. Their position was indefensible and increasingly overrun; it was every man for himself. Abner, witnessing the army's collapse, took who he could and slid down the backside of Gilboa, using the same road that the Philistine war wagons had used only moments before. The Israeli formation was fast crumbling. The Philistine commanders were on the prowl for Saul and his sons. They were spotted isolated, wounded, and vulnerable. Desperately, the three brothers and their father, Saul, and his loyal armor-bearer Naw-saw circled up and were not giving up without a fight.

Saul knew this was the judgment of God spoken through the ghost of Samuel. Saul lamented, "It is hard to admit defeat. My chief regret is the loss of you, my sons, who are my dearly beloved. Know that where we find ourselves is the will of God. You, my sons, are good men and will see His face this day, and my prayer is for the forgiveness of my many sins, for I am a weak and shallow man and have not been obedient to God's will in all things, neither things above nor below. By His mercy, if not justice, your brother Ish-bosheth may save our house and our name and be the next rightful king of Israel, I pray. But know this, I will fight to the end, protecting you and me, and will strike at every heathen before breathing my last."

The Philistine infantry closed in, and a desperate but futile rumble ensued. While the family fought like cornered lions, the Philistines killed Saul's sons, Jonathan, Abinadab, and Malchi-shua; each fell protecting his brother. Saul fought as a man possessed, taking a slew of enemies while holding his ground. With great delight, the Philistine archers marked him and showered him with a swarm of sharp-toothed barbs. Saul was limping but remained upright and bled from every wound. Finally, exhausted and knowing that his end was near, Saul turned to Naw-saw, his armor-bearer, and said: "Draw your sword and run me through, or these uncircumcised pagans will attempt to keep me alive to humiliate me and then kill me screaming in pain and horror." Regrettably, Naw-saw could not lift his sword and, for the first time, went against his master's wishes and did forgo his last command. Saul, in a moment of desperation, fell on his blood-stained sword. When Naw-saw witnessed the king's lifeless body, stabbed through, and punctured with a host of enemy arrows, Naw-saw's heart died within him, and he fell on his sword, for the pain of living was more significant than the fear of death and dying. At that moment, both David's prophecy and Samuel's curse came to pass.

Only a very few Israeli soldiers had managed to dodge the carnage and the defeat of Gilboa. They ran either by foot or by a horse's hoof to the bordering Israeli settlements. Their cry was as loud as it was disturbing. King Saul and his sons had fallen, and the army of Israel was in shambles. In turn, gossip and bad news fly on the twin wings of disaster and mayhem. An army of chin-waggers carried the message of desolation. Many nearby Israelite villagers ran for their lives, leaving the Philistines in turn to occupy the whole of the territory.

Some Amalekites, known to be unlawful scavengers, followed the engagement closely, even scavenging so close dodging spears and arrows. They would hurry in sometimes within a bowshot of an ongoing struggle, stripping the dead and the dying of weapons and armor, and any and all things valuable. When a scavenger got caught, he suffered torture before being put to a long and lingering killing.

After a battle, some of the victors would re-enter the killing fields. These warriors would end the suffering of any friend or foe alike who was desperately holding onto the last breaths of life with no hope of relief; they were called "finishers." This act entitled them to what spoils they could gather up and cart off, and they could do this legally by right of conquest and compassion.

Regular Philistine finishers were stripping the corpses of armor, weapons, and personal possession as the customary spoils of war. When they happened upon the fallen Saul, he was among a mangled pile of dead bodies. His armor was bound about his body, but his crown and his bracelet of authority were missing. Saul was lying face down and hard upon his ornate blood-stained spear. Captain Padi knew what to do with the body. The Philistine commander decided: "Cut off Saul's head and strip him of his armor. These royal trophies will attest to an overwhelming Philistine victory."

Padi dispatched messengers throughout Philistia, proclaiming the news in their cities and temples of his overwhelming triumph. They put Saul's armor in the house of Ashtoreth and fastened his and his son's corpses to the wall of Beth-shan.

The indignity done to Saul was an insult to all of Israel. When the inhabitants of Jabesh-Gilead heard of the outrage committed by the Philistines in the appalling violation of Saul's body, this outrage would not be tolerated or go unpunished. All the valiant men agreed and traveled only by night, protected by the cover of darkness.

They secretively took the corpse of Saul and the bodies of his sons down from the wall of Beth-shan. They came to Jabesh and burned them there with dignity and honor, befitting a royal monarch. A holy man took their bones, buried them under a tree at Jabesh, and fasted seven days in sackcloth and ashes.

CHAPTER SIXTEEN

Death Is the Messenger

David was back at home in Ziklag, fresh from the Amalekite slaughter. He was enjoying two full and beautiful days of rest and recreation. He was settling in with his recently rescued wives Abigail of Carmel, the wife of Nabal, and the pleasant Ahinoam of the Jezreel. The two women could not show him enough appreciation for their return to freedom and their renewed lust for life. Each wife tried to outdo the other with the gifts of ease and comfort, and David was subject to constant pampering. Ahinoam was as excellent a cook as Abigail was demure. David also basked in his newfound wealth. God had given the abundance of herds and flocks, a bounty enough in the making of a king. The men and their princes were gathering to David's standard; the army of God was forming around him.

The smell of a delicious leg of lamb was wafting through David's almost completed rebuilt villa. As far as prince Achish was concerned, David, the son of Jesse, was still an honored Philistine vassal. Three days after David's triumphant return home, he directed the labor and resources needed for Ziklag's resurrection. Stopping at the unsecured gate, a bedraggled stranger presented himself; his clothes were ripped open, and he had dark dirt streaks. A residue from the grease and blood of battle was all about his head and face. The sentry challenged, "Who goes there, and what is wanted?"

"My name is Eviyl, and I have come out of the camp of Israel. I escaped the slaughter of battle in the Jezreel valley. I have come a long way with news and royal spoil for David, the son of Jesse and the future king of Israel, and only to him will I give these glad but grave tidings."

The gate parted soon after the sun cast a long shadow. The stranger was stripped of all weapons and brought to the door, where David, his brothers, priest, advisors, and bodyguards presented themselves. Eviyl, when seeing David, fell to the earth and paid homage.

David commanded, "Stand up—tell me where you are coming from, all full of dirt, tattered, and torn."

"My name is Eviyl, and I have come out of the camp of Israel."

David, his curiosity piqued, asked, "How went the battle?"

Eviyl, looking down upon the ground, solemnly voiced, "It went badly, my lord. I barely escaped the massacre when the army broke ranks, and it was every man for himself. Many are fallen and dead, too many to count. Israel fared badly. We never surrendered and fought to the last." Eviyl knew what he said next could very well mean his death. He sorrowfully let slip, "King Saul, Jonathan, Abinadab, and Malchi-shua are also dead."

David snapped, "How do you know this for a certainty that these men are dead? Did you witness the fall or when they took their last breath," David demanded.

Eviyl gulped down his fear and continued, "In my hasty retreat and either by fate, chance, or accident, I came across Saul's and his sons' final stand on Mount Gilboa. My eyes beheld a standing figure leaning and straining on his exquisite spear, a beautiful armament of carved ivory with a blood-stained upper shaft; he used it as a crutch. He was stung with many arrows and was struggling to keep himself upright. His crown was still fixed and announcing his identity. A gaping bloody gash stained his chest. The man, larger than life, called out, 'I am Saul, the king of Israel, and my three beautiful sons lie dead at my feet.' Philistine corpses were piled high and all about them. They took many enemy warriors with them to the grave. At that very moment, the sound of rumbling chariots and pounding horses' hoofs was bearing down on our location. We heard the approaching pounding. Saul called to me, and he was unsure whether I was flesh and bone or a ghostly specter. 'Speak—answer me if you are real.' I answered, 'Here am I,' Then Saul asked, 'Who are you?' I answered, 'I am an Amalekite, and I stand with Israel.' Saul then commanded, 'If you are with Israel, I command you to stand up on me and slay me. I am in anguish; my beloved sons are dead at my feet, and my life is still whole within me. My fearsome enemies approach with evil intent in their hearts; they will humiliate me and torture me to my very last breath.' I rose and did as he commanded me. I stood upon him and slew him. I took the crown that adorned his brow and the bracelet of supremacy that was on his arm and have brought them to you, my lord. I have traveled an exhausting distance and at great personal risk to deliver these holy badges of authority to Israel's next king."

The now-quivering man opened his tattered bag and held out the royal items, one in each hand. It was as if a great wave of sadness and remorse had swallowed up David in one great gulp. Then David took hold of his garment and made a great tear [or a Kriah, acknowledging that the flesh is all but a covering, like cloth is to the body, and the rip releases the spirit of loss and remorse]. All the men about David followed the rending and said, "Blessed are You, Adonai Our God, Ruler of the Universe, the True Judge."

David was troubled with sadness and anger at the news of such a loss. David's eyes flashed red as he inquired further of the young man, "Who are you, and from what is your tribe?" David was searching for credible evidence of the truth or a lie.

Eviyl avoided eye contact and knew that sometimes the messenger of such evil tidings is immediately put to death.

Eviyl answered, "I am the son of a stranger and Amalekite."

David beckoned Eliab, Abinadab, Shammah, and Abiathar for a whispering counsel.

"What say you? This heathen has a fanciful story; is it believable? It seems a farfetched tale at best. I think he was a scavenger and closely followed the battle to see what he could scavenge from the dead. I believe he came upon the dead body of Saul and saw an opportunity for riches and to curry favor in the delivery of the crown and the bracelet. Whether this Amalekite enemy has done the deed or not, it matters not, for he has confessed it by his mouth. He has taken the blame for the slaying of the Lord's anointed. He has now put this evil at my feet. What say you as to the disposition of this thief and confessed murderer?"

Abiathar spoke first. "Lord, the young man's plea moved me, but I do not know what to make of it. The death of the royal family sorrows me, but in truth, Saul had ordered my father's murder, so I will stand moot on the matter of further bloodshed."

Eliab moved in close and privately whispered, "I believe that he came upon Saul by accident and that he did dispatch Saul as he had stated. The detail that confirms his story is Saul's spear. He described it perfectly, the object of Saul's power that had become his prop to keep him upright. Saul wielded it as a scepter of judgment and was never out of his reach. The same spear, little brother, that he hurled at you early on at the dinner table. The only other time it was out of his grasp was when he tossed it to Doeg to kill Ahimelech and the eighty-five priests who wore the linen Ephod.

"So, this observation confirms his words. I am convinced that he did finish off Saul, as he had stated. But, consider this, little brother: The killing of the Lord's anointed is a delicate matter and must be discouraged at all costs; for you, David, are also the Lord's anointed. The execution of this man is an opportunity to send a message through all the coasts of Israel. That anyone thinking of killing you, or any consecrated man, is in jeopardy of both man and God's vengeance. Particularly a king who has been set apart by God would be all but committing suicide."

David understood the messaging perfectly.

Abinadab then sounded, "Little brother, unless we forget, you remain a vassal of Achish, prince of Philistia. Who better than you to receive the crown and bracelet of authority? Would this not serve the Philistine interests for you to be king? I believe the Philistines are behind this chance and highly suspect encounter. But in any event, this messenger must be dispatched. It will give vent to your sorrow in the loss of Jonathan, your closest and dearest friend."

David now looked to Shammah, who nodded and said, "All that can be said has been said. Follow your heart and quell your grief."

David stepped closer to Eviyl and hissed, "How come you were not afraid to raise your hands to destroy the Lord's Anointed?"

David then gave the sign of vengeance to his eager bodyguard and said, "Go fall upon him." The blade was sure, and the brute dispatched Eviyl to death with one blow to his neck. David felt a sense of relief from his pent-up rage from the loss of his friend, and he roared at the fading breath of the dying messenger, "Your blood is of your own doing, and it is upon your head alone; for your mouth has testified against you by saying, 'I have slain the Lord's anointed.'" David and all his company found an emotional release in the brutality of a blood sacrifice. All were free to mourn and weep until evening. They fasted girded about in sackcloth and ashes in memory of Saul, Jonathan, and all the slain princes.

David was stirred to his very core and overflowed with conflicting emotions. His best friend in all of creation, Jonathan, whom he loved more than his own life, was no more. Saul, the king of all Israel, had sought his life through desert waste and forest thicket. Now he lay dead—slaughtered by an infidel. *Saul was my relentless adversary. Was he not the opposition that formed me like a lump of wet clay on the potter's wheel of life? A shepherd boy that has been set apart by God Almighty to be the next king of Israel. Have not the hands of Saul prepared me mightily for this royal stewardship over God's chosen people?*

David needed to express himself and put his pain into creativity. So, he lamented with the words of a song for the burial of the dead. For Saul, Jonathan, and all who had fallen on Mount Gilboa.

"Also God told them: 'Teach the children of Judah the song of the bow, know that it is found in the book of Jasher.'"

David lamented Israel's loss in song, "The beauty of Israel slain upon thy high places; how are the mighty fallen!

Tell it not in Gath, carry not the tidings in the streets of Ashkelon.

Lest the daughters of the Philistines rejoice, Lest the daughters of the uncircumcised triumph.

Upon the mountains of Gilboa, let there be no dew, no rain upon you, nor fields of great offerings!

For there, the shields of the mighty vilely cast away. The shield of Saul was not anointed with oil

but from the blood of the slain, and from the fat of the powerful,

The bow of Jonathan turned not back, and the sword of Saul returned not empty.

Saul and Jonathan, beloved and pleasant in their lives; even in their death, they were not divided.

They were swifter than eagles. They were stronger than lions.

You daughters of Israel, weep over Saul, who clothed you in scarlet with splendor.

Who put ornaments of gold upon your apparel?

How are the mighty fallen amid the battle! Jonathan slain upon the high places.

I am distressed for you, my brother Jonathan: very pleasant were you unto me; thy love to me was

wonderful, passing all, even a women's desire.

See how the mighty fall and the instruments of war perish!"

CHAPTER SEVENTEEN
For Want of a King

David was too long in Ziklag and felt irritable and discontent. In all outward appearances, he remained a valued vassal to Achish, the Philistine prince. Many still considered David a renegade and an outlaw, residing within Philistia's protective borders. He yearned to be back inside his familiar home and customs of Judah.

David prayed mightily to the Lord to dispel the fog of confusion and for the direction of travel, saying, "Shall I go up into any of the cities of Judah?

And the Lord said unto him, "Go up."

David inquired further, "Where shall I go up?"

The Lord replied, "Unto Hebron."

Once asked and answered by God, David felt compelled and considered it a commandment, not to be dismissed or taken lightly. So, he gathered up the people into the town center. He stood upon a high wall so that all might hear the voice of his yearnings. The day was sunny and blue, and there was not a cloud in the sky. Babes went silent by a greedy mouthful of mother's milk; the crowd hushed in anxious anticipation, for David would always speak of new adventures just over the next horizon. The only sounds were the braying of asses and the constant bleating from the sheepfolds.

David surveyed the crowd and paused until inspired. He commenced,

"Friends, family, and soldiers of the most high God: I have inquired of Adonai, and He has mostly graciously answered me, in that our destiny will be to return to our homeland and familiar culture of Judah, and so back to Hebron. King Saul is dead, and, so, too, our need to evade and escape, and seek shelter in a heathen's nest. All those who wish to stay and make this your home, a Judean outpost, can do so. For it is given to you to choose, as it has always been, even from the beginning. I would implore you, though, to ask of God—where all wisdom and knowledge resides—to receive your witness before coming to a decision. May God bless you and keep you. As for me and my house, we will obey and abide by the promptings of God."

David prepared all his needful things, as well as his wealth of flocks and herds—but with a touch of sadness for leaving some fast friends and his comfortable living. Still, David had a glad hope for his next adventures. He would seek the will of the Lord in all things. David's two wives, Ahinoam the Jezreelitess, and Abigail, Nabal's wife, the Carmelite, accompanied him, for neither could abide long separations from their warrior-poet-and-musician husband. So, too, all the men who sought after him out at the cave of Adullam. David's nomad army of discontents and the 200 that attached themselves after the deliverance of

Keila. They all gathered unto him once again, for now, they were respected warriors in the legion of David. So they came too, every man with their household, and followed their hero David to the cities of Hebron, for they would follow him to the gates of hell if need be.

Before departing, David sought the counsel of Achish and was immediately presented to the prince. "My old friend, your generosity has been grand and gracious. Your war with Israel, for now, is over. You have protected your trade routes and have expanded your interests in the Jezreel Valley. It will be a long time for Israel to recover from your brutal humiliation. My master and a long-time enemy have gone the way of all flesh."

David swallowed hard and choked back a tear, for his grieving was still tender. He continued, "I have become restless, and my men are becoming rusty and dull for lack of conquest. I have counseled with my God, and He has directed me to return to my Judean origins. I am well prepared and eager to leave with my men, wives, flocks, and herds. But, before I depart, I wanted, no, I *needed* to pay homage to my benefactor and beg for your leave."

The gesture moved Achish and, with a sigh, he implored, "I would prefer for you to linger as my vassal, for in time we will face each other again, but hostile and on the field of battle. So, know this, my friend: I will make every attempt to kill you, but with love, honor, and respect."

Both men laughed, saluted each other, and David departed before Achish had a change of heart.

Gossip and rumors often travel faster than the flight of ravens. So the news of David's slow-moving procession of sheep and goats was thoroughly announced to the whole of the Judean province by washwomen and fast-moving merchant caravans. Moreover, the generous gifts of spoil that he had captured from the Amalekite raiders and, in turn, speedily gifted to the princes of Judea, preceded David's arrival, all but guaranteeing a hero's welcome.

Upon entering the city, the train met with a festive welcome. The Lord of the town made a long-winded speech giving David and his following choice land for homes and stables for their array of livestock. The nesting process for the beautiful Abigail and the pleasant Ahinoam had commenced with heartfelt passion. All of David's men gained the status of respected citizens. Some even had families and were soon engaged in raising young households. Some even took up the labor of sowing and planting. But, most were discontent with the roots of family and were natural vagabonds who preferred the unsettling business of pillage and plunder.

The new moon of promise brought with it all the princes of Judah. David was now made aware that a council of noblemen had convened and that he, David, son of Jesse, was overwhelmingly selected to be the anointed king over all of Judah. The last princes had arrived in the dark of the night, and now bright new dawn found the town center overflowing with happiness and laughter in the preparations for a royal coronation.

"Abiathar," David commanded, "You will anoint me, and place Saul's fallen crown, raising it up and upon my head, and his bracelet of sovereignty, you will also place on my right arm. It is only fitting, priest, for, unless we forget, I am already the anointed king of all of Israel. Every step I take and every breath I make will be to this end, for the Lord God has sealed my destiny. My wives will flank me, Abigail to the right and Ahinoam to my left, for if I would be your king, they will certainly be your queens."

The ladies smiled at each other and then curtsied to their beloved husband for bestowing such an honor.

David continued, "My dear brothers, Eliab, the firstborn, and next unto him Abinadab, and the third, Shammah. Once, you were simple sheepherders, but now you are three brothers to a king and, so, princes and noblemen of Judah." All of David's men attended, and all of Hebron came out in support.

The rowdy crowd held their collective breath when Abiathar commenced, saying, "David, son of Jesse, anointed as a youth to be a king, even before you had conquered the giant Philistine Goliath of Gath. Your destiny is now forever intertwined with Judah and Israel. I bless you that you will forever seek the counsel of Adonai, our Lord God, and that He will bless you and keep you, and you shall be our good shepherd king—to preserve and protect the kingdom of God upon the earth, and to have your name enshrined in the mind of man and God, forever and forever."

David stood up from bended knees, a new king of the Jews, and the crowd erupted with joy and thanksgiving for the protection of a new monarch. Each Judean prince approached and knelt on one knee, proclaiming his loyalty and allegiance. All the other nobles lined up to give their pledge of devotion. Once the devotional concluded, the senior elder addressed the fledgling sovereign. "Your Majesty, the men of Jebesh-Gilead have rescued the bodies of Saul and his sons from the wall of Beth-shan—a monstrous blasphemy and insult to our God, to Judah, and all of Israel. All their fearless men went by night and retrieved our honor and our shame. They came to Jabesh and sang songs of worship and praise around a roaring cremation pyre. The brave heroes then took their bones and buried them under a funeral cypress in Jabesh, and they fasted for seven days."

For his first decree as king, David sent messengers to the courageous men of Jabesh-Gilead, who served their master well. The royal message delivered his heartfelt reflections as if spoken directly from the lips of the king. "Blessed are you of the Lord, in that you have shown this kindness unto your Lord, even King Saul and his sons, that you have given them an honorable burial. Our Lord has shown you truth and compassion: I will also reward you for this kindness and your gallantry in putting to rest our insults and sorrows. Accordingly, now let your hands be strengthened and remain courageous, as it was for your master Saul, whom you had honored, even in his death. I have been set apart and anointed the king of Judah, and so I am your new regent and count you as fellow servants and warriors to our most high God, Adonai."

The news of David's rise to glory and his ever-expanding power troubled Abner. If David went unchecked, he could easily step up, and with little or no resistance, he could usurp Israel's crown and gain ultimate power.

Abner had sworn to continue Saul's kingly line of succession. So a timely political solution required a reprieve from armed conflict. Moreover, he needed to gain time while David grew accustomed to his new kingly duties and authority. Ultimately, Abner, the son of Ner and Saul's sworn captain of his host, summoned Ish-bosheth, Saul's only remaining legitimate son and the sole rightful heir to Israel's throne.

The candles flickered from the constant draft in the waiting room. Ish-bosheth was always sickly and was still battling a recurrent fever when he inquired of his father's uncle, "Abner, you demanded my presence. What is so important to raise me from my sickbed?"

Abner grunted, "Your recent illness has saved your life. Perhaps we can increase your good fortune if we hurry."

"Speak plain, Abner. What are you trying to say?" Ish-bosheth coughed again and again.

Abner heightened his stature. "If you would be king, we must gain the loyalty from all the other tribal princes before David realizes our weakness and attacks, taking the crown by storm and force of arms. Our standing army nearly suffered annihilation only three months ago."

Ish-bosheth agreed. "We will invite all the necessary nobles into the forming of a strong military alliance, and small Judah will never think about taking up arms against us once I am set apart as their king."

Abner nodded. "Yes, yes, exactly. The only problem is that time is against us. If we send out formal invitations to the princes, we all but invite intrigue and delay. In the meantime, we will be giving David time enough to rally his growing forces and attack us without a suitable defense in place as we wait helplessly for all the princes' endless bickering and agreeing to petitions of favors. We will also be hard-pressed to find the time to submit to meet in a formal setting while ensuring that none will be insulted or neglected. No, we must go now and implore them separately and give each tribe the honor of anointing you king personally and then doing this in every tribe. This action must be taken and completed before David gets this same inclination of our intentions and beguiles the powerful leaders to his banner. May God forbid that his elevation should ever come to pass, as it will mean our certain death and an end to the house of Saul forever."

Ish-bosheth, wiping his runny nose, nodded and spoke. "I agree with your scheme, Captain Abner. You are as cunning as my father always had said you were—Aaachoo!"

Abner took Ish-bosheth by chariot, hurried to Mahanaim, and then made him king over Gilead, Ashurites, Jezreel, Ephraim, Benjamin, and Israel. Ish-bosheth was considered a weakling and not long destined for this world. Mephibosheth, the son of Jonathan, was considered the more promising of the two and the more likely heir to Israel's throne, but he was still a child. The agreement was that Mephibosheth would be a prince regent, sharing the title of alternate king for five years and six months, giving Ish-bosheth sufficient time to either prove himself capable or succumb to his many illnesses and die. This ploy would also ensure a seamless transition of power and not require any further rancor or debate. Ish-bosheth, Saul's son, was forty years old when he began to reign over Israel independently of Mephibosheth's shadow for two years. Ish-bosheth proved reliable, if not substantial, under the tutelage of Abner, son of Ner.

The house of Judah grew and thrived as they followed the dictates of David. David was king in Hebron over the house of Judah for seven years and six months.

Border disputes between Israel and Judah began to erupt into armed conflicts. The army of God increased as many flocked to

Hebron and the rising star that was David. Ish-bosheth appeared sickly and weak, and his army thinned for lack of an imposing strongman. Yet, try as he might, even Abner could not hold back the incoming tide that was God's will.

Abner obtained an audience with Ish-bosheth, now the sole and recognized ruler of Israel. The room was stuffy and moist. Thin shafts of light reflected the thick dust, and it echoed sneezes and coughs.

"What is it, Abner? You always have some bad news to make worse my already bad day. Speak up, for I have an appointment to see an Egyptian physician, a renowned healer!"

"Your Majesty, I am concerned with the ever-growing might of David and Judah. Our border skirmishes are getting more ferocious and impossible to defend. Therefore, I propose we move our capital to Gibeon. It is much more defensible. Moreover, it is in the territory of Benjamin and is near to Gibeah and your extended family. Besides, it gives us easy access to the borders of Judah. I can take a spearhead of the army and set up a temporary headquarters there, and when organized, I can send for you when it is safe, and you can relax and feel secure in your new home."

Ish-bosheth nodded and said, "Abner, I trust in your judgment in all these matters, although it does seem a bit extreme. You do have my permission to proceed as long as you feel that it is essential. I will endure this challenging hardship of moving my household."

Abner gathered up the best of his army and went out from Mahanaim, and headed for Gibeon.

A banquet of spies was the first to notice the gathering and destination of Israel's army. David was immediately alerted, for he had a network of loyal informants working as merchants and servants. They reported any suspicious activities, from alehouse boastings, pillow-talk ramblings, and the tongue-wagging of servants and washwomen. Rumors speedily arrived in Hebron that an Israeli force with chief captain Abner had gone out with a Gibeon destination. David called upon Joab, the middle son of his sister Zeruiah.

Joab found David on the open field, where the snap of arrows and lunging spears became a regular and deadly sport. "You have summoned me, uncle? What is your pleasure, lord?"

David, without hesitation, let fly and scored a perfect bullseye. He saluted his favored nephew and voiced his concerns. "I have received a most troubling dispatch in that the army of Abner is on the march to Gibeon. It is up against our borders, and with all the recent battles, I fear they might be preparing for an invasion. I want you to command the army and flank their advance until you can determine their intentions. Nephew, we will not attack unless provoked or you have determined their intentions are hostile. I do not relish battles that are Hebrew against Hebrew, for we can easily bleed ourselves nonexistent. At some point, we will have no strength against the next time we meet the crushing might of the Philistine heathens."

Joab took the army on an intercept course, but many men in a headlong pursuit are nearly impossible to conceal. In a lush, open field surrounded by an ancient forest, they met at no more than a stone's throw across the pool of Gibeon. A lingering stalemate ensued, producing an invitation for a truce sent and accepted for a discussion on how best to lessen the bloodbath of an all-out conflict. It was a cunning remedy on how best they could move forward with honor and dignity from their current deadlocked positions. The captains met on either side of the pool.

Abner introduced a solution and said to Joab, "Let us each take twelve of our most fearless warriors and meet at the edge of this Gibeon pool. We will speak of our differences, and if we cannot settle by argument, let us fight, but only the twenty-four, and whoever prevails, even if only by one, let their house take the field. The other house retires and returns every man to his place. Each army will observe from either side of the pool and sustain the outcome in good faith."

All agreed on the future needs against the Philistine invaders and the ultimate conservation of needed warriors. So Joab, the son of Zeruiah, and David's servants went out and met together by Gibeon's pool, one group on one side and one group on the other side.

The conversation began with polite barbs and sarcastic abuse that quickly turned into yelling and screaming personal insults. Finally, Abner had had enough and called out to Joab, "Let the young men now arise and let us have the play of war, the sport of swords that decides the fate of nations."

Joab agreed and said, "Let them arise."

Twelve stood from Benjamin, which pertained to Ish-bosheth, Saul's son, against twelve of David's servants. The fight was fierce and deadly, for the insults had sparked a seething hatred and a stark life-or-death enmity. With swords drawn, each wrestled and caught his fellow by the head, and they thrust the point of his blade deep into his rival's side, destroying vital organs. All perished, but one who had endured but was severely wounded no longer wished to live and favored, instead, to go the way of all his dead comrades. He fell on his sword, and he so, too, perished with his friends and enemies alike.

No, not one survived the ruthless bloodletting. The place was hence called Helkath-hazzurim, or "the place of sharp blades," which is in Gibeon.

Abner and Joab withdrew to their encampments; every man's wrath cried vengeance, and now there was no turning back. Both sides were howling for a fight. The battle commenced in deadly earnest; there were no tactics or strategy; it was more like two packs of ferocious wolves tearing at each other's throats; it was a melee of blood and carnage. They fought the whole of that hot, sunbaked day.

Finally, after an epic struggle, Abner lost, and the men of Israel were with him. David's servants would have slaughtered every man, for no quarter was asked, and none given. So it was less than a retreat and more of a desperate route when Abner yelled out, "It's every man for himself."

Joab was the chief captain, and he was like a father to his two beloved siblings, Abishai, the oldest, who had a desire to lead but was dwarfed by Joab's cunning, and Asahel, the youngest, who was fleet and made perfect by God in the speed of his feet.

As the battle splintered, Asahel caught the wary eye of Abner fleeing headlong from the melee. Asahel took chase, knowing full well he was the only one who could match him stride for stride and could overtake Abner's legendary gait. Asahel reasoned that, if he could kill Abner, he would be rewarded with honor and glory and help seal his uncle David's destiny in capturing Israel's throne. The race was on.

Abner picked up his pace when he spotted a young man bearing down on him, running like a wild deer. Asahel focused on his prey. He went straight as an arrow's flight, not veering even slightly to the left or right, gaining an inch or two on every stride. Abner looked behind him and thought he recognized his pursuer.

Abner called back, "Are you Asahel?"

"I am."

Abner, knowing the nobility of his family, yelled back, "Turn aside either to the right hand or to the left. It is not giving up or giving in but pursuing a fleeing enemy, only someone younger and not as wise in the art of war and killing. In that, you might prevail and take his armor as a spoil. The great prize that is my armor will not be yours this day."

Asahel would not turn away from his single-minded pursuit.

Abner, in good faith, turned back one last time and warned, "Turn aside, lad, for you will leave me no choice but to take your life and bring you to an untimely end. How, then, can I face your brother Joab?"

Asahel was hell-bent on his capture and coming within a stride of striking distance.

Abner then stopped dead in his tracks. He gingerly spun his deadly spearhead to his rear, the lethal point aimed squarely at his pursuer's oncoming belly. Abner took a backward step, placing his heavy hand on the blunt end of the shaft. He jabbed with all of his might, using Asahel's unstoppable forward drive.

Asahel ran into the sharp, deadly weapon. It caught him under the fifth rib, and the blade pierced straight through, sliding past his backbone. Asahel was still standing from the sudden impact until Abner released his spear, and then Asahel's torn body crumpled to the ground.

Many young men were hard-pressed to keep up with Asahel's and Abner's fever-pitched pace. Finally, some stalwart friends came upon Asahel's fallen and mutilated body. They stopped and stood voiceless and motionless over their fallen comrade. Joab and Abishai did not stop or even pause for a moment to mourn their dead brother. Instead, they continued their pursuit by doubling their efforts to capture and kill Abner and all his men with a renewed vigor.

The last of the sun was on the horizon when they came to the hill of Ammah, a short hill only a few cubits tall that lies before the entrance to the town of Giath, on the outskirts of the Gibeon wilderness. Not wishing to be slaughtered, the vengeful brothers halted their pursuit.

The children of Benjamin gathered around Abner on a nearby hill and became one troop. Abner considered a counterattack but counted heads in the twilight and concluded that too many had fallen and that a further battle would be suicidal. Abner called to Joab—now a fading silhouette—before the night swallowed up the last of the light. "Shall the sword devour forever? Do you know that we will reap a stark and bitter ending if we continue with this battle? For later, when we could have counted on each other's help against our common foe, the Philistine pagans. Our call for help will come back empty and void, for they will be no more. How long shall it be before you command your people to stop pursuing the killing of your Hebrew brothers to our mutual utter destruction?"

Joab, moved by Abner's plea for common-sense mercy, replied, "As God lives, unless you had decided to hold your plea for peace, surely then, in the morning, every one of my people would have risen and followed his brother until there were none left to hunt." Joab blew a shofar horn, and all his people stood still; they pursued Israel no more. The fighting ended with the shrill dying echo of a dark, lone trumpet call.

Abner was relieved at the reprieve of hostilities. He knew Joab thought tactically; this could be but a temporary pause, or even worse, a ploy so that he and his crippled army would let down their guard. But, on the other hand, Joab could be preparing for a final and devasting offensive of vengeance and retaliation for his younger brother Asahel's killings. For what better time than now for the killing stroke to be delivered and end a fledgling blood feud decisively?

Chief Captain Abner rallied his captains—as few or as many who remained breathing. Then, in a shrouded murmur, he spoke his concerns. "Men, we will not linger here in the killing fields. We will neither seek rest nor take time to bury our dead. Captains, take as many men as needed and set up small campfires around an empty perimeter. Joab will camp for the evening, and we will appear to be doing the same. But we will leave this place with the cover of night and walk through to Mahanaim. We will pass over the Jordan and through all of Bithron back to safety and home."

In the morning, Joab found an empty encampment and the dying embers of numerous unattended campfires. Joab followed Abner's trail to the borders of Benjamin. Once he knew that the enemy had long departed, he doubled back to count—and then bury—in all, his nineteen dead warriors. Joab and Abishai counted so, too, their younger brother Asahel, whose body would find rest in the family's tomb in Bethlehem. Abner's fallen sadly numbered 360, and as Hebrew brothers, they were also given rest in the earth that was their mother.

With grief and relief, Joab marched with his men all the next night and came upon the welcome sight of Hebron and home at the break of day.

CHAPTER EIGHTEEN
The Intrigue of Generals and Kings

Constant skirmishes, battles, conflicts, clashes, and fights highlighted a war that dragged on for years between David's house and the house of Saul. David's forces grew larger and deadlier, and Saul's house became weaker by losing its resolve. Yet, no decisive encounter could tip the balance of power or proclaim an undisputed champion; life went on. Warring became routine, if not predictable, during this period of bloody carnage. Some were born, and some died, and some were taken and given in marriage. The times were uncertain, painful, and stressful, with no end in sight.

David remained active and vital through all the years of warring. He planted his seed with varied wives and often in his new capital. He had six sons from six of his seven wives. David joyously sired among the lush lawns of Hebron. Amnon was David's first son, followed by Chileab, Absalom, Adonijah, Shephatiah, and the baby boy Ithream.

As the war progressed, Abner gained more and more control and authority. While Ish-bosheth was sickly and weak, a pathetic creature relegated to the shadowy realm of an anointed puppet king. Ish-bosheth was becoming more agitated at this seemingly bizarre turn of events and his apparent loss of power.

King Saul had kept a favored concubine. She was more than a harlot but less than a wife, and her name was Rizpah [meaning "hot stone"], the daughter of Aiah. Saul often remarked that her name was best said in a sensual whisper: "Rizzpaah." Rizpah was a raven-haired beauty, slender and wistful; she moved and swayed like a willow in the wind. Her hips had a carnal beckoning that would transfix the gaze of both aged men and young boys. She had conceived and then gifted Saul with two healthy but illegitimate baby boys, Armoni and Mephibosheth. She was a devoted mother nonetheless, and after Saul had passed, she remained well treated as an honored courtesan; she maintained her standing and rank in the court of King Ish-bosheth.

One day a tasty morsel of palace gossip reached the embattled monarch's sensitive ears. The word was secreted to Ish-bosheth by none other than his court jester. "Sire, the gossip is that Abner and Rizpah were behind closed doors, with nothing observed but sounds of heavy breathing, moans, and groans of ecstasy confirming the throes of ardent lovemaking. Of course, I cannot say with any degree of certainty about the accuracy of these rumors. But like a fool, I do know this one thing, that there is no man alive who can refuse Rizpah's beguiling charms or fail to warm the bed of this comely wench once she sets her mind on a catch."

The alleged indiscretion disheartened Ish-bosheth; it was a slight to his father's honor, and it could not go unpunished. He usually would not have taken issue, but Abner's growing power was threatening, and he felt he had to exert his waning authority.

So Ish-bosheth commanded Abner into his presence. Abner had not heard of any rumblings or warnings. The war with Judah seemed to have settled into a stalemate, and Ish-bosheth had never bothered to get himself involved in any of the strategy sessions.

Abner entered the main room and saluted Ish-bosheth. "Majesty, you have summoned me. I pray it must be something of an urgent nature or a matter of great importance," he uttered with an air of flippancy. Other than for some slack-jawed body-guards, the great hall was all but empty.

Ish-bosheth dispensed with all the social niceties and got right into his judgment of immodesty without any supporting witness or facts. "Abner, it has come to my attention that you are having inappropriate and erotic relations with Rizpah, my dead father's favored concubine. Is this not so?"

Abner flushed with anger at the slight. He growled at the intrusion on his highly respected moral character—however accurate the accusation may have been. The guards present hid their faces and slunk back into the shadows as Abner raged. "Am I like the head of a dog that seeks Judah as its new master? Must I remind you of who has been in opposition to Judah's tribe, and I alone set you up in opposition to David, son of Jesse? Have I not shown respect to Saul's family and by my close, faithful attachment to you, Ish-bosheth? It has been in my power to have delivered you many times into the hands of David. It has been in my control to have done so. Today you slander me with baseless gossip of sexual indiscretion with this woman who is neither a widow, for she was never a wife nor attached to anyone alive in any event.

Ish-bosheth, how can you feel justified in belittling me in public after all I have sacrificed for the house of Saul and you, my flesh and blood? I have gone against God's will for Israel. I knew of God's oath to put David on the throne of Israel, and still, I followed my promise to your father and supported you in the hopes of keeping our house alive." Abner was hot, inwardly furious at himself for allowing this insult to reveal a deep-seated sense of order and justice. It brought him to the remembrance that God's will cannot be circumvented or disallowed, for ultimately, it will come to pass. "I have knowingly gone against God's word," he declared, head bowed, with almost a sigh, "and I have prepared myself for the eternal consequences. As God has sworn to David, I vow to remove the kingdom from the house of Saul and put in place the throne of David over Israel and Judah, from Dan even to Beersheba."

Ish-bosheth did not summon his guards to arrest Abner. Instead, he considered for the briefest of moments to put him in chains and have him executed. But as he sat on his throne, sweating and shivering, he also knew that Abner could slay him with his bare hands, and even the guards would more than likely support the general. So, Ish-bosheth answered not a word as Abner breathed in three more breaths, turned his back on the king, and stormed out of the throne room, never looking back.

Abner prepared a heartfelt letter of negotiation, proposing to conclude this conflict and repent from the vain attempt to evade God's will regarding the nations of Judah and Israel:

To David, son of Jesse, king of Judah

The Lord God Adonai has decreed that you, David, had been set apart as ruler of Israel and all of God's chosen people.

Does not the land already belong to you? And, by God's law, it remains yours? Therefore, make a pact with me, and my hand will help you obtain the throne of Israel peaceably and without any further bloodshed or loss of life.

Your servant,

Abner, son of Ner, Chief captain of the host of Israel

Messengers proceeded to Hebron, to King David's residence with all haste—for peace was at hand, and all parties were weary of the intrigue and the constant fighting. David received the surprise message with understanding and immediately sent a letter back from a position of strength.

To Abner, son of Ner, Chief Captain of the host,

I will make a treaty with you, but one thing I require at your hand, in that you will not see my face nor get my agreement unless you bring back to me the wife of my youth, even Saul's daughter, the princess Michal. She is my lawful wife but given to another. Her restoration to me is the only remedy. The whole matter has been an insult to my household and me, personally. This condition is non-negotiable before I agree with your petition. I must retain good stewardship over my family before being deemed worthy to ascend to the stewardship of the realm.

David, son of Jesse, king of Judah

Abner was puzzled, for he believed that David would have embraced his offer without condition or exception. But, on the other hand, he did not have the authority to repeal a consummated marriage and reinstate a previously revoked union. These intrigues were the provinces of kings.

You had to persuade the king, that in turn had to agree, for he was the only legitimate and recognized authority. Only Ish-bosheth had the power that could unravel this complicated plot. What Abner had already proposed to David could easily be viewed as treason by Ish-bosheth. Abner now had to make sure that the army and the palace guards were on his side before making such a declaration.

The setting was dark and ominous. The dark antechamber had a chill of pending doom. The fire in the hearth seemed to be gasping for air. Ish-bosheth raised his hangdog face. "What is it, uncle? No good news, as usual, I suspect."

Abner commenced and went straight to the point. "Nephew, another full attack by the forces of Joab and Judah, and the kingdom will crumble like a sandcastle. We lose all our property, titles, and life if we continue with this fruitless fight. I have written to David, and he is open to an agreement. We could very well save our good standings and be brought under David's dominion, as he would be the king of Israel and Judah—either that or death and disgrace. David asks only one thing, that you void Michal's unlawful marriage to Phaltiel; the greatest difficulty will be to send back the dowry to Laish from your very-diminished coffers."

Ish-bosheth shook his head as his depressed state physically worsened. Then, in a moment of emotional exhaustion, he accepted the certainty of defeat and uttered, "What now, uncle?"

Abner contained his glee, for he could see the end of the old regime and the promise of new beginnings of life and prosperity. He even imagined keeping his esteemed rank as commander of the armies, with all its rights and privileges.

But, in an uplifting tone, Abner continued. "I will immediately send messengers to David, explaining your submission. In addition, he will undoubtedly send you a message confirming your agreement and demand his wife returned to him as a gesture of good faith; in this way, it is all legal and proper."

David received a message from Abner, in which he stated that Ish-bosheth would concede and that he was expecting David's request or, if he preferred, his *demand*.

David set about composing his conditions to regain the wife of his youth.

Ish-bosheth, son of Saul and king of Israel,

Deliver me my wife and your sister Michal, for I had won her by the quest of delivering one hundred foreskins of our sworn Philistine enemies. I had given two hundred foreskins because the Lord was with me. I had kept my bargain with your father, the king who was greater than his daunting challenge. What God joins together, let no man put asunder; I need to be reunited with my wife by the king's decree, and this must be in place before any league or agreement between you, me, and Abner, son of Ner, is struck.

Signed, David, son of Jesse, king of Judah.

Having little or no choice, Ish-bosheth sent for Michal and took her from her husband Phaltiel, Laish's son. Then, reluctantly, Ish-bosheth delivered David's wife, Michal, back to David, her lawful first husband. This turn of events helped to bolster David's claim to the throne of Israel. Abner handily gifted the required political concession and rattled his sword to ensure compliance.

As Michal's caravan trudged southward, Phaltiel tagged along, cherishing every waking moment. He wept, lamenting the loss of the love of his life. He followed behind Michal like a lovesick puppy until reaching Bahurim, east of Jerusalem, on the Jordan

Valley's road, close to the Mount of Olives. At that crossroads, Abner stepped up and sternly demanded, saying, "That is as far as you go, Phaltiel. Return home, and do not come any further or suffer the fury of David. It could very well cause your death for the crime of adultery. David will soon be king of Israel and would take your dogged refusal to depart as a personal insult."

Abner was in a full peacemaking mode and wished to bring back a gift to David even more precious than his beloved wife: Israel's promised crown. As agreed, Abner mounted his steed and traveled throughout all the realms. He spoke with the princes and elders, saying, "You wished for David, in times past, to be king over you. Now is the time to agree. The Lord God has spoken it, saying, 'By the hand of my servant David. I will save my people Israel from out of the Philistines' hands and out of the hands of all their enemies.'"

Abner spoke to the elders of Benjamin—his tribe and Saul's tribe—as they would be the most reluctant and hardest to convince. Begrudgingly, allowing a Judean prince to become the reigning monarch. But, for the sake of peace, it seemed a good thing to Benjamin and all of Israel. The agreement was that Abner would come to David in Hebron, accompanied by twenty of his most loyal and trusted bodyguards.

Upon a high tower, David spied the train headed his way. David was glad for his wife and the end of the fighting, and Abner, as an ally. He thought, *Perhaps, I have a new chief captain who is long in the tooth, with tried-and-true battle experience.*

David yelled out in excitement, "Prepare the fatted calf; a reason for rejoicing will soon present itself at the front gate—a prince of Israel and a former enemy, now a comrade with the promise of peace on his lips."

People cheered Abner's arrival as if a conquering hero. David met Abner at the front gate; Abner dismounted and took a knee in homage. The assembled crowd cheered, for this was a sign that the war was over. The group of guests moved into the great hall and to the seats on the overflowing banquet table.

David sat at the head, and Abner took his position to his right and in the place of honor. After several toasts of dark-red wine, the conversation started to flow freely, and former enemies began to relax in each other's company. As it was his way and custom, David complimented with sincerity for a job well done. "Abner, I know Ish-bosheth's royal decree that gifted the return of my first wife, Michal. But make no mistake that I know full well it was by your mediation and skillful maneuvering that my honor and my wife returned to me."

Abner, feeling obliged to help David to rise to his exalted position as king of Israel, whispered into David's confident ear, "Thank you, my lord. I must confess I feel young again, setting off on this quest. I will get up and go at first light, and I will gather all the rest of Israel unto to my lord, the king's influence. I will ensure that the holdouts must agree that you are the king of both Judah and Israel. Once I explain to the tribes the dire necessity of your coronation, I am sure they will readily agree and support your sovereignty. The tribe of Benjamin quickly decided on the correct course of action once I laid out the facts before them. In time, the rest of the tribes will fall into line. I am confident that no more than a simple nudge is all that is needed to capture the rest of the nation's hearts and minds. After that, you will rule and reign over all that you desire."

The morning overflowed with gratitude and expectations. So many found words of loyalty and commitment readily exchanged. David said, with a broad smile and a wink, "I look forward to when next we meet. I need a skilled chief commander. We will speak of this again after my coronation. Go in peace, Chief Captain Abner."

Abner smiled broadly and bowed his head in respectful submission and hurried off on his daunting mission to gather up Israel for the sake of God's direction and David, the son of Jesse.

The dust had barely settled in Hebron from Abner's peaceable departure, and everyone had returned to their daily chores.

Joab entered from the far side of David's compound with great treasures from a successful and bloody raid. Joab was boasting and bragging while unloading his plunder. Finally, a tax collector, who began his tally for the king's portion of tribute, happened to mention, "This has been such a very unusual and extremely eventful day, and it is barely noon."

"How so?" Joab inquired.

The taxman reflected, "Abner, the son of Ner, was treated to a banquet in his honor last night and has recently departed in peace and good tidings from the king." Joab, flushed with rage, dropped a piece of captured armor. It crashed loudly upon the ground. He angrily sought out David for a royal tongue-lashing.

Joab barged into David's refuge, a place where the king retreated for contentment and serenity. The chief captain commenced his wrathful spewing without leave or permission: "What have you done, and in what contradiction were you thinking? Look at the fact that Abner came to you, our sworn enemy. Do lions excuse their prey, praise them, feed them, and then let them escape back into the wilds with little more than a fare-thee-well? Abner is now far gone and beyond the hands of justice. Did it not occur to you, uncle, that Abner, the son of Ner, came only to deceive you, only as a spy to observe? He now knows your comings in and your goings out and all that you are about to do. He will try to trap you and catch you in your naive gullibility."

David was in too good of a mood to let his disturbed nephew upset him. "Nephew," David scolded, "I will excuse your bad manners and will not allow you to sour my mood on this glorious day. I understand your hatred and the blood feud you perceive with Abner. He killed your brother and my nephew, but Joab, this is war. It is not personal, and it has been my understanding that Abner pleaded with Asahel to turn aside, and your brother refused to give quarter. Abner is repentant and will seek my good in gaining my dominion over Israel and Judah. He is also the most experienced chief captain in all of the land, and he will be a certain asset with our likely coming battles with the Philistine mongrels. Go now, Joab, so I might continue composing."

Joab's fury, already inflamed, now heightened when he heard of David's plan to recruit Abner for chief captain over all the forces of Israel and Judah. If that transpired, he would lose his position and authority and be subject to the man who had slaughtered his younger brother.

But Joab thought it best to keep the king's counsel, and he begged the king's leave. As soon as he had made it to the stables, he gathered some trusted servants and told them, "Go now and, with all speed, catch up with Abner, the son of Ner, and say to him that David had for him further cautions that David had neglected to impart and would beckon Abner to return to him and at once. He might hear these important thoughts that David would relay to the noble Abner, son of Ner." The messengers caught up with Abner and his twenty men at Sirah's well, but David knew nothing of Joab's deadly scheming.

Joab debated with his older brother Abishai. "I have sent for Abner to come back in the false inquiring of David. I say we take our kind words to the dark shadows near the gate, where none travel, and slay him out of the sight and witness of his twenty men, and we will have to make sure that we keep a company of men around to protect us. There is the secluded void, and we can take our vengeance there and satisfy the blood of Asahel that cries to us from the dust. For even greater concern has arisen that David may very well take my position as chief captain and bestow it upon Abner. We have the reason, and the might with which we could kill our enemy for a twofold purpose. What say you, Abishai?"

"I agree with your proposal, brother, but my concern is our uncle's punishment. He is ruthless when crossed. He may very well seek our lives."

"I do not think so, brother," Joab responded, shaking his head. "We are, after all, the blood of his blood and flesh of his flesh. Besides, our house is mighty, and I command the army. No, he will lament and curse us—that is for certain—but our lives we will not forfeit. No, the timing is also in our favor; he is recruiting the allegiances of the tribal elders; he cannot also attempt to fight his own family."

The assassins had well prepared by the time Abner returned to Hebron. Joab greeted Abner with feigned respect and the cunning of diplomacy.

Joab bowed and announced, "Abner, son of Ner, I regret missing your honoring banquet, and, since your departure, David speaks highly of your integrity. However, I have some personal thoughts I wish to convey out of earshot of all present. Would you mind dismounting, Abner, and following my brother Abishai and me for a pressing conversation behind the private gate?"

Abner nodded in agreement as he was curious as to what was so important. Once in the void, Joab leaned in, as if to whisper in Abner's ear, when Abishai quietly slipped a dagger to Joab's hand. Joab, without remorse or hesitation, shoved it up into Abner's fifth rib, not a word uttered, and a fool's shock of utter betrayal lit up his face and froze his lips. It was only for the briefest of moments until he exhaled life's last breath. Abner's final view was the gloat on Asahel's vengeful brothers' smirking faces, taking out their long-awaited blood-feud vengeance.

A short time had passed when David heard a commotion of armed conflict down and around the front gate. Abner's men knew that something dreadful had happened to their commander. A servant, fearful but willing, told David, "Forgive me, sire. I bear terrible news. Joab has killed Abner for the killing of his brother Asahel."

David was stunned and wished to distance himself from blame; he proclaimed, "I and my kingdom are guiltless before the Lord forever from the blood of Abner, the son of Ner. So let it rest on Joab's head and all in his father's house involved in the conspiracy, whether young or old, rich, poor, sick, well, alive, or dead. There is no doubt that Joab and Abishai have together slain Abner because he had killed their brother Asahel at the 'field of sharp blades' that is in Gibeon."

David's eyes glared at Joab. He then commanded all the people with him, "Tear your clothes and bind yourself about with remorse, and mourn before the body of Abner."

It was a rushed burial because Abner's righteous remains needed covering before sundown. David followed the procession with guilt and tears of sorrow. Finally, Abner found rest in his family's sepulcher in Hebron.

David lifted his voice weeping at Abner's grave, and his sincere, heartfelt display touched all the people.

The king grieved over his former enemy and his recent powerful ally. David cried, "Abner, you died not as a fool dies. Your hands not bound nor your feet in shackles: as a man dies before wicked men, so you fell."

All the people wept again over Abner. The servants prepared food for mourners, and some people brought meat to David, but he refused to eat. While it was still day, David swore, "Let God do to me and more if I taste bread or anything else until the sun goes down." The people took notice that the king was fasting, and it pleased them. For all in Israel now understood that day that it was not the king who had slain Abner, the son of Ner. David announced to all his servants, "Know that there is a prince, and a great man has fallen in Israel this day. I am weak this day even though I am the anointed king, and these men, the sons of my sister Zeruiah, are too strong for me. The Lord shall reward the guilty of this evildoing by giving the same measure of wickedness to the wrongdoers."

CHAPTER NINETEEN
The Boast of Oafs

Bad news gathers speed carried on the winds of trouble and misfortune. Ish-bosheth's ears tingled with the dark dispatch regarding Abner's murder in Hebron; it was like being struck with a bludgeon. Ish-bosheth's hands went feeble, and his knees buckled; all of Israel was troubled on his behalf. The gravest fear was that Chief Captain Abner was on a peace and reconciliation mission—and yet had met slaughter just the same while under King David's directed protection.

Ish-bosheth had two captains, huge in body but weak in mind: Baanah, the mastermind, whose talents lay in inflicting pain and suffering, and Rechab, his partner, who would go along just for the fun of it, as brothers often do. Both men were the sons of Rimmon, a Beerothite, and counted as the children of Benjamin. Both men oversaw raiding parties and were known for their greed and gluttony. Nevertheless, they readily accepted elevation as captains for their size and bloodthirsty temperament, and this also because the army of Israel was thinning, and pickings were slimming. The disturbing news from Hebron had carried Ish-bosheth to his bed and was now abroad in all the land. These evil tidings sparked a fire of ambition that ignited into a murderous plot to curry favor and position in the army of David.

"Rechab," Baanah began, "we have an opportunity that has fallen into our laps."

Rechab, confused, as usual, said, "Lap? But I am standing up."

Baanah shook his head and whispered, "Let me buy you a cup of wine, and then both you and I will create a lap for this unique opportunity to nest." The two settled into dark shadows lit by a single candle, surrounded by kegs and barrels.

"Speak up, Baanah," Rechab insisted. "Ish-bosheth is a dead man. Without his captain Abner to rule from behind the shadows, Israel will fall to David. Mephibosheth, son of Jonathan, crippled by a nursing accident, is still a child and will not be considered a suitable regent. No, King David will be king of both Judah and Israel.

"Ish-bosheth must die, and for us, my friend, we can hasten his fate and save King David from staining his hands in the killing of an anointed king. I am sure we are in store for great rewards, both in rank and treasure. My plan is simple, but we must act quickly before someone else seizes this opportunity or David attacks, and then Ish-bosheth will increase his household guards and change his routine."

Rechab nodded and smiled; in a low whisper, he said, "I like it, and my lap is filling up with warm expectations. What is your plan, brother?" Baanah poured another round of dark red wine and growled his displeasure, fearing that their plan had been discovered when a serving maid approached. She turned abruptly in her tracks and left the two alone to hatch out their murderous plot.

"Tomorrow is the day," Baanah whispered. "With pure evil intent, we will approach King Ish-bosheth's mansion. Right at high noon and during the heat of the day. There will be, more than likely, no one or too few to bar our way. If challenged, we can pick up some barley to feed our charges and then show them the innocent empty wheat sacks. It is the same time every day that Ish-bosheth takes to his afternoon nap. He will be lightly unattended and ripe for the killing. So, tell not a soul of our plan, and we will, by craft and cunning, do this assignation together."

The following day, everything was as usual. The day was going to be a hot one. The brothers kept a wary eye on the royal residence, observed tradespeople's everyday comings and goings, and marked fresh meat, wine, and cheese deliveries. The sun hung high in a cloudless sky when the back entrance emptied of all signs of life.

"Let's go, Rechab," Baanah commanded in a low tone. As he had half-expected, there were no challenges to their home invasion—for even the guards were napping, taking their cue from the sleeping monarch's afternoon ritual.

With stealthy silence, the twin assassins mounted the darkened staircase. Ish-bosheth lay fast asleep, Baanah lifted the point of his sword, and with both hands, he stabbed through to Ish-bosheth's heart just under the fifth rib. At the very exact moment and with a mighty whack, Rechab separated the king's head from its torso to quell any dying cries for help. He then lifted the gore-dripping trophy from the blood-soaked bed and put it in his handy wheat sack.

The familiar face was the needed proof of their deed and would leave no doubt in confirming their kill; indeed, it would speed the collection of their just rewards.

The brothers hid in a small cave on Mahanaim's outskirts; they were pleased with themselves at the ease of their execution and basked in the thoughts of a future filled with honor and glory.

A chorus of shrill shofars broke the still of early afternoon and trumpeted the news of the king's murder. Bedlam erupted throughout the realm; every nook and cranny was thoroughly searched and explored, but the culprits were nowhere in sight. Baanah and Rechab patiently waited out the hours until the rising of the new moon. The dim-lit crescent allowed the assassins to escape undetected, guaranteeing safe passage through the plain of Jordan and the sixty-eight miles to Hebron and King David's well-guarded stronghold.

Through valley oasis and barren wilderness, the journey was daunting and dangerous. What made it worse was the constant flies attracted by the blood-soaked bag and the awful smell of rotting flesh. Meanwhile, overhead, a kettle of vultures circled, hungrily following the scent of death.

Three days later, the ragtag and weather-worn brothers staggered in their final steps to reach David and the Hebron gate.

"Who goes there, and what is wanted?" sounded the familiar call of a dutiful watchman.

Baanah returned the challenge: "We are friends of the king who bring him an enemy's head, and so we have together created a vacancy for David, son of Jesse, to fill in the kingdom of Israel." Saying thus, he retrieved the decaying head of Ish-bosheth by the hair and displayed it to gain access to the compound.

David was alerted to the two ghouls who were begging for an audience. The brothers cheerfully strode to the bottom steps to stand below David, alongside Eliab on the upper porch. Rechab and then Bannah took his turn and reached into the blood-stained and fly-infested wheat bag. They produced the less-than-pleasant head of Ish-bosheth. Rechab, with an air of superior achievement, proclaimed, "Behold the head of Ish-bosheth, the son of Saul, your enemy, which hunted you tirelessly to take your life. We have avenged you, my lord, from Saul and his posterity this day. We have done this thing only for your benefit and in your service." Rechab spoke boastfully, spewing every gruesome and vivid detail depicting the killing of Ish-bosheth.

Upon hearing of the manner of death to Saul's only remaining son, David was furious at this brutal and monstrous assignation. He addressed Baanah and Rechab in the harshest of terms. "You sons of Rimmon, as the Lord lives, He, and He alone has redeemed my soul out of all adversity. When a young Amalekite adventurer told me that he had slaughtered Saul and brought me his bracelet of sovereignty and his crown of gold, he mistakenly thought he was bringing me some good news. I took hold of him and killed him in Ziklag. He thought, like you two, that I would have rewarded him for his evildoings. How much more when wicked men have slain a righteous person in his own house and upon his bed? Shall I not also require his blood that is on your hands and take you away from the earth this very day?" David needed no council, and he abruptly commanded to the twenty guards present, "Kill them, completely without mercy or hesitation. The very sight of these ruffians sickens me. Then cut off their hands and feet. Their hands because they have wielded evil against a righteous man, and their feet for they quickly ran to mischief by their wicked design. Hang their bodies over the pool so all can see them in Hebron, and so, too, for a stern warning to anyone participating in such outrageous behavior that they, too, will swiftly suffer death and humiliation." The task of dismemberment commenced as David's breath finished uttering the last of the sentencing.

David esteemed the head of Ish-bosheth and laid it to rest with all due respect and proper reverence, befitting an anointed king of Israel. It was buried alongside Abner's body in his sepulcher in Hebron.

CHAPTER TWENTY
The Capital of Kings

Every obstacle and barrier had fallen; every stumbling block was smashed or overcome. Finally, after seven long years, Israel had come to its senses with the dark veil of indecision replaced by the bright light of understanding and wise judgment.

Then came all the tribes of Israel honoring David and coming to his capital in Hebron. Israel spoke with one voice, saying, "Witness for yourself, for there is no doubt that we are of the same bone and the same flesh. When Saul was king over us in times past, Saul led us out and brought us back to Israel. The Lord has tasked you to feed my people Israel, and you, David, shall be a captain over Zion." So all the elders came to Hebron and agreed to make a union with David before the Lord. They set him apart as holy unto the Lord and anointed David as king over Israel. David was thirty years old.

David was the regent of two kingdoms, and, as such, needed a capital befitting his two crowns, one of Judah and one of Israel. David pondered his choices, and with certainty, all agreed that it was necessary to be the sprawling city of Jebus (also known as Jerusalem). The Jebusites were a clan of the ancient Amorite peoples, who were descendants of Canaan, descendants of Ham, the son of Noah, who was before the flood. Jebus had been an open city by treaty with Judah and Benjamin ever since the early conquest by Joshua and Caleb. They had quarters and ready access, and they called the place "Jerusalem," or "the city of peace." The Jebusites were fierce when it came to keeping control of their fortress city. It was a Canaanite gem, for much commerce and trade passed through its ancient gates. It was a crossroads and an oasis to many merchant nations.

The allure of Jerusalem was its location and defenses. Jebus sat at the top of a very high hill, surrounded by seven hills that lessened the plague of fierce desert dust storms. Its thick walls were impenetrable on three sides. There were narrow paths that led to small, easily defended gates. The city flourished, having an underground freshwater supply. The citadel remained challenging to conquer for its abundance of water. The walls on the only accessible side were high and thick. But David wanted it mainly because it was close to the kingdom's center; Jerusalem was the ideal location for the new capital city. David would have it.

David had two well-equipped armies to make his wishes a reality. He and his men formed about the mighty walls of Jerusalem. David called for the Jebusite governor of the city and demanded, saying, "We have come to take this place and the whole of it; we will allow you to maintain your rights to all your properties and landholdings. I and my priests, elders, and judges will govern and abide by the laws of God and Israel. What say you?"

174

The governor chafed behind his mighty walls. He was outraged by the proposal and asked, "Are you and your nation not the posterity of Abraham?"

David agreed and spoke up, so his words would reach to the top of the parapet. "I am, and we are, but how does this matter enter into our demand for a bloodless occupation?"

The governor responded, "It matters greatly, for Abram, your forebear, had given his oath that his posterity would never conquer the city of Jebus by force of arms. For the consideration that we would relinquish all rights and claims to the cave of Machpelah. The resting place for all of your patriarchs. We have it recorded upon Jacob's death and when he was buried next to his father, Isaac. We fashioned a brazen idol inscribed with Abraham's oath for all to witness. There are two men affixed with their mouths forever open. One is Isaac, who was blind, and the other Jacob, who was lame. The idol is a reminder that Abraham's oath is forever and can never be destroyed or broken. The brazen idol is found in the center of the marketplace and is guarded day and night by Jebusite guardians. Unless you take away the blind and the lame that is the enduring reminder of the oath of Abraham, you shall not come into the city." The governor was confident that David would uphold Abraham's sacred promise and not violate the patriarch's ancient agreement.

David was concerned and hated that he had to break Abraham's commitment to gain access to the metropolis, which sickened him to his very soul. David could not overcome the tall, thick walls of the Jebusite fortress; it had to be captured by wile, wit, and cunning. David came up with a subtle plan. The army retreated to a hill overlooking the city. No campfires struck, and so, too, no torches were visible. David called forth and addressed all his captains: "Whosoever can get up from the outer gutter gate by the way that looketh eastward, where the waters run out from the right side and kill the Jebusite guardians and destroy the blind and the lame idol, and by doing so deny the oath of Abraham. The destruction of which vexes me deeply but is necessary for the benefit of Israel. He who can accomplish this feat of daring shall be my chief captain and have my eternal gratitude."

Joab was already considered chief captain but had found disfavor with David for Abner's assassination. The lesser captains spoke among themselves. Joab stepped to the front of the pack and spoke up: "The blind and the lame idol that is Abraham's oath shall not stop us from coming into the house of Jebus. I will take a small force, destroy their pagan idol, secure the gate, and open it—so be wary of my signal. I will wave forth a torch at the entrance when ready. When you make your advance and capture the city, most will be still asleep and unaware of our stealthy intrusion."

Joab and a small squad navigated the cisterns and climbed up through a well in the dark, dousing their torches. The silent patrol engaged the Jebusite guardians and made quick work of them in the shadows, and with a battle-ax and hammer-blade, destroyed the brazen idol of the blind and the lame. They stole into the night through the deep dark of the fourth watch and killed the half-asleep guards by stealth and the cunning of liars. Then, as promised, Joab produced a blazing torch and opened the gate to David's and his army's delight, for nevertheless, they took the stronghold of Zion, which is also known as the city of David.

Being true to his word, David found some choice land upon which to build a house, and he paid for it in full to Ahithophel, the current landowner. This transaction signaled that the new government would legally and properly agree to Jebusite property rights. He was giving the sense that it was not like an armed invasion but a subtle change of administration and that it would be business as usual.

David made his home in Jerusalem, and he hired local crews of stonemasons and laborers. David then zealously began reinforcing the walls of his new capital. He started from the milo defense tower, the highest point in the city. When all defenses were secure, then, and only then, did he proceed with the work inward.

David and his city grew great, for the Lord God of hosts were with them both great and small.

CHAPTER TWENTY-ONE

Master of the Breakthrough

Hiram was the king of Tyre, an ancient Phoenician port city located three hundred and thirty miles to the north of Jerusalem. He was impressed with David and his achievements. Hiram also needed a solid alliance to protect his southern trade routes. Jerusalem remained ideally situated as a chief caravan waystation. Hiram thought it would be advisable to curry favor with the new up-and-coming regional power. David was well known for his courage and daring; Israel would be a strong ally and a trusted and lucrative trading partner.

Hiram sent messengers of goodwill to David in Jerusalem. He also sent an abundance of fresh-cut lumber, skilled carpenters, and master masons, who—by a royal commission—provided David with a mansion of cedar.

David, almost giddy, stood overjoyed with this bounty, and it became apparent that the windows of heaven had opened. God was exalting David's kingdom for the sake of His people Israel.

David felt that, having been given so much in his youth and being full of health and vigor, this was an obvious sign from God to spread his seed liberally, ensuring that his kingdom, and therefore God's kingdom in Israel, would last forever. So, the young king took for himself more concubines and wives from both Jerusalem and neighboring kingdoms. He sired eleven children in the fertile fields of Jerusalem alone.

David also maintained a royal household in Hebron, where he had sons and daughters, adding to his ever-expanding nursery. In part for its higher elevation, he favored life in Hebron. It felt more like home with its rural settings, and he could better relax with fewer demands from ambassadors, palace politics, and the constant infighting of ministers. David saw Jerusalem's hustle and bustle as a fortress and a stronghold, and, at best, a necessary and secure bastion against invasion.

The Philistines had held their peace, hoping that the Hebrews would destroy themselves in an ongoing and vicious civil war. They had hoped that the Hebrew immigrants would be too weak to struggle against an inevitable return to slavery, extermination, or expulsion from the land of Canaan. The Philistine princes were surprised that David, the former vassal of Prince Achish, had been anointed king of both Judah and Israel. Moreover, David had now gained control of Jerusalem, the former Jebusite stronghold. These revelations, coupled with his new alliance with Hiram, king of Tyre, posed a mounting threat. The Philistine princes counseled together, and to a man, agreed that it was now time to strike, before Israel became a fearsome and dangerous adversary once again. The five Philistine princes, including David's old friend Prince Achish, recruited and equipped their armies. Achish recounted his flippant remarks when dismissing David from his kingdom years before. He had promised to fight to the death without mercy or quarter, and now this prophetic remark could very well come to pass.

After ten days of enlisting the strongest warriors, all the Philistine armies gathered with one objective, to seek out David. They pitched their tents and camped in the valley of Rephaim.

A well-trained Hebrew scout had been alerted to a massive movement of men, wagons, and chariots coming up the valley of Sorek from the south and west. It was the whole of a mass military invasion, come to destroy Israel.

The day was sunny and pleasant with a light warm breeze and not a cloud in the sky when an overheated messenger reached out for David's attention. "Your majesty, the Philistines have gathered for a massive attack. But, strategically, they are now encamped in the valley of Rephaim, or the place of giants," he said, gulping for air.

David wiped the messenger's brow and spoke, "Take a breath, for I have been half-expecting this menacing turn of events. David gave the young man a flask of cool water and said, "Refresh yourself, for this news must travel far and wide, throughout the whole of the nation and beyond our borders, even to Moab."

David hastily summoned a council, including Joab, Eliab, Shammah, and Abiathar, the high priest. David met his trusted Mighties at the mansion entrance. The great hall of David's royal residence filled up quickly with the clatter of swords, spears, and nervous chatter. The council was hastily called to order with several thunderous claps from Abiathar.

Once there was silence and order, David began addressing the elders and the assembly of captains, "Make no mistake, the Philistines have come for my head. Prince Achish is now aware of my deception when I was his trusted vassal. He has discovered my slaughter of the Gershurites, Gezrites, the Amalekites villages, and their men, women, and children. Achish has been made the fool in the eyes of all the other princes. They were going to invite me to join them in the battle of Mount Gilboa as a trusted brother. Achish vowed on his honor to my reputation and standing. He now hates me above all others, and all the Philistine princes have sworn an oath of blood to seek me out either at the stronghold gate or valley floor. What say you, Captain Joab? Do we defend or attack? What course of action best suits our chances for victory over the Philistine mongrels?"

Joab shook his head. "My lord, we seemed not to be of one mind about whether to attack in the open or defend in close quarters. Some say this stronghold is an impregnable fortress, but so, too, thought the Jebusites, and my lord had proved them wrong. In the open, we can easily maneuver and strike them at will. I agree our best strategy goes with me down to the hold of Adullam, and this strategy frees us from the concerns for the well-being of women, children, the elderly, and the ill and crippled."

David agreed and then questioned his older brother, "What say you, Eliab?"

"We know now how to protect the gutters and the gate; we can accomplish a stalemate with little or no loss of life. They will tire of the siege and withdraw until another day."

David replied, "Hmm, how long before the food runs out? Do you not remember the siege of Keila? No, brother—we will go down to the hold and leave Jerusalem as soon as possible."

David immediately set about sending out messengers through the length and breadth of his newly acquired realm, commanding all his forces to meet him down at the cave of Adullam. It was the very same place where he had called upon God, and God had answered him with the assured safety of his mother, father, and brothers. Thus, the miraculous, spontaneous gathering of his four hundred ill-assorted outcasts and misfits at that very spot became the spearhead of the army of God.

The only thing that travels faster than bad news is good gossip and the wagging tongues of washwomen; Jerusalem was astir, and a crowd collected bellow the ramparts to hear the king's words. Climbing high above the waiting crowd, David stood upon the western parapet as the morning sun rose at his back. He addressed the waiting crowd and all who were within hearing. David's stance, a blazing silhouette, demanded their undivided attention, some raising their hand to brow to shield their eyes against the blinding glare. A hush of silence blanketed the anxious mob.

David stretched to his full height and stature and began. "Praise be to our God Adonai, and may His words be on my tongue. Let me put your fears to rest and dispel all rumors and gossip. Once again, the Philistine horde is making war, and I believe it is fear of our growing strength and because of me. I was once under their direction and protection, and I am above all others they hate and seek to destroy—me, your king. They will stop at nothing to achieve their wicked ends. The harvest is at hand, and there is no time to reap enough from the fields and threshing floors to sustain the city through a long siege. If I stay, it will only welcome suffering, starvation, and death. I will leave Jerusalem for the hold of Adullam, and there I will call upon God—who has answered my prayers and directed my path when no man would seek after the welfare of my soul. If I stay here in the fortress, there will be a long and lingering siege and a high cost in misery. I will not be able to maneuver the army if backed into a corner. Three of the Mighties will accompany me to my stone lair—my most trusted bodyguards—Jashobeam, the mighty slayer of eight hundred with a spear; Eleazar, who was with me at Pasdammim [or the border of blood]; and lastly, Shammah, who had slaughtered an entire troop of Philistines. These are the Mighties that will join me at Adullam so that Jerusalem will not be molested or assaulted. The army of Israel will gather to me there, and God will direct our footsteps."

David bid his wives goodbye, and he departed at first light for his bastion of prayer and meditation, where he often sought refuge as a boy; it was thirteen miles west of Bethlehem. It was still morning when David entered the familiar cavity; it was rugged and uninviting, but it served a higher purpose. Within the tight space, he received direction, inspiration, and much-needed revelation.

In four days after his leaving, David's call to arms had tingled the ears of Israel, and the army of God gathered to him at the rocky cavern.

David, God's Chosen Crucible

Then, without warning, the Philistines had spread through half of the surrounding countryside, hot for his capture. So David was making the best of a troubling situation. But to make matters worse, the ghosts of disturbing boyhood memories haunted the chilling crevice. For there he was again, hiding from his enemies.

The water of Adullam was barely drinkable and had a bitter, chalky taste. David whispered his longing, not expecting that anyone would have taken him seriously: "Oh, that one would give me a drink from the sweet living waters of the well of Bethlehem, found at the very gate. I remember many a sweltering day coming in from weeks in the sheepfold and longing for that simple refreshment and the cool sweet taste of home and family." The Philistines now had a garrison occupying Bethlehem, but David was more concerned with the coming invasion that was threatening from the north and west.

Jashobeam the Hachmonite [thou will make me wise], Eleazar [God has helped], son of Dodo [his beloved], the Athonite [brother of rest], and Shammah, son of Agee the Hararite. These three Mighties overheard David's longings and set about on a quest for the love of their king. The three slipped outside and out of hearing. Shammah quietly uttered, "I believe we are all thinking the same thing. We are bored and restless, waiting for the rest of the army to rally at this inhospitable gap. We all seek a hero's distraction. I propose capturing a pitcher of the highly valued sweet Bethlehem water from the deep well at the heavily guarded gate by stealth of night or brute force. All three of us should present it to the king to quench his thirst for righteousness's sake. Our king's expression of love and affection will also confirm our skills and lack of fear of the Philistine invasion.

Our exploits will then inspire the army against the Philistine invaders, and our names will be enshrined in stories and sagas of God's chosen people for all time." All three put forth hands in a solemn agreement.

The three Mighties started at first light and traveled the day, avoiding spies, scouts, and outposts. They hid in the shadows until the beginning of the second watch—midnight. It is when all the guards were still sleepy and unsure, and uncertain as to if dreaming. The three scaled over the town's back wall, unnoticed, and silently made their way toward the town square. They crouched as they went across the dark courtyard but were spotted when a sentry spied three shadowy figures scurrying toward the well. A gang of Philistine soldiers immediately set upon the three, and they fought as men possessed. Shammah and Ishbaal held off ten men, giving Eleazar time to break through the spring-fed well and filled it to overflowing from the tipping bucket. Eleazar joined the fray again as the three almost joyfully fought back into the enveloping darkness through the now-open gate. The trio traveled stealthily back to David for the rest of the night by hiding in the underbrush and dodging torch-lit patrols.

The daylight found the three Mighties on a thirteen-mile return to quench the king's desired thirst. Their parched lips were dry, but not a drop of the precious liquid was tasted. They boastfully presented the prized pitcher of sweet home waters on bended knee to the king. They took turns telling a tale of their bravery and how they broke through the Philistine guards to obtain this offering of living waters at Bethlehem.

King David, deeply dismayed at this reckless adventure, sternly scolded the three. He took the pitcher in his hand and poured it on the ground, in an offering unto the Lord, "May God forbid that I drink this gifted sacrifice—only God is esteemed enough to receive such adoration. Shall I drink the blood of you men that have put your lives in jeopardy? You have risked life and limb, for such feats, either great or small, belong to the Lord, and the Lord alone." The three Mighties were downcast from the righteous scolding, but accepted it like true men of valor.

The Philistines lodged in the valley of Rephaim. They gathered at their sacred high grove surrounded by many wooden, brass, gold, and quarried idols. Their stand was two and one half miles north and west of Jerusalem; there, they would invoke ancient heathen spirits to overthrow the power of the Hebrew God before staging their invasion.

All of Israel gathered from the four corners of the realm and traveled to the hold of Adullam. They were in search of their anointed king to find their needed leadership. David knew now that it was time to counsel with the Lord and earnestly pray for divine direction. The king dismissed everyone, for he preferred to be alone whenever he called upon God and sought relief for his tormented soul. He knelt in the very same spot as before and inquired of God, "Shall I go up to the Philistines? Will you deliver them into my hands?"

The still, small voice of the Lord answered, "Go up: for I will doubtless deliver the Philistines into thine hand."

David exited from the dark-mouthed cave into the sunlight of the spirit, immediately strengthening his steadfast resolve. His face was bright with the grace of God, and he proclaimed with a sure and steady voice, "I have sought counsel with Adonai, and my faith is full to overflowing. My confidence waxes strong in the Lord of Hosts, and I remain committed and unwavering to His omnipotent commands. We have neglected nothing, and all our arrangements are in place. We shall prove ourselves once again able to repel any invaders of our sovereign nation, Israel. We will hold fast and outwit and outfight the Philistine menace, however long it takes. We will prevail as one, for God is with us, and with steadfast resolve, we will protect and defend our sacred homeland. Alone we are weak. But together and with the might of God on our side, we are strong. We shall not relent until victory is ours, as it has already been given to us by our Creator. We shall resist with sureness and courage and so dispel any misgivings. We will fill all the breaches with brash-dogged determination, no matter how long it takes. We will, and we shall prevail: this is my pledge, and the Lord of Hosts goes before us." All went quiet as the words stirred every man's heart. Then a rumbling broke into a raucous cheer of acknowledgment. The encouragement was widespread and sincere. All agreed wholeheartedly to go forward to Rephaim and the valley of giants.

The army of God hastily organized and set forth, banners and flags snapping against the stiffening winds of war.

David and his army endured twenty miles of a forced march. They halted only when one of Joab's advanced scouting parties alerted David to the enemy's whereabouts and urgently disclosed, "We kept to the shadows of deep ravines and boulders as we crept upon our bellies to the most northern edge of Rephaim Valley, and what we came upon was a view of a mountain covered with Philistines. There was a large gathering of people at the very top—with raging fires, chanting, and it seemed to me like idol worship. There were chariots and horses in abundance and many infantry tents pitched at the mountain base, too many to number."

David realized that they were preparing for a full-out assault on Jerusalem, only two and a half miles away to the south. The only obstacle to the heathen assault was the army of Israel. The coming dark prohibited waging a night battle, especially when trying to ascend in force up steep highland walls. He also speculated that the Philistines were too busy with their religious rituals, and they were still far enough away that his movements had gone unnoticed. Eliab, Abinadab, Shammah, Joab, and David's thirty chief captains attended a council to determine the best course of action. David stated, "If we stay, we fight at first light. Going up in the dark will be treacherous at best. On the other hand, if we hold our position here and form battle lines, there is too much open ground, and we will fall prey to the Philistine chariots. What say you?"

Joab spoke up. "I say we pitch here. If we depart, where would we go? The men have been marching all day and have had only an occasional break. For the men to gather strength and ward off fatigue, they need a full night's sleep."

Shammah, a tight-lipped brother known for keeping his own counsel, had a confirming insight. "I have considered our problem, and I agree with David. As yet, we have gone undetected." All agreed that the army would encamp there in the coming twilight without warming fire or any revealing torchlight.

The heathen legions struggled to organize, and then, a command echoed against the mount's stone walls. It was Padi, the renowned Philistine strategist. "We will attack Jerusalem, their mighty stronghold, and there we will fill our coffers with spoils of gold so that each man can buy ten kegs of wine. With ransom enough to lure a comely wife and slaves enough to endure her endless nagging of household chores." A laugh of familiarity rose and then just as suddenly subsided. "But, most decidedly, we will finally rid ourselves of those troublesome multiplying immigrants and their constant challenge to our ancestral lands of heritage."

Padi started issuing commands to his lesser captains as order began to emerge out of confusion. The Philistines were masters at forming tactical ranks; chariots and their bowmen came up from the rear as the infantry spearheaded the army in columns of three. Once the battle was raging, the mobile chariots could reinforce breaches anywhere the battle lines began to splinter.

A threatening red sky met the day when David summoned his captains and laid out his battle plans. He gravely asserted, "Our best hope—and our only hope—is to gain the high ground. If we remain on the flats, the enemy chariots will slay us with impunity; our only chance is to overturn them on the slopes.

"A three-pronged attack, then. One corps to the right and one legion to the left, holding back the center strike force. The right and the left will attack at the same time. The enemy will rush to reinforce their flanks and will be weakest in the center."

The army was set in order and made ready as commanded. The skies over the mount had eerily blackened when three blasts from the shofar horn signaling the advance sounded. The Israelites set themselves to march when suddenly, and before a forward step touched the ground, the windows of heaven opened, and the Lord cast down great hailstones from above—the enemy suffered a great pelting without mercy or pity. Horses reared and stampeded, forcing their driverless chariots to flip over. This chaos caused a parting in the enemy defenses. There was a breach, as the breach of waters like unto the separation of the Red Sea. David and his forces ran up the break and exploited the opening. He had become the point of the spear and edge of the sword. His army took heart at his fearless daring. His most valiant three Mighties surrounded him. They formed an unstoppable killing machine, slashing and stabbing (and sometimes slipping and sliding) as they pushed uphill through a veil of hailstones, ice, and blood. Israel took full advantage of this opportunity and hurriedly scaled to the heights. Once Israel reached the top, the Philistines soon melted away from the torrent of tumbling boulders and well-aimed rocks that sealed Israel's overwhelming victory.

The enemy's army split in two and then finally crumbled. Their retreat was so sudden that they left behind their wood, brass, and gold idols, some taken as spoil, and their wooded gods burned the next night to ward off the high mountain chill. Then, in the glowing firelight, David blessed his men, saying, "The Lord has broken forth upon my enemies before me, as the breach of waters. Hereafter and forever, this place is now known as Baal-perazim 'or the lord of the breakthrough.'"

CHAPTER TWENTY-TWO

When Baka Trees Bleed

The Philistines were thoroughly humiliated at the battle of Baal-perazim. It cemented their seething hatred for David and Israel—a hatred that grew ever more vicious and desperate. Spitefully, Achish and the other Philistine princes agreed they would use all their wealth and power to entice the Amalekites, Gershurites, Gezrites, Shurites—or any willing Canaanite—to join their war, even if it meant going beyond their borders and recruiting the feared Egyptian charioteers. All this to ensure the success of a great invasion of Israel and the slaying of David.

« « « » » »

A peaceful year passed, and in the meanwhile, David and Israel continued to strengthen and prosper. But, now that the harvest vines again bent with plenty, war once more was on the horizon. So Israel enlisted spies, scouts, and informants—for now, Israel was a land of milk and honey, surrounded by a host of enemies that envied her treasures and would have those riches for themselves.

A spy of some renown, Eliyahu Ben-Shaul, was dusty and dirty from a sleepless journey. He begged for admittance to gain access to the ear of the king. Eliyahu presented himself in an adjacent and private anteroom, for he had won David's confidence on many previous occasions. Eliyahu bowed in homage. David then inquired, "Eliyahu, I am glad for your work and acknowledge your sacrifices of family, friends, life, and limb for the sake of Israel. I know, when you come to Jerusalem, there is terrible trouble in the making. Speak up, my friend."

Eliyahu had dark, piercing eyes and hair and skin blacker than midnight. He leaned into the light and out of his comfort of shadows. "Your Majesty is insightful as usual. The Philistines have, yet again, spread themselves in the valley of Rephaim. It is an invasion force, three times greater than at the battle of Baal-Perazim. They have aligned themselves with all of Israel's most vicious and determined enemies and shall reach their full strength of numbers in about four days hence."

David replied, "Thank you, Eliyahu, for this vitally important information. I am grateful to you, and so is the nation."

David summoned his messengers, alerting all the tribes to the imminent threat. He then called his brothers, captains, and Abiathar, his high priest, to a war council. The noisy gathering quieted after a loud shout.

"Order! I say, elders, princes, and nobles, David ben Jesse, king of Israel and Judah commands your attention."

The loud crowd died down to a hiss of whispers. David attempted to lay out his divine plan, and so he began, "I have prayed and had asked the Lord if we should go up against this formidable heathen horde." The Lord replied, "You shall not go up; draw your forces behind them in the place where the mulberry [or Baka trees] are most plentiful. When you hear the sound of a great army going in the tops of the trees, then and only then shall you rouse yourself from your hiding place. For then, you will know and doubt not that I am YOUR LORD YOUR GOD, who goes out before your very eyes. For it is I that strike down your mortal enemy, the uncircumcised Philistine."

David was so confident in God's promise that he did not wait for the army of Israel to gather from the outlying provinces. Instead, he assembled his inner circle, Eliab, Abinadab, Shammah, Abiathar the high priest, and Joab, his chief captain. David adjourned his trusted group into the shadows of a side alcove and out of hearing of any guards or servants that lurked within earshot. He began laying out his plans in a subtle whisper: "Brothers, I believe we have an opportunity here if we act quickly and decisively. The Philistines have amassed a great army in the valley of giants and will not expect our attack this quickly. I have counseled with our almighty God, and He has assured me that He will go before us, so it matters not that we are few or many. Therefore, as secretly as possible, I propose that we set out immediately with my devoted six hundred, the Jerusalem garrison, and any nearby warriors to avoid announcing our intentions to the enemy."

Eliab spoke up, "Brother, I believe your proposition stands doomed to failure. We should take our time and gather all the men we can and prepare as best we can. The forces of the Philistines are greater than we had ever previously encountered. If we leave Jerusalem undefended, especially now during the harvest, it would not be prudent; I contend that it is too risky and even a foolhardy strategy. Therefore, we should plan well and gather strength before taking on such an expedition."

"Eliab," David countered, "do you believe me when I say God has promised us a victory and that He will go before us? He has given me a sign as to the very moment when the army of heaven, even vengeful angels, will proceed before us into battle."

Eliab had to concede, "I believe that you believe, dear brother. As usual, I understand that you are determined to face down the might of another Goliath with your childlike trust in God. As for me, I will again use your faith until mine becomes as sure and steady as yours, little brother." All agreed to David's proposal and hurriedly prepared to witness if faith alone could conquer the unimaginable—an empire's worth of ferocious enemies.

There was little or no fanfare when David and his small band departed from Jerusalem. The route was hidden to the casual eye and thwarted liars' and spies' ability to discover David's destination of Gibeon. There he would encircle the rear of the Philistine invaders and catch them unprepared and unaware of his presence.

The Philistine commander Padi was expecting a direct assault from the entire tribal army of Israel in the same direction and manner as they had done the year before. He concluded that it would take David time to recruit such an army and prepare it for battle. Even so, General Padi believed that he had enough time to make ready his siege and capture Jerusalem.

David's hastily recruited army moved swiftly; they traveled between valley floors and mountains peaks, keeping to the lowlands, moving faster than rumors and the flight of ravens. Lastly, David and his band of dedicated men reached the outskirts of Gibeon at twilight. They pitched in secret and rested for the night, for dawn would test their faith of will and their sharpened killing skills. At first light, David gathered his mighty men of valor.

"I am your king—but make no mistake: the Lord God is your commander. He has directed our every step and has witnessed our inevitable victory. This day you will see His might and His promises realized right before your very eyes. We have taken the necessary actions, and now we wait upon God to reveal Himself. We are to linger behind the screen of the Baka trees [or the trees that bleed]. The Lord has whispered to me, 'When you hear the sound of a great army going in the tops of those trees, then and only then shall you rouse yourself from your secret place. For then, you will know, and do not doubt that I am your Lord, your God, that goes out before you to strike down your mortal enemies.' We will wait and remain poised and ready for the promised sign; let no one make a move until we observe the bending of branches and the rustle of leaves. The Lord's time is not our time, and His ways are not our ways. In so, that He may do His work, His strange work; and bring to pass His act, His strange act."

The day had passed without even a whisper of a breeze. The buzz of flies and the bite of bugs grew intolerable. It was as if some evil force was trying to dislodge, dissuade, or make them reveal themselves to the observation of enemy scouts and stop them from accomplishing their mission. Some of the men were getting anxious, and a few pressed hard for David to retreat. Night fell hard, with fearful misgivings and bitter, impatient grievances. It seemed as if the darkness would last forever.

The waking enemy camp was close enough to hear the neighing of horses and the clatter of chariot wheels. David's men were fearful that the slightest utterance could give away their position. Even their breathing remained short and shallow.

The sun of a new day gave up its first rays, with a great sound of an army marching through and high above the Baka treetops. David stirred his forces with the loud blast from a single shofar horn, and every man rushed to witness God's mighty arm of vengeance. All the king's men glanced over the valley rim to observe a great uproar as if an invisible band of killer angels was churning, slashing, and stabbing the Canaanite revengers, creating a whirlwind of destruction. The pagan army was being cut down and was now on the run. So the shout was, "Every man for himself!" lending speed to a glorious route. The army of David joined in with heaven's forces and destroyed the fleeing Philistines, from Geba to Gazer.

CHAPTER TWENTY-THREE

The Arc of the Ark

Israel now cleansed all her mortal enemies through God's omnipotent hand, and David established his capital at Jerusalem. He was obliged to honor the Most High by gathering all the men chosen, thirty thousand in all, mighty vessels of righteousness. David addressed the festive crowd and all those who had remained loyal, even beyond the wilderness stronghold and high mountain passes. Everyone there either hailed from Baalah or Kirjath-jearim to Judah's borders. David loved them all, just like family.

He began: "Brothers, priests, nobles, captains and friends, and all who have placed their faith in me and Adonai, our great Creator. We will now go together as one people to fetch up the choicest treasure in all of Israel, even the Ark of the covenant. It has been the sign and symbol of God's presence with us since the days of Moses. It is the object and primary focus of our worship and service to Adonai, our master. The Ark or 'The Name,' saying *Hashem* in reverence, even the name of the Lord of Hosts, the infinite, eternal, and absolute Being, the Lord of armies above and below; whose habitation is between the cherubim that overshadow the mercy seat. We honor the Ark; it belongs to Him and Him alone. Our amazing Ark has a vibrant glow and seems to have a light of its own, with a skin of highly polished gold. Therein are two large stone tablets wrapped in the holy commandments deeply inscribed by the mighty finger of God. These divine instructions were set aside for His prophet Moses on Mount Sinai. ["Sinai" means the bush in the clay desert or the place of enmity]. The commandments remain our beacon and our light so that we might navigate back into the presence of our loving heavenly Father. There is also a bowl of fresh 'manna,' or 'what is it?'—the corn of heaven, with the texture and taste of coriander: warm, nutty, spicy, and sweet orange-flavored. The manna not only fills the belly but also guards against illness and plague. When we were in the desert, only one day's helping was the required allotment. Hoarding was discouraged by worm and by rot. On the eve of the Shabbat, a double portion remained delicious through the whole of the next day. Manna reminds us that God's word is fresh and alive and feasted upon daily and twice again on a holy day. Also present in the Ark is Aaron's rod, which God had made in the twilight of the sixth day of Creation. The scepter represented the power of the priesthood and made a permanent connection to God Almighty. Aaron's rod put forth buds and produced blossoms, and it bore ripe almonds, an acknowledgment that the house of Levi was forever the keepers of that eternal priesthood."

David turned his attention to Abiathar, saying, "You hold that very same priesthood with all its rights and privileges. Would you acknowledge that the rights of the priesthood remain inseparably connected with the powers of heaven? Remember that the powers of heaven cannot be controlled or handled, only upon the principles of righteousness and with an eye single to the glory of Jehovah."

The crowd shouted as with one voice, "Amien and Amien." The joyous mob was eager to begin the procession to repossess their holiest artifact.

Preparations were well underway when David called upon Abiathar, his friend and his high priest. Abiathar—which means "the father is great"—was the son of Ahimelech, which implies "brother to the King"; Abiathar's father often went by his familiar name Ahija—brother." Ahimelech was the son of Ahitub, Phinehas the younger, whose name means "the bronze-colored one or the colored one," was Eli's firstborn son; "Eli" means "elevation." Eli was the high priest at Shiloh and a direct descendant of Levi. Abiathar was one of the few remaining Levites since the massacre of the eighty-five priests who wore the linen Ephod. King Saul had ordered their slaughter and of everything that drew breath in Nob, including the animals.

David hugged his dear friend and said, "You have schooled me well in the contents of the Ark, and for this, I am forever grateful. However, I now have a concern that only you can answer. Therefore, the command is that no one may carry the Ark of

God, but only by the Levites. For the LORD has chosen them to take the Ark of God and to minister before Him forever."

"Speak on, my lord; I am here to serve."

"Abiathar, since you had the Ark at Nob, the house of God, for a very long time, how should I proceed to carry it back the seven miles from Aminadab's home to Jerusalem, without offending God?"

Abiathar pondered at length David's urgent request and attempted a solution. "There are four gold rings attached two on each side, and two poles of acacia wood sheathed in gold. The cartage requires four Levites to carry the Ark, and at this time, we seem to be lacking three Levites, although the Ark had suffered transport by a driverless Philistine cart pulled by two kine, or cows, that had never known a yoke or plow. The Philistines seemed to have done this without suffering the wrath of God. The Philistines did not know of the commandment and would not suffer God's anger because of their ignorance; God does wink at certain times. Perhaps—and just chancing a guess that the Lord would permit a cart again—one pristine, never used before, and one only made clearly for this singleness of purpose. The sons of Abinadab have been caring for the Ark for a long time. None have suffered death or injury, which is an encouraging sign. But I am not completely certain of their lineage, as all the sons of Aaron are Levites, but not all Levites are the sons of Aaron. The Lord God will adopt some in righteousness; that was told to me by my father. We will have to lift the Ark onto the cart, and their help will be essential. Then they can shepherd the Ark in the cart back to Jerusalem. That is my opinion and my advice, my king."

David had found the answer he was hoping for, and he added, "I will order an unspoiled carriage, and on the flooring, I will place an unspotted sheepskin so that Ark will ride in comfort."

David and all the people were in a joyous and festive mood. All were singing, dancing, and playing musical instruments. There were cascading harps, and psalteries strings were blissfully plucked. High-kicking women shook timbrels. Coronets and their warm, mellow tones floated above the procession while cymbals clashed like thunderbolts. The people were going out to bring their God-box home to rest among them in the city of David. The new cart and the uneasy oxen covered in garlands went out before them, setting out for Gibeon. The eager crowd proceeded to the house of Abinadab. Uzzah, meaning strength, and Ahio, meaning his brother, were the sons of Abinadab. Abinadab's house had basked in the glory of the Ark, and this had urged David to give the honor of piloting the freshly made wagon to his two sons. They would help to convey the Ark of the covenant to reside forever in Jerusalem. Uzzah and Ahio had maintained the Ark by polishing the gold and cleaning and its surroundings. They had developed a spiritual connection and would suffer a longing and a deep sense of loss at its departure. Abiathar, Nachon, Uzzah, and Ahio hefted the Ark into the waiting cart. The brothers were more than ready to accomplish God's will to help secure its final and hallowed destination.

The uproar of the pageant had simmered down to jubilant praise and worship. Then, the roads became uneven, potted, and rutted from the endless wagons that had come before Nakhon's threshing floors. The oxen jumped, and the Ark slid violently back and forth on the sheepskin flooring. Uzzah jumped down from the carriage seat to protect his precious cargo. He walked along the pockmarked road when suddenly the oxen kicked, and the Ark tipped and threatened to flip. Uzzah instinctively reached out; he braced his legs and planted his feet and was well-grounded. The gold-sheathed Ark shifted and touched his outstretched hands. There was a sharp, commanding snap and a faint blue spark, followed by a white flash like a lightning bolt. Uzzah's hair lifted, and there was the smell of burnt flesh. Uzzah went rigid and then just as suddenly fell back, dead. The cart righted itself, keeping safe and intact its precious cargo.

Through this incident, it seemed that the anger of the Lord kindled hot against Uzzah, and God had killed him immediately for his error. David was confused and displeased because the Lord had made a breach upon Uzzah. Prayerfully, David named the place Perez-Uzzah [or the violation of Uzzah] because Uzzah had broken God's holy commands.

David was saddened and afraid of God, and so were all the people who were with him. David pondered his failings and sought comfort and counsel from Abiathar, his Levite high priest, who was also perplexed and puzzled at the sudden turn of events. Gravely David inquired, "My priest—was it the use of the cart, or was it the sudden physical assault, that now God is disturbed with my meddling? Tell me, priest, what is on the mind of God? How should the Ark come to me in Jerusalem? If men fall along the way, perhaps even the Lord will strike me down for this folly. Tell me, Abiathar, for I am a man of war who loves his God, and now I find myself thoroughly mystified on what to do next so as not to offend my Lord, God forbid in the likes of the accidental death and well-meaning breach of Uzzah."

Abiathar was lost in thought for a very long time as silence invaded the conversation.

"I believe there were two insults; for the first one, remember that it is required that, before touching the Ark, a solution must be made, consisting of the ashes of the red heifer and a dram from a pitcher of living waters. A person that is to touch the Ark must thoroughly wash their hands in the solution. The second was using a cart. The Philistines had used a cart to return the Ark to Israel but were ignorant of the divine protocols, so they were not held liable. Once the cart was out of their possession, it crossed back into Israel. The kine stopped in the town of Beth-Shemesh. The people there mobbed the Ark and attempted to lift the lid of the box. They were hoping to see the face of God. But instead, their rash insult caused many of them to die. Uzzah's death is unfortunate, but the Lord has signaled his displeasure, in that a person would treat the Ark as a common item that an ordinary person could molest. I think it is wise to pray that the Lord does not take any further vengeance for our disobedience. I suggest that we do not continue our journey to Jerusalem until we can better determine the extent of displeasure and avoid His fury. So let us adjourn to the closest house of a known and righteous Levite for cover and protection."

The nearest Levite, through God's omnipotent plan, was but a stone's throw away. The man's name was Obed-Edom, who lived on Gath's borders and hailed as a Gittite.

Abiathar wisely counseled, "Better yet, my Lord, to leave it with this Levite. What better place to let it rest for a season and give our Lord time to ease His wrath and so call upon His abundance of mercy?"

David spoke to Obed-Edom, "I have a treasure that I need to leave in your custody, even the Ark of the Covenant. I am the King of Israel and Judah, and I will require your obedience in this delicate matter. I will pay you handsomely for its care and protection and will be along for it as soon as I deem it acceptable and desirable by God's will."

Obed-Edom was hesitant at first after hearing of Uzzah's downfall—but in the end, he agreed to the king's plea of dire necessity.

CHAPTER
TWENTY-FOUR
A Naked Breach of Modesty

The Ark found rest in the house of Obed-Edom for three months. The home of Obed-Edom prospered, the fruits of his ground grew lush, and his vines did not cast off their fruit before its season. His herds and flocks flourished with a blessed increase. His Levite sons were encouraged in the study of the Torah. By all outward signs and appearances, the Lord's wrath was satisfied.

The words of redemption reached the eager ears of David, saying, "The Lord has blessed Obed-Edom's household and all that comes within his reach because the Ark of God resides under his roof with care and protection."

David called for Abiathar and Zadok, the priests. In turn, the priests gathered the Levites Uriel, Asaiah, Joel, Shemaiah, Eliel, and Amminadab to hear the good news from David's lips. "Priests and Levites, it is time to retrieve the Ark and place it under the covering of the awaiting booth until the Temple rises from the ground and so that God may find a permanent dwelling place here among us in Jerusalem. This time we will do it right, for none other than Levites should carry the Ark of the Covenant—for they are the chosen ones to minister unto Him and forever. I have called you because you are the chief of the fathers of the Levites. I need you to sanctify yourselves, both you and all of your brother Levites, that you may bring up the Ark of the Lord God of Israel to the place prepared for it in Jerusalem. The first time you attempted transport, it failed because you did not make ready, and the Lord God made a breach upon us, for we relied on the understanding and reckoning of men. Because we were making an offering for the Lord, we somehow felt exempted from His justice and His laws. Wherefore, now let every man learn his duty and to act in all diligence in the task assigned to him."

Abiathar nodded and grinned in joyful anticipation. "My Lord, I have considered this task and the safest way to accomplish this challenging mission. But, yes, and most certainly, we need to call forth all the Levites, from the surrounding tribes with their singers of songs, their musicians, doorkeepers, and porters one and all.

"Our faith in the Lord includes understanding His timing," Abiathar continued. "When we first attempt travel, this time, we need to go only but six paces, the very same number as the number of days it took the Lord to finish all of creation; then on the seventh day, He rested. On that count, we need to commemorate the seventh day of rest by offering up seven bullocks and seven rams, and we need to do this before we take even another step. I believe if we sanctify ourselves and have the ashes of the red

206

heifer mixed with living waters before touching the Ark, we will be grounded in the Law and shielded from God's wrath. Since we know that Obed-Edom found favor in the eyes of the Lord with regards to the Ark, I would suggest that he be set apart as a porter, as well as his five sons, Shemaiah, the firstborn, and Jehozabad, Joash, Sacra, and Nethaneel. All Levites are to help in the Ark's transport."

"I agree," David stressed. "If there are no more questions or suggestions, let us get this procession organized, set apart, and begun."

David assembled all of Aaron's children, Levites, by inheritance and set apart God's ministers. David again gathered all the house of Israel. The elders and the captains of thousands joyfully paraded in front of the Ark of the Covenant. They were joined at the gates with shouting, cheering and singing by Chenaniah (David's master of the song) and all his singers. The rousing sound of shofar trumpets, cornets, and cymbals made a joyful noise with psalteries and harps reaching the heavens.

David called upon Abiathar to bring forth the linen ephod vestment and the Levite robe of fine-twined linen. "Abiathar," David proclaimed, "I feel so close to the Lord that I have lost the forbidden knowledge of modesty. Therefore, I do not need the kethōneth [or the apron symbolizing Adam's leaves to hide his nakedness from the Lord]."

Abiathar did David's bidding and said nothing, for David was bursting with the love of God in that he was far beyond the earthly concerns of decorum.

David danced with all his might, for he overflowed with the spirit of God. His flimsy linen robe hiked up above his girdle.

David, God's Chosen Crucible

His kicks were to heaven, and he leaped and whirled as a man possessed. When David spun, the linen robe raised high above the confines of polite society, and with awkward glances, maidens blushed to witness the king of all Israel in all his glory.

As the Ark crossed the gate and came into the city of David, Michal, Saul's daughter, looked through a window and saw David leaping and dancing, and she despised him in her heart for his moments of base immodesty.

The holy procession had reached its destination, placing the Ark amid the tabernacle that David had pitched in the heart of Jerusalem. David then offered burnt and peace offerings before the Lord in the number and manner befitting the jubilant assembly. So many had gathered to witness the historical recovery of Israel's most precious treasure.

Once the holy ordinance concluded, David rose to where all could see and hear him. All stood as he raised his hands to heaven so that he could bless them, "My priests, my captains, and my friends who are my people of Israel. I am your prince, but only God is your king, and I ask Him in The Name to bless you and keep you, to see to your happiness and protection. Let the righteous be glad this day, let them rejoice before God, yes, let them be exceedingly glad and rejoice upon the mountaintops. Sing unto God, sing praises to His name: extol Him that rides upon the heavens by The Name, and rejoice before Him. He is a father to the fatherless, and a protector of widows is God, and now is in His holy habitation. God sits with the solitary families: He brings out those bound with chains: but the rebellious dwell in a dry land waiting on His mercy and love like a spring of living waters to quench their souls. The Ark of God has found its way home; blessed be The Name of the Lord."

In humility and reverence, David became a servant to all the people, even among the whole multitude of Israel. He served the women, as well as the men. He gave each one within reach one cake of bread, a good piece of flesh, and a bottle of wine. When all the people were satisfied, David sent everyone home to their own house, having filled his high commission as a servant to all Israel.

David then sought out his household to bless it with his presence and find rest and peace, with his loving wife Michal at his hearth and fireside.

Michal was a raven-haired beauty. She was the daughter of Saul and the bride of David's youth. She had personally saved his life by helping him escape from her father's henchmen. Michal had then borne the indignity of being given to another man in marriage, Phaltiel, when her father had disavowed David's legacy. Eventually, she was brought back to David through Abner's workings and the agreement of her brother, King Ish-bosheth. But things were all so different now. Three years had passed, and again she was being put through yet another disgrace. She realized that David, now king, was still the ill-mannered shepherd boy not accustomed to living with polite society. Only, now, he would be unrestrained in his appetites, for he had outlived her father and bested all his rivals. And so—at this point—whatever David wanted, he could now take—including all the women who had just seen his nakedness.

Michal's eyes narrowed into angry slits.

David entered the gates to his Jerusalem estate to find Michal on the front steps with hands-on-hips, foot-tapping loudly, and eyes red with flame. His guards had barely shut the door when she lit into him. David quickly ushered Michal into the king's apartments, attempting to shield their row from spying eyes and gossipmongers.

Michal screeched, "Why does the king of Israel debase himself in public, and under what circumstances?" she glared. "Did you lose your entire army on the battlefield? Are you the vassal of Prince Achish yet again?"

David's face flushed, and he was about to open his mouth. But, instead, she screamed, "Who are you to put on such a vile and disrespectful display, like some common ruffian in the town square? How could you ever think it was appropriate to show the king's nakedness to a gaggle of giggling high- and low-born women?"

"I respect all women alike." David immediately regretted saying it out loud. So, he tried a different tack in his explanation. "I am not afraid to be naked in front of the Lord. He has known all of me since birth, and He accepts me naturally as he made me."

"From what I saw, it seems that half the wanton women in Jerusalem saw all of you, as well, my husband! Are you looking to add more to your growing stable of concubines, then?

"For you shall not have any one of them and revisit my bed-chamber. I am King Saul's daughter and a princess by heritage, and I do not consort with someone who would make a shameful spectacle of himself."

David was sweating, despite the steady cold wind that whipped at his flimsy robe. His face flushed with rage, he thought for a moment, confounded and unable to answer. Then he stood erect and girded the robe tight around him.

"Maybe I should just pack you up with your household and send you back to Phaltiel, serving both of our purposes," David spat with wrath on the tips of his lips.

She sneered at him for the first time.

"If you do, you may as well pack up the crown of Saul for Phaltiel, as well." Michal gave David a gaze that could stop a charging elephant.

"The Lord God has said that you would be king of all Israel, but He gave no condition for how long you would keep the title."

David gulped.

"You need me more than I need you! If the seed of Jonathan lives, and my father's other seven grandsons draw breath, you will be an illegitimate heir to Saul's kingdom in the eyes of eleven of the Twelve Tribes unless you are married to me. That is why you brought me here in the first place, isn't it?"

In his heart, David knew this to be true. He bowed his head in submission and decisively uttered, "So be it, princess, and as you wish, wife of my youth. We will remain, man and wife, but in name only, but forever and a day, we will live separate lives."

Michal would live in her own home close by to David's palace; she would receive a pension, servants, and a living allowance, suitable to her elevated position, and for the rest of her life. But the two never shared a bed again. David would never have his seed tainted by the house of Saul. Michal would die childless but, on her terms, and with her quiet dignity intact.

CHAPTER
TWENTY-FIVE
A House of Cedar, Prayer, and Thanksgiving

K ing David sat serenely in his house, for the Lord had given him rest roundabout from all his enemies; even the Philistine threat remained dampened. But his mind was always in motion. Soon David became restless and anxious without a border to defend or new lands to conquer, for he was the ever-eager man of action.

He summoned Nathan, the prophet, who came forth into the king's private and well-appointed apartments. David greeted him with all the deference and due respect expected of a prophet of God. David began, "Look around you, Nathan, I dwell in a house filled with the fragrant smell of fresh sturdy cedar, but the Ark of God dwells within flimsy curtains and is subject to sudden changes in the weather, desert winds, beating rains, and the scorching sun."

Nathan nodded. "God will hear all that is in your heart, for the Lord is with you."

Young men shall have visions, and old men shall have dreams—and as he promised that night, as Nathan lay upon his bed, the Lord spoke to Nathan, his prophet.

"Go and tell my servant David: Thus, saith the Lord, 'Thou shalt build me a house for me to dwell in, for I have not resided in any house since the time that I brought up the children of Israel out of Egypt. Even to this day have I but walked in a tent and a tabernacle. In all the places where I have walked with all the children of Israel, have I ever spoken a word with any of the tribes of Israel, whom I commanded to feed my people Israel, saying, Why have you not built me a house of cedar? Now, then, so shall you say unto my servant David, so saith the Lord of hosts, I took him from the sheepcote, from following the sheep, to be ruler over my people, over Israel. I was with him wherever he went. I have cut off all his enemies from out of his sight. I have made him a great name, like unto the name of the great men in the earth.

"Moreover, I tell you that the Lord will dwell in the house that my people build.

"I will appoint a place for my people Israel and plant them to dwell in a home of their own and move no more. Neither shall the children of wickedness afflict them anymore, since I commanded judges to be over my people Israel. Moreover, I will subdue all your enemies.

"It shall come to pass when your days expire, and you must go the way of your fathers, I will raise your seed after you, which shall be of your sons; I will establish his kingdom. He shall build me a house instead of you, and I will establish his throne forever. I will be his father, and he shall be my son: and I will not take my mercy away from him, as I took it from him that was before you. I will be his father, and he shall be my son. If he commits iniquity, I will discipline him with the rod of men and with the stripes of the children of men. But I will settle him in my house and my kingdom forever, and his throne established forevermore.'"

Nathan became unsettled with the news and immediately went forth and requested an audience with the king. Nathan walked into the banquet hall in a stark and somber mood. He pounded his staff three times, bringing the noisy gallery to order. In the ensuing silence. Nathan beckoned David to join him in a private chamber to voice God's words for his ears alone.

"Your majesty, the Lord who knows the end from the beginning has given me a dream," and he began reciting word for word according to his divine instructions.

David was confounded and somewhat perplexed at God's blunt rejection of his offer to build Him a house of prayer. A house of fasting, a house of faith, a house of cedar, and the house of God, so that He may have a permanent dwelling place and reside amongst His people Israel here in Jerusalem.

The king took solace from the promise that his name and his seed would go on forever, and it would be his posterity that would build the temple to the Almighty.

David took a sullen moment with mixed emotions and then asked Nathan, "Why did the Lord God deny me?"

Nathan shook his head and looked David squarely in the eyes. "I told you all that the Lord had imparted to me—and all that I heard, I repeated. I would implore you to go to the Lord and speak your heart and mind, for you will find what you seek. Remember, David, that His thoughts are not our thoughts, and His ways are not our ways. It would be best to prepare yourself for an answer that may not be to your liking or your immediate understanding."

David took the advice of the sage and retired to a private closet to speak his heart and his mind, saying, "My Lord, my God, I have in my heart to build you a great house of cedar, stone, gold, and silver, the greatest house in all the world, and I stand denied. Therefore, I pray thee allow me this task that I might show my gratitude and my love for taking me out of the sheepcote and making me a king of your people Israel."

The word of the Lord came in a still small voice, for David knew his soundings. "You have shed blood abundantly and have made great wars: You shall not build a house unto my name because you have shed too much blood upon the earth in my sight. Behold, a son shall be born to you, who shall be a man of rest; and I will give him rest from all his enemies round about: for his name shall be Solomon, and I will give peace and quietness unto Israel in his days. He shall build a house for my name, and he shall be my son, and I will be his father, and I will establish the throne of his kingdom over Israel forever."

David found comfort and solace in the blessing of his house and lineage. He prayed with a heartfelt thanksgiving with insight and knowledge that surpasses understanding. "O, Lord God, the word that you have spoken concerning your servant, and concerning his house, to establish it forever and do as you have said.

"Let your name know only praise eternally, saying, 'The Lord of hosts is the God over Israel: and let the house of your servant David find eternal establishment before you.' Therefore, now let it please you to bless the house of thy servant, that it may continue forever in your sight: for you, O Lord God, hast spoken it: and with your blessing, let the house of your servant be blessed forever."

David returned unto Nathan and spoke all he said and heard. "I will not build the house of God, for it is a house of peace, for I am a man of war. But my posterity will do so, for the Lord God is the great architect and master builder, and in his hands are the holy compass, level, plumb line, and square.

"I will gather the building supplies, the finely polished stone, brick and mortar, gold, silver, and brass vessels, and so, too, the much-needed cedar in abundance. I will also gather all the most elegant furnishings, both holy and temporal. I will, in time, recruit all the necessary masons, carpenters, and highly schooled artisans."

David paused and continued, "Why is it that cedarwood is so desired, among all the exotic woods He could have chosen? Is there some spiritual reasoning that the Almighty God so highly prizes its qualities?"

Nathan was pleased to answer David's weighty question, "First, consider that cedar never shrinks, and so reminds us never to shrink from our duty to God and man. It never swells, and so we should swell not with vanity or ambition, nor seek the acclaim of men, but only seek the esteem of God. Cedar does not warp: reminding us not to twist our minds in the lust of the flesh. We are to refrain from the lust of the eyes and forgo the pride of life. Most importantly, remember that cedarwood is resistant to pestilence. It reminds us to resist the termites of little sins of gossip and backbiting and the little indulgences that lead directly to the sheer cliffs of disobedience. It fights rot and decay, a reminder to evade the mildew and rot of conceit, contempt, and jealousy. For all of God's children are on equal ground: whether prince or pauper, sturdy or lame, we are all transparent in His sight. He sees through our frail bodies and into the secret chambers of our hearts.

"Finally, the cedar tree roots travel deep into the ground and extend three times the crown's height. Yet, it stands firm and immovable, a demonstration of the love of God for us and a reminder to be resilient and steadfast in the Lord's work. It is the wood of incense, and its fragrant aroma is a sweet savor unto the Lord."

David was pleased with this spiritual insight and mused, "The cedars of Lebanon, of course, for my God is God, and I will obey—standing firm and immovable in him that I fear, love and trust."

CHAPTER TWENTY-SIX
The City of Chariot Bridles

The Ark of the Covenant was now joyfully housed in the city of David. Pilgrims flocked to Jerusalem from all over the kingdom and far beyond its borders to pay homage to Israel's holiest treasure. The added revenue afforded David the ability to expand Israel's army to protect and defend its fragile boundaries. Secreted knowledge came to David from a well-placed network of spies and liars. In addition, the Philistines were in the grips of political upheaval. Maoch, the king of Philistia, was old and wine-besotted, and he was losing touch with reality. His only son Achish and his grandson had both died at the battle of Baal-Perazim. Philistia was without a unifying monarch and no clear line of succession. The Philistine princes were all vying for the vacant crown, and sometimes heated arguments turned into hostile armed conflicts.

The armies of each of the tribes gathered, and David called a war council at Hebron. David's two nephews Joab and Abishai, his three older brothers, Eliab, Abinadab, Shammah, and his three Mighties, Ishbaal, Eleazar, Shammah, and all the captains of thousands were in attendance. The great hall overflowed with hopeful judgments and challenging arguments. Abruptly Abiathar called the gathering to order, as it was his duty to announce the king's arrival.

David gravely began. "Welcome, my friends, family, and brothers in arms. I will put to rest all rumors and get right to the heart of the matter. I have commanded all our available forces to gather and ready themselves for a decisive battle. It has come to my attention that the Philistine princes are warring among themselves and are in disarray. I believe this to be an opportunity for victory over our ancient sworn enemy. Prince Achish, my former friend, has died as my embittered enemy. His father, King Maoch, is long in the tooth and unable to govern. There is no clear-cut bloodline of ascent. Because of this, each prince is making his claim, and armed battles have become everyday occurrences. The Philistine borders are almost defenseless, and their cities are vulnerable to attack. When joined together, the princes are at once a formidable adversary. Separately and independently, though, they are weak and are ripe for the picking. If we act quickly and decisively, we can destroy our most hated enemy. In doing so now with one heart and one mind, they will never rise again to threaten our nation."

The crowd eagerly agreed, so noted by the banging on the wooden tabletops with closed fists and upright cups. David continued, "The key is Gath, the stronghold of Maoch, it is still the center place, and when that has fallen, the other Philistine cities will surrender. Think of Gath as the Philistine mother city, a metropolis of power; liken it to a horse's bridle; it is where the reserve chariot legions stand ready. If we can take charge of those strong reins, we can force all Philistia to our will and dominion. Then, when Gath rests, we will attack; we will keep all city-states separated. We begin the assault before dawn and appear suddenly from out of the shadows. We will prevail with this divine tactic, for God has decreed it and has already seen it. We will capture their wealth and their weapons of war, and this will endow us with the ability and resources to achieve even more and greater victories until all the enemies of Israel are defeated."

David detailed his final strategy to the assembled army leaders. "I will take the chief command to Gath. I have assigned Joab, Abishai, Eliab, and Abinadab to four smaller corps, stage end-to-end attacks against Gaza, Ashkelon, Ashdod, and Ekron. These will stall any attempted rescue of Gath and stop combing any Philistine legions, leaving our main strike force against Gath freed up to do our deadly work. Timing is critical; we will commence our attacks on the morning of the third day when the cock crows—and before anyone rouses from their beds. The Philistines will withdraw behind their tall walls and bar their gates until they determine the invading army's greatness. Once we have subdued Gath, we will leave a holding garrison in its place, and with all due haste, I will relieve each corps in turn, starting first with Ekron, then in order Ashdod, Ashkelon, and lastly Gaza. Once the prince of each besieged bastion realizes your numbers are not menacing, he will open the gate and pursue you with all the forces at his disposal. Stay in place as long as it is possible, and then retreat and blend into the surrounding countryside. The chase and their fruitless search will leave the city unattended, and we will move in and take possession of each town, making ready for the army when they return empty-handed."

David's commanders departed that night with little or no fanfare. Instead, each captain took their company to their assigned stronghold—each with steadfast determination and a secure hope of divine intervention in the conclusion of a successful outcome.

David's main force chanced upon a wagon train of wine merchants heading west. David halted the procession to gather information. The merchant's kegs and barrels were a tempting target for the host of dry and thirsty men. David had different plans. He sought out the caravan master and inquired, "I am David, king of Israel, and I need to know your destination."

A rotund fellow with a large red nose—fittingly acquired from the many hours of sampling his beguiling merchandise—spoke up: "I am Yayin, the master of this enterprise. We are on our way to Gath to fill the wine store of King Maoch and fulfill our annual contract. However, I would warn you that interference with my appointed rounds will bring you a harsh response from the Philistine monarch, who has grown fond of my enchanting vintage."

David, with a charming smile, agreed, "Yayin, my good fellow, you need not take another step, for I will buy all that you have—carts, horses, wagons, and the lot if you would be so kind. I also need your clothes, sandals, belts, turbans and all your scimitars. Please be assured, sir, that I will deliver this precious cargo to Gath personally."

The offer thoroughly confounded Yayin, but a hefty purse of gold was more than a fair price. Moreover, King David had promised to deliver the wine, and Yayin's armed guards could certainly not defend against the king's whole army if they decided to seize his goods outright.

A change of clothes was in order, and Yayin and his men left in the rags of beggars, but they held high a heavy purse of gold and the gratitude of a powerful sovereign.

David summoned his captains to unveil his improvised plan. Under a nearby oak, he put forth the finer details, "Gentlemen, this bounty is a Godsend. We can now enter Gath via the front gate. We will disguise ourselves as wine merchants. There will be little or no inquiry from any curious guardsman. We will give a full skin of wine for a bribe to any challenge to our passage to the palace. Once the king is in our custody, we will have him give the order to open the gate, and then our army that has been patiently waiting outside the walls can come flooding into the city and surround the palace. The Philistines will yield, and it will be a bloodless invasion. The timing is also perfect; we will continue through this day and easily get the wine wagons through the sundown gates. Our army will remain on the borders hidden by the cover of night. I will signal with a flaming arrow when their entrance is achievable. Our other legions will not attack until tomorrow's dawn, and this will give us the required time to follow up on their planned deception. I pray we have enough time to get to Gaza before we are discovered and avoid heavy losses. God's will be done."

A young captain named Nikud stepped up, first hesitated, and then suggested, "Please excuse my simple thinking, sire. Still, according to your brilliant plan, our entire army will not be necessary for every city after securing Gath. So, I suggest we can take a thousand and break off from the main body and go down to Gaza and help capture the castle—and so put the Philistines between two armies."

David nodded and was pleased with the young captain's plan. "Yes, I agree with you, Nikud, and you will lead that expedition to reinforce the assault on Gaza.

"Now, if there are no other suggestions or concerns, I and my three Mighties will dress for the part and assault the Philistine gate with the vintage of guile and cunning."

David's wine caravan began its intoxicating ruse at the Philistine entrance just before nightfall lockdown. The evening watch's sparking torches cast wavy shadows as David and his wine wagons approached the compound.

"Who goes there, and what is wanted?" The common challenge uttered a thousand times guarding the city entrance came back unanswered. Instead, the crier was about to speak out in a more menacing tone when Ashbaal, one of King David's Mighties, broke the unsettling silence. "It is Yayin here, King Maoch's supplier of fine wines. We are in a hurried attempt to slake the king's unquenchable thirst, and he wants our delivery tonight instead of on the morrow." Then the acting "Yayin" voiced, "It is my pleasure and honor to help quench the thirst of such fine gate guardians." He gingerly handed over several skins of wine to the night watch, which ended all further discussion.

The plan had worked better than he had imagined. David and his costumed merchantmen went completely unchallenged as they entered the king's pantry. A jug of wine, a goblet, and a silver platter gained access to the king's private apartments. King

Maoch was grateful for the rushed delivery of his much sought-after pain-numbing elixir until a sharp dagger was thrust at his throat, clearly targeting his exposed windpipe.

David spoke softly and clearly into the king's ear. "I am David, king of Judah and Israel. I do not seek your life or your kingdom. I am only attempting to subdue an enemy so that they will no longer invade my borders. Therefore, I need you to order your gate to be unbarred and opened. Your timely compliance will spare your life and the lives of many others."

Maoch agreed, and soon the gate swung open. At once, a fire arrow was launched and streaked across the dark horizon. The army of God then flooded through the open gate and disarmed the guards. David's men took their threatening position high above the city's ramparts while the rest rushed to reinforce the other bastion invaders.

Each Philistine princedom fell in an unstoppable chain of events. Once David conquered the Philistine strongholds and subdued all the princes, King Maoch had no choice but to ally himself with Israel. Moach then assigned his chariot forces as a submission gift to guarantee that David would not destroy Philistia.

The Philistines had always had a metal-smelting advantage over the Israelites in that they were renowned workers of iron. Almost all the armor, hardened metal weapons, horse bridles, and chariots that the Israelites owned had been taken in battle or stolen from fallen Philistine soldiers. Now the Israelites could learn to make all the metal items they ever needed or wanted.

CHAPTER
TWENTY-SEVEN
East of Edom, North to Moab

The great victory over all the Philistine princes spurred David and his Israeli army to turn their attention to protecting their often vulnerable southeastern borders. Edom to the far southeast is where the king's highway crisscrossed from Aram and the Euphrates in the north to Egypt in the south. Trade was often preyed upon by Edomite raiding parties, which were hostile to the interests of Israel. Edom also had large deposits of copper and iron, desperately needed metal resources to fuel David's growing imperial ambitions. So, David called a war council that now included Seranim, the Philistine prince, and his fearsome chariot legions. David began, "Edom disrupts our trade and is often hostile to our interests. With the addition of Prince Seranim, his infantry, and his legion of Philistine war wagons, we now have the upper hand. The time is ripe to strike to protect, defend, and enlarge the stakes of Zion." All agreed, once the bitterest of enemies and now the best of friends. The Philistines, for their participation, would receive a fair share of spoil and slaves.

Israel's unbeatable army crossed over the Jordan and east to Edom, shielded by Maon's wilderness. They promptly engaged the kingdom's hapless defenders. The infantry clash was brutal and bloody, supported by the deadly accurate Philistine chariot archers. The Edomites fought bravely and took many an enemy with them to the grave, but they were soon overwhelmed by the sheer force of numbers. The king of Edom suffered capture while trying to retreat, and by David's rigid command, he was swiftly put to death, dismissing his desperate bargaining pleas for mercy. The king's beheading signaled an end to the brutal armed conflict. Some less courageous dropped their weapons and begged for pity immediately, while others battled valiantly to a glorious death.

David ordered, "Let no enemy leave the field alive. Kill them all—every one.

"Let us now go to every city, village, town, and hamlet, and we will leave no fighting-age men standing. Instead, the women and children will be rounded up and sold as slaves so that Edom will rise no more to trouble the king's highway."

Abishai, the son of David's sister Zeruiah, killed the Edomites in the valley of salt, [or at the salt springs of Tedith, a league from Palmyra], with eighteen thousand slaughtered. This action sent a strong message to all who would fight against Zion to fear a deadly reprisal.

David put strong garrisons throughout all of Edom, and Edom became David's servant.

The Lord preserved David wherever he went.

Moab was never a friend to Israel, more along the lines of a devious and hostile adversary. Once David subdued Edom, Moab became more troublesome. There was an uneasy truce that had existed between David and Pahath-Moab, the Shilonite. He was one of the many sons of Sheth, who were themselves the Anak or giants of men. In addition, Ruth, David's grandmother, was a Moabite—making David a person of Moabite descent.

Moab had once given refuge to David's family, as well. When David was a fugitive and an outcast from all of Israel, David had been fearful that Saul would use the capture of his family as a bargaining chip and that this would lead to his capture and eventual death. And so, Jesse and Nitzevet, David's father and mother, had sought and found refuge in Moab. They lived out the rest of their lives with safety and were comforted up until the old king died, but the two had recently passed away. Moreover, rumor had it that Pahath-Moab was not so kind to the old couple because of his renewed hatred of Israel.

The fragile peace with Israel had ended.

Moab raiders now hijacked much of the eastern trade, including the life-sustaining wheat barges that plied the Dead Sea. The caravan routes to Israel passed through the Moabite territory and the shallows of the Beth-bara, a well-traveled fording place of the Jordan River Valley. Moab harassed almost all of Israel's trade caravans; many suffered plundering, and caravan merchants routinely were slaughtered. Invasions into Judah by the Moabite giants had become regular, and the massacres of entire towns and their outlying villages were becoming commonplace.

Merchants, tradespeople, and high council elders of struggling towns, villages, and hamlets sought an audience with the king to voice their plight and make a desperate petition for his assistance. "We need to stop the all-too-regular raids of our exposed southern borders," they said. These frequent invasions needed addressing, for it was halting all trade in both directions. The townspeople and the merchants demanded military action to secure homes and livelihoods. Any delay could mean that the outlying regions would become subjects of the giant Moabite raiders.

Their appeals were heard and acknowledged, and David promised the delegation that he would take swift action before they departed. A war council convened. David addressed the gathering. "We are fresh from our great victory against Gath, the mother of the bridle of the Philistine horde. I believe for now, at least for the time being, we can put away that troublesome enemy and turn them into an uncertain ally. But now we have another old enemy that has again reared its ugly head. The Moabite giants have cut off almost all trade from our eastern borders and have ransacked Judean and Amorite villages with brutal regularity. An invasion into the wasteland and to the castle tower of their all-seeing eye would be fruitless. We cannot carry supplies enough for a long siege and cannot afford to leave Israel unattended and unguarded for such an extended and prolonged absence. This collection of marauders is less like an army and more like the group that took Ziklag from us many years ago. If we brazenly approach them in force, they will scatter and disappear like a vapor, vanishing into the desert wilderness. Does anyone here have a winning strategy?" An unsettling silence was the order of the moment, as all mulled over this puzzling challenge. Finally, at just about the time frustration was about to overtake reason, Joab, with a glint in his eye and a confident smile, stood up.

"Uncle, it seems that we cannot go to Moab in force and expect even the slightest hope of victory. So we will have to trick Moab to come to us."

All in the room looked around with bewilderment, and then David glared. "Is this some riddle? But, nephew, please speak your mind—and make it plain and simple for the rest of us."

Joab bowed his head in respect to his uncle's veiled slight and continued, "We will set up a grand caravan of gold and silver, spices, precious stones, and weapons of war enough to fill the coffers of a king's ransom. We will further give wings to the flight of rumors by asking everyone involved to keep this expedition confidential. Then let us whisper about which route we shall take as we pass through Jerusalem and what day we will ford the shallow waters at Beth-barah. We need to present an irresistible temptation for the whole of the Moab raiders, one that they cannot easily ignore."

David was pleased. "Well, Joab, I can see you are a man of reasoning, but I cannot afford to lose such treasure. What if your plan fails? What say you, Joab?"

With cunning on his mind, Joab responded, "There will be no wealth in the caravan, sire—only the appearance of wealth. Only with ornate and shiny boxes and baskets, filled with weapons and covered with cloth and straw. In this way, the baggage train will appear to have only the trappings of treasure; their greed and far-reaching tales will do the rest. Each fearless warrior will be disguised as a foolish merchant, and at the right time, will stand their ground, waiting to engage the enemy marauders. They will cut loose the cargo and withdraw the weapons at the first sign of trouble, and then circle up and make a stand. That would give us enough time to make up the distance and surround the Moabite raiders from the outside to deter any escape attempts.

"The plan is that the caravan will take their regular eastern route, following the Jordan south to the crossover at the shallow waters of the Beth-bara. Our army will shadow them and take the southern course through the hills, mountains, and valleys and remain out of sight to any Moab scouts. We will close the distance when approaching the Beth-barah. I believe this will be where Moab's forces will strike because that is where I would engage. If they do not emerge there, we will fall back and follow the well-traveled trade route east to Nobah and Jogbehah. Our patience will count more than courage; they will come like wolves in the night, and of this, I have no doubt. We will, and we can, capture the whole of the Moab legion and snare them in their greedy piracy."

The convoy stealthily outfitted behind closed doors. Rumors and gossip went abroad like wildfire. Shills whispered abroad that this valuable caravan was to be kept secret and in the closest confidence.

The army of Israel was camped well outside the gates so as not to arouse suspicions. The company departed on a matching course, and outriders kept a wary eye on the wealth passing before their eyes. They prepared to report back to David in the event of any enemy movements. As the procession moved closer to the shallows, the distance between the two parades lessened. The foggy nights were unsettling as well; your hand would disappear in front of your eyes, and campfires and torches were of little benefit.

On the morning of the third day, the caravan crossed over the Beth-barah when the Moabite raiders attacked in force. The convoy warriors grabbed for their hidden weapons and circled up their camels and asses, fending off the marauders as best they could.

Joab called out, "It is time to mount our attack. We have caught the enemy unawares. The Philistine war wagons are lagging far behind the charging infantry. David ran to the forefront, as was his custom, slashing and stabbing like a whirlwind. Joab and Abishai fought as a team of brothers, creating a ruthless killing machine. The chariot legion circled the conflict, closing off any escape routes. The Moabite king had himself even ventured out because of the rumors of a secure victory and a grand prize. Trying to escape the massacre, he suffered slaughter by a host of arrows that abruptly ended the conflict.

The battle was sore because the Moabites were giants in stature, young and unyielding. David's blood was up from the fight when he commanded, "Gather up the remaining enemy—it is time to make an example."

The dazed soldiers were now easily herded into one group. David said, "Make me a measuring line of three cubits and a span; mark the place on a spear."

After doing this, he said, "All those who are taller than the mark, put them face down upon the ground. Then, take another measure of one cubit in the length of a reed and lay it across their shoulders. If it is longer than a cubit, make another line and have them face down upon the ground. For all the rest who are left, once again, have them face down upon the earth."

Joab looked puzzled about this odd request, for never had such a killing ever been attempted. "What end is this separation meant to accomplish, my most mysterious uncle?' Joab questioned.

David was amused and replied, "Well, my confused nephew, how do you think that we can put away menacing giants and all that is strong and fearsome? With this slaughter, we can ensure that their brutality will no longer threaten us. Today the only men left alive will be small and weak, and they will never again threaten Israel with hostile intent. Have your men divided the two lines yet? The one line for the strong and the other for the tall. We will pierce them all in their temples with the mouth of the sword until they are no more—the very same removal as when Jael struck the head of Sisera with a sharpened tent peg. Let the third line of men go as witnesses to publish both near and far in what to expect when you trespass against Israel."

With their king's death and their fierce warriors' destruction, the Moabites became David's servants. But unlike the Edomites, they were not cut off or destroyed as a people. Instead, they brought gifts, offerings, and yearly tributes to the throne of David and Israel.

CHAPTER TWENTY-EIGHT

The Laming of Warhorses

After many wars that expanded Israel's wealth and borders, a short rest was needed and enjoyed. Nahash, the king of Ammon, had recently perished and returned to the earth. Nahash found rest with the honors befitting his royal station. The national mourning was grievous and long-lasting, and the wailing had spilled over to the notice of Israel. Hanun, the king's son, now reigned in his stead. Abiathar and David's brothers and his two captain nephews, Joab and Abishai, were summoned for their advice and consent. David was more suspicious than grieved, as he called his inner council to order.

"King Nahash had shown kindness to me in the days when Saul was pursuing every rumor to my whereabouts. He had offered me his support and hospitality when my parents and my brothers found refuge in Moab. He said that I was an enemy to his enemy, and so he would count me as a friend."

"But there has been an uneasy peace since my coronation," David detailed. "My spies have continuously warned me of a hostile military presence along our border with Ammon. Nahash hates Israel and has always lusted after our extinction. I fear his son Hanun will pick up that mantle. I was considering sending a delegation to give my condolences and the comfort of respect for his loss. While they travel through to the capital, tell them to keep a sharp eye and a grounded ear to the possibility of a troop buildup and all signs of coming hostilities."

Joab heartily agreed, "A brilliant ploy, as usual, my uncle. We can send an olive branch and at the same time get the lay of the land and determine any unfriendly intentions in and by the reception afforded to your ambassadors of solace."

All wholeheartedly agreed with the scheme, and David, as usual, thoroughly coached his servants before their departure. The diplomats traveled east and north to the kingdom of Ammon. Before entering the heavily guarded compound, King Hanun and his princes were alerted to David's emissaries and were deeply suspicious of a possible twofold mission.

The princes asked, "What do you think about David, the warrior king who has just recently conquered both Edom and Moab with savagery and unbridled brutality? Do you think that he now has suddenly and miraculously had a change of heart by sending comforters to ease the king's heartfelt grief? We all say, 'No, of course not.' Do you think this leopard has changed his spots overnight? David sent his servants to you only so they could search the city and spy it out, and so see how best to overthrow it!"

King Hanun may have been gracious to David's envoys, were it not for his princes' warnings of David's cunning; they convinced him otherwise, raising the specter of a sinister plot against his kingdom.

David's envoys met the king's men in the outer courtyard by the well of the fountain. Suddenly and without warning, a gang of armed guards rushed in, surrounding the startled party of envoys. A prince of high standing and rank spoke down to the now-frightened group of delegates. His voice crackled with outrage: "Why have you come here to spy for David, the warrior king of Israel?"

A lowly priest named Anav gulped hard and spoke up. "Please pardon me, my lord, but we have come only to give comfort and aid in honoring the memory of the great king Nahash, who had shown kindness to David, our sovereign and king. We have come on his behalf to honor the fallen monarch, a gesture of goodwill and peace between our two great nations."

The prince responded with scorn: "Fine words, young priest—but your deceit is blatant. The prince turned his attention to his fellow nobles, still seething with hostility. Then he announced within earshot to all present, "Let us blind them all with hot pokers, leaving one eye unmolested. In this way, a new vision can lead them back from where they came, one that will send a clear message that the street fighters' scheming does not so easily blind us, and we will match David's ruthlessness measure for measure."

King Hanun was listening and closely observing from the shadows of a nearby alcove. He stepped up and into the light. "Alas, my much-too-eager ministers, this is an overly vicious response. We remain uncertain as to the real intent of these messengers. To honor my father's passing, though, I will agree with your judgment, and we will send a message of ridicule. We will let David know that we are well aware of his cunning and are prepared for war with Israel if that is his wish. Instead of blinding these visitors, we will shave off half of their beards—because it seems that half their purpose was for comfort, and a half was for spying. Also, cut off half of their garments at the waist, exposing their buttocks for all the world to see that Israel has no modesty when engaging in deception and betrayal."

The group mocked David's ambassadors in such a manner and then handily sent them on their way, living messengers to echo the lack of fear and utter disdain for David that remained held by King Hanun and so, too, by all the Ammonite people.

Upon returning to Israel, the scorned group acquired clothes to cover their nakedness, and each of them shaved the remainder of his beard so it would all grow back evenly. They came as far as Jericho and sent the news of their shameful encounter by messenger to David in Jerusalem. David, to honor them, went forth himself to meet them because the men were much ashamed.

David gave comfort to his agents. Still, he was sore in his criticism for the insult when told of their ridicule at the hands of King Hanun.

The king gently engaged, "Men, my heart is sorrowful for your treatment, but I praise God that your injuries have been only to your pride and that you were not maimed or suffered a loss of life. Be assured that my heart is heavy from the insults directed at me and suffered through you. Linger here in Jericho until your beards have grown back. Your grateful king will meet all your needs and wants, and your loyalty and your service to Israel do not go unnoticed. Linger until such time you deem it proper to reunite with your loved ones in Jerusalem."

King Hanun knew that his words of discontent would tingle the ears of Israel, and he understood that his scorn and mistrust would soon require a deadly reckoning. With his mourning complete, he concluded that Israel's army would swiftly come to invade his kingdom. So he took it upon himself to set a trap. He hired the Arameans of Beth-rehob, the Arameans of Hadarezer, king of Zobah, twenty thousand footmen, King Maaca's thousand men, and King Ishtob's twelve thousand men.

With Ammons threatening military buildup, David no longer needed an excuse to extinguish a competing threat to his northeastern borders. Calling forth his military leaders for a council of vengeance was in order. Joab, Abishai, his first and second chief captains, his three brothers, his priest Abiathar, and all his Mighties came running. The banquet hall was filled with both the hunger for food and the need for news.

The hearty meal quickly filled empty bellies, and all had drunk wine enough to loosen tongues. Then David's high priest Abiathar, as usual, called the high council to order:

"Noble warriors, captains, family, and friends: the king would speak to you of a grave and pressing manner."

David rose from the king's seat and firmly began his speech. "I have been personally insulted. No, all of Israel has been offended by King Hanun of Ammon. I propose we address this slight, which now has become more than an ill-placed jest. Hanun has engaged many thousands of Arameans (Syrians), chariots, and footmen in recent weeks.

"The only reason he would gather up such a force is to plan an invasion of Israel. With this in mind, I propose that we strike first and catch them unprepared while they are unorganized within their borders. Then, Joab, my chief captain, will gather the army and cross the Beth-barah and cross over the plain and attack the Ammonite capital city of Rabbah, the city of waters."

Rabbah rests in the narrow valley of the upper Jabbok River. On both sides of the stream, the wadi Suwaylih comes from the north and west of Rabbah, and wadi al-Dhulayl comes in due west of Rabbah before they merge a bit further south at their capital. Hanun's castle is a well-fortified citadel and sits on the northern cliff overlook. It stands towering over the north side of the city. It has polished pointed parapets, and from a distance, it looks like a crown of gleaming arches, and so "the Royal City."

David pressed, "If we can make haste, we will take them unawares and unprepared."

All agreed, noticed by the loud pounding on the wooden tables. Messengers briefed then hastily dispatched, recruiting all the forces Israel could muster, including the recently enlisted Philistine chariot legion, which had hurriedly charged through the shallow fording waters of the Jordan. They traveled the plain east of the Jordan unopposed and reached Rabbah's towering walls soon after the break of day. Chief Captain Joab and his brother and co-commander Abishai organized their legions, preparing to storm the barricades. Instead, the gates suddenly flew open, and the Ammonite army flooded out in battle array opposing Joab's forces.

"This is better than I could have hoped for," voiced Joab to Abishai. "Taking a walled city is both dangerous and tricky, and it usually requires a lengthy siege and the twin allies of starvation and disease. But here they are in the open and outside of their protective compound—and, better yet, there are no Arameans to trouble us." The battle lines formed, but just before the command to step into the struggle could be uttered, a rumbling sound arose from the south. A dense cloud of dust signaled a rush of Aramean chariots and twenty thousand footmen. They were hastily lining up to battle to the rear of Israel's formation.

Israel found itself caught, wedged between a hammer and an anvil. King Hanun had executed a well-baited trap. His ready warriors stood at the gate as the surprise was about to be sprung. Abishai called to Joab, "Brother, we will be pressed to death and utterly destroyed. What say you, Joab?"

Joab could think on his feet and commanded, "Well, little brother, we will divide and conquer. I will take all the choice men and put them together with the Philistine and Canaanite chariots against the Arameans. I will deliver the rest of the people into your hands to attack Ammon's army guarding the city gate. If the Arameans (Syrians) are too strong for me, then you shall reinforce me. But if the Ammonites are too strong for you, then I will come to your aid. So be of good courage, brother, and let us play the game of war and brace ourselves as men, for our people, our cities, and our God. Let us fight with all our might, mind, will, and strength, and let the Lord do what He had already known to be right."

The Philistine chariot legions engaged the Aramean chariots, creating a twisting whirlwind of carnage. Joab's aggressive Philistine coaches soon gained the advantage, and the Aramean war wagons fled the field. Joab turned his infantry loose, and a bloodthirsty frenzy of hand-to-hand combat erupted. The Ammonites watching the slaughter lost heart and retreated behind the protective walls of their capital city. Joab found Abishai in a lull of the battle, covered in blood and gore, his breath coming in sharp and shallow. "Brother, we have avoided destruction by the slimmest of margins. If we give the enemy time to reform here on the battlefield, it might not be to our advantage."

"We should retreat, then," replied Joab as he helped Abishai into a chariot. "We are in no condition for a prolonged siege against Rabbah. So let us withdraw back across the Jordan so that we can fight another day."

The withdrawal was swift through the open plain, crossing the Beth-barah and the Jordan back to Jerusalem. The Arameans did not pursue them because the Ammonites made no signs of leaving their stronghold. Instead, the Arameans fled north to regroup at Helam [or the citadel], just south of Succoth and west of the Jabbok River crossing at Penuel. A messenger was hastily dispatched to Hadarezer, king of Zobah, informing him of Israel's battle and ending in a tie. Haradzer replied to hold in place, that he would recruit all his vassal states north of the river Jabbok, and that Shobach, the army captain, was bringing reinforcements and would meet them across the river.

Joab, entering Jerusalem, at once sought out the king. Joab still smelling foul from his recent ordeal, approached David, insisting on giving him the bad news personally. "Uncle, it was an ambush at the gates of Rabbah," and then he explained in detail the near destruction of the army of Israel. "When the Syrians (Arameans) retreated, I had a scout follow them to warn us if they were reforming for another attack. He has since reported back that they were holding at Helam, a fortified stronghold just south of Succoth."

David extended his hand, attempting to console his nephew. "You have done a man's work, nephew; be not sorrowful or ashamed; God has His ways, and His ways are not our ways. I will now gather the rest of the militia from every part of the nation. You, my dear Chief Captain, have brought back the vital chariots and the army intact. I will personally lead the next attack and spur on our forces to their very best effect."

David then paused, and then he continued. "I have had a vision, nephew; we will not cross the Jordan at the Beth-barah, for they will be expecting our crossover there."

Joab looked confused, and he questioned David. "But, sire, that is the only fording place other than the A-barah, and that is too far up by the Galilee."

David smiled with the divinity of insight. "We will travel north, allowing the Jordan River Valley to conceal our movements from the Ammonite defenders at Rabbah. Then we will cross over just below where the Jabbok and the Jordan come together."

Joab looked confused. "Uncle, there are no shallows there. How will we accomplish this impossible feat?"

David excitedly smiled. "That is what I saw in my dream. We will cross over the river with ropes and rafts. The Jordan narrows there, and, even better, the enemy will never expect us to come from that direction in force or mass."

Joab was physically excited and voiced, "That is a brilliant move, uncle! I will take an army group of a thousand into Manasseh, and we will prepare there for the full crossing with ropes, rafts, and planks."

As he said, David did, and a militia army gathered to join Israel's army north of Jerusalem. Once organized, they met up with the Philistine chariot cohort that Joab had miraculously kept intact. The militia army grew as the hosts went northwards on the west side of the Jordan River, picking up companies of tens, then fifties, and even hundreds. Again, David's plan was working perfectly. The river flow was low this time of year, and chariots, horse wagons, and infantry made it over the river swiftly and with no loss of horses, supply wagons, or chariots.

When King Hanun heard of the Israelites' movements on Jordan's east bank, it was too late to gather or hire more troops. He could not even pull back his companies stationed to repel his borders coming up from the Beth-barah.

Captain Shobach, thoroughly caught by surprise, had only hours to rally his forces, regroup, and defend against an enemy onslaught.

The two vast armies collided just south of Succoth at the Aramean stronghold called Helam. The Syrian chariots and the Philistine war wagons pounded out the ominous sound of approaching stampeding hoofbeats with vengeance and fury, growing ever louder. The ordinary foot soldiers with shield, sword, and spear clashed violently in the battlefield center, meshed together, and engaged in ferocious hand-to-hand combat.

A swirling battle ensued. The chariots were like whirlwinds, colliding and disappearing in thick brown clouds of powdered dust and sand. Israel was now valiantly led by David, who remained at the forefront of the battle. He fought like a man unafraid, refusing to give ground and spurring on his men to greater and greater feats of daring and heroism. The vicious combat had reached its bloody climax when the lead chariot bearing the Syrian chief captain Shobach was overwhelmed and overturned. The captain and his driver suffered slaughter, along with sixty others.

David slew the men of seven hundred chariots of the Syrians and forty thousand riders. The Syrian second captain ordered a withdrawal before the Israeli assault turned into a total massacre.

David had won the field and the day. Standing in the back of a Philistine war wagon, he addressed his mighty men of valor. "Conquering soldiers of Israel, be at peace, for we have done the Lord's good work this day. We have bruised and beaten our enemy for a second time and have put him to flight back beyond his borders. We have won the battle, but the war is still in question. Our enemy will regroup and re-emerge, and, like a wounded animal, be more dangerous than before.

"Nevertheless, we are here, and it is now that we shall proceed to finish what we had started. Let us now see to our dead and wounded. Succoth is only a stone's throw from a place where we can find temporary shelter. We can resupply, and we can repair our battle-scarred chariots from the hulks left behind here on the battlefield. In doing so, we can re-engage our invasion of Aram (Syria) and sever the stranglehold of Hadarezer, king of Zobah, and his dreams of expansion into our borders and territories. Let us cross over the Jabbok at the shallows and proceed through the ruins of Penuel. That is the very place where Jacob wrestled an angel and received the blessing of Israel for all time and eternity."

The army was bloodied but inspired as they cheered their fearless commander. They had seen him fight as hard or harder than any one of them. They understood that he fought for God and had their and Israel's best interests at heart.

The news of the defeat of Aram at Helam spread like wildfire across the province by the swiftness of wagging tongues and gossipmongers.

Some of the less loyal vassal states that Hadarezer had recently conquered started a rebellion, sensing his weakness. Hadarezer was now in a real dilemma. He could not launch a strong attack against David until he put down these revolts. The knowledge of David's advance had reached Hadadezer's ears, and his only alternative was to split his forces. He had to deal with both the invasion and the uprisings at the same time, as half his army was on their way home when Israel slammed into the rear of Aram's weakened legion. It was Israel's third encounter in six months against the powerful and chariot-strong Arameans. The battle was ferocious, and no quarter was asked or given. David made it into the center and pressed relentlessly upon them, urging his men forward. The Aramean center collapsed, and the battle became a total rout. Israel pursued, and the bloody slaughter of the Arameans extended to the gates of Hamath.

David's men scaled the lightly guarded city walls, fighting through the gates and opening them from the backside. Within fifteen minutes, David had broken into the secure hold to find King Hadarezer.

"Your Majesty," David declared at the point of his sword. "We have come to the end of a long and bloodstained road. Pray to your gods—for either standing tall or on your knees, you are a dead man!"

The king lunged at David, who deftly sidestepped the blade and, at the same time, drew a dagger from his waistband with his free hand. The two princes collided as the killing stroke struck, piercing the king just below the fifth rib. King Hadarezer crumpled to the ground, spewing blood, and with a final gurgling breath, exhaled a death rattle at David's feet.

The battle was still raging outside the town walls as the Syrians from Damascus arrived to help Hadarezer. David left the confines of the city and continued his rampage; his army slew twenty-two thousand Syrians before the rest fled away. David had now extended the borders of Israel as far north as the banks of the Euphrates River.

The spoils of war were plentiful; the Syrians had many treasures just for the taking; it was one of the many benefits of building an empire. David now laid claim to a thousand Syrian chariots, seven thousand riders, and twenty thousand footmen. As commanded by God, David reluctantly hobbled all of the remaining Syrian horses; the horses could still be used as beasts of burden but no longer as weapons of war. After all, David retained one hundred chariots as swift messengers to connect his growing and far-flung empire.

Israel put military garrisons in Aram-Damascus. The Syrians became David's servants and brought gifts of tribute and bounty. David took the shields of gold that were on the servants of Hadarezer. He brought them along with a mountain of brass to Jerusalem. Hadarezer's enemies were now David's friends, and King Toi sent his son Joram with gifts and offerings of vessels of gold and vessels of silver. All these spoils were collected eagerly and dedicated to God for the building of His temple. A house of cedar, a place of prayer and learning, a home for God was in the making.

The Lord preserved David wherever he went.

CHAPTER TWENTY-NINE

Lust and Deception

Bathshua, or the daughter of wealth, was born to Eliam, also known as Ammiel. Ammiel was one of David's thirty-seven Mighties. He was the son of Ahithophel, the chief counselor of King David. So wise were the counsels of Ahithophel that advice-seekers felt as if they were enquiring of an oracle of God. Some rightly reasoned that David purchased the adjacent land from Ahithophel. David had decided to build his house next to the seer's residence to have ready access to the depths of his understanding, wisdom, and knowledge.

Ahithophel summoned Bathshua into his study for some grandfatherly advice, "My precious granddaughter, you are now of the age to understand our inheritance and our lineage. My name, Ahithophel, means 'One onto Another'—and our ancestry is as follows: Eliphelet was the son of Ahasbai, the Maacathite; Eliam, your father, is my son. I tell you this because

246

I am a Gilonite. I am from the Judean hills, the little town of Giloh. My childlike curiosity soared with the constant study of the Torah, and soon my small village became too confining. I pleaded with my father to let me leave for years, but this was against his worried wishes. Finally, he relented, and I was free to seek my destiny. My mother quietly placed a water flask, a loaf of bread, and a few pence in my hand—at the time, I thought this was a king's ransom. Then, lovingly and with a holy kiss, she gave me her most precious blessing. I then headed out to the open city of Jebus, the crossroads of commerce and learning, to seek a young man's fortune."

Bathshua impatiently voiced, "Grandfather, is this going to take much longer?"

Ahithophel sighed. "Just a few of your precious moments, my dear child. For it gives me much pleasure thinking that someday you might speak of me to your children and so, too, to their children, so please indulge me.

"When I arrived at Jebus' main gate, there was a penny tax to enter the city. The guard there told me this was to discourage beggars and paupers, who I could see huddled in droves outside the city walls.

"I did not want to give up half of my fortune, as I had not eaten in two days. Suddenly a beggar approached me from out of the crowd and stumbled, faint, at my feet. I helped him up, but he was too weak to stand. He finally spoke and apologized, 'Sorry, sir, it is just that I have not eaten and was hoping you could spare a penny for alms at the gate so that I might live another day.' I was so touched and so compelled that I did give him half of my holdings.

247

"He whispered his gratitude and told me, 'Kind sir, there is a far eastern gate called the Eye of the Needle; there is only enough room for one man to pass through, and there are no tax collectors there.' I needed my last penny for bread, so I went as the old beggar suggested. It took the entire day, and I was tired and beyond hunger. I arrived to find a small caravan of twelve or so camels in the very process of being unloaded. The baggage of each camel was being hefted and tirelessly carried through the narrow opening. Once freed from its burden, the camel was brought to its knees and shuffled through the tight passage. After a while, the young caravan master called out, 'Are you going to stand there idle? How about giving me a hand before the gate closes for the night and makes this drudgery a misery?' I did so, and we finished up in the fading light.

"'My name is Orach,' he said. 'I am a merchant, and this is my first caravan; I would not spend my hard-earned money on the taxes demanded at the gate from those damned Jebusite vultures. What is your name?' 'I am Ahithophel,' I told him. Orach nodded his recognition and then continued, 'Thank you, Ahithophel, for your hard work. Let's bed down the camels and unload one last time, and then we can feast and speak of business. What say you, Ahithophel?' I was exhausted and famished, but the promise of a feast was enough to regain my strength.

"Good fortune had smiled on me. My dear child, that teamwork was the beginning of a lifelong friendship and a profitable business partnership. We were closer than brothers until the day of his death. In time I no longer had to go on the grueling caravans. I negotiated trade from the Euphrates in the north to Egypt in the south, and our wealth increased in abundance each year. The business success afforded me the luxury of studying under the great masters, scholars, and rabbis. I had purchased this land and built my mansion upon it for your grandmother and me, which she dearly loved before she died.

"For most men, these experiences would have meant a satisfying life, but either fate, fortune, or God has now given me a second chance for a new adventure."

"What do you mean, grandfather? You are speaking in riddles."

Ahithophel gently confessed, "I need just a few more moments of your priceless patience, now, while I explain an account of my life that you might even find exciting.

I was returning from Egypt, the master of a one-hundred-and-fifty-camel caravan. It was the most massive caravan ever to travel the king's highway. It was just before we were about to enter Zion's gate when we abruptly halted. It is no easy task to stop such a convoy suddenly; some of the camels slammed into each other, and merchandise was dislodged and scattered. There was a large, jubilant procession that went before us. Women were singing and dancing; the mood was joyous and festive. King Saul led the parade, accompanied by a young lad lifting high with stress and strain what seemed to be a giant's bloody head. Later I found out that the lad was David, the son of Jesse, our current king and benefactor. Soon the procession had passed, and we proceeded to our warehouse to unload our cargo. There was a gala feast that night. Saul kept a mansion when the city fortress was called Jebus, but Saul's seat of power was in Gibeah. The Israelites of Benjamin and Judah had quarters in the open city, and even back then, they referred to the stronghold as Jerusalem.

"I needed some relaxation, and so I ventured forth that evening to the celebration. Torches were blazing; the music soared over the uproar of laughter. Israel was celebrating a miraculous victory of good over evil. The head of a giant was speared and pinned on a pike. A grisly trophy, dreadfully displayed, was front and center—and covered in flies. I was taken aback by the horrible sight, but I could not look away.

"A youth approached me from out of the crowd; he then introduced himself. 'My name is David, son of Jesse, and I am the slayer of the giant Goliath, who insulted our God.'"

I replied, "My name is Ahithophel, the merchant, and I have never slain a giant, a dragon, or a sea monster, but I have caught many a robber on the run, my brave young warrior." We both laughed, and from then on, we became fast friends.

"David then asked, 'What do you think of this rotting trophy?'

"I think it has served its purpose. Sorry to say, it is gruesome and not worthy of a hero, and worse than that, it grows foul with decay.

"David questioned, 'What should we do with it?' I answered, 'Bury it outside the city walls. I know of such a place, a high mound just above the cemetery garden, and we can call the place Golgotha, or the place of the skull. It can there be an everlasting memorial to your victory.'"

"So, we dug a pit, laid the head to rest early the following day, and quickly covered up the flies and the rotting flesh. Since then, I have been David's friend, mentor, and advisor. He would seek out my counsel on many matters these many years. As a result, I am now one of David's chief ministers and a most trusted and personal confidant. When David conquered Jebus and made

Jerusalem his capital, he purchased the adjacent lot from me to have ready access to my wisdom and knowledge, and that is why the king is now our neighbor.

"Now, my dear granddaughter, with your mother's recent passing, you and your father have been invited to make a new home here with me, for we are family. Bathshua, you are now the lady of the house, requiring a particularly formal etiquette because of our nearness to royalty."

"Thank you, Grandfather. That story was—I must admit— most enlightening." Bathshua bowed and fluttered her dark, beguiling eyes.

Ahithophel, being aware of the impatience of youth, nodded in response. "Certainly, my dear, and thank you for honoring me with your attention."

Bathshua, encouraged by their recent intimacy, voiced, "Grandfather, you say I am a woman. Why must I still be treated like a child? I am only allowed out with a chaperone and attired with veils and restricting robes. How am I supposed to find a husband?"

Ahithophel smiled and nodded. "Ah, the eagerness of youth to be counted as wise. It does leave one confused when plucking the forbidden fruit of passion. The hot embers of emotion cool in the stark light of reason. In time, my dear, we will find you the proper match, a man of wealth and standing, someone who will cherish you, who will take care of your every need, want, and desire. These conventions are well established and reliable. Love will come in time, tested and true, and it is, after all, for your greatest good and benefit."

Bathshua reluctantly agreed to her role but set into motion a rebellious plan of adventure. Bathshua's father, Eliam, was never at home because of an endless stream of wars from King David's never-ending conquests and nation-building. Ahithophel was always next door, serving in the court at the pleasure of the king. Bathshua's mother had recently died, and in her passing, Bathshua was a very bored mistress of the household.

One star-struck night, Bathshua made a shocking proposal to Almah, her ever-loyal body servant. Bathshua whispered her heart's desire, "Let us go out after twilight, and I will dismiss the household servants so that our comings and goings will go unnoticed. Let us invade the night bazaar, where young soldiers are known to gather to sing, dance, and keep their wine red in the cup."

Dressed as maids, the two adventurers set off in the hopes of experiencing some forbidden fruit and shedding the confines of duty and convention.

Upon reaching the festive bazaar, Almah exclaimed, "Look at all the people, and look at all the young men. There are flocks of them, sturdy and strong, and so many men to choose from!"

Bathshua giggled and was about to speak when she felt a presence. Someone was directly behind her; she quickly turned and saw the most handsome man she had ever encountered. His locks were long, dark, and unbraided. She had a strange tingling, as if she were in the presence of a young lion. Her heart skipped a beat, and her breath caught in her throat. Everything fell away as if they were the only two standing in the crowded street. Bathshua was spellbound, caught up in a whirlwind of strange emotions.

"My name is Horite," he confidently declared. "I am a stranger to Jerusalem, and I have just returned as a victorious soldier in the army of Israel. I am on a promised leave, and this is my first time in your amazing ancient city. Please, beautiful lady, tell me your name, or I shall die in anticipation for an introduction to such a perfect vision of loveliness."

Bathshua blushed, captivated by the stranger's enticing flattery. Then, bracing herself and taking a deep breath, she exclaimed," Sir, you are a stranger, a tempting diversion—I grant you that—but a stranger, nonetheless. Consequently, I remain warned of such passing encounters as unladylike and suspect."

Almah nodded in agreement, and both women turned to walk away. Horite stepped quickly to bar their way; he bowed an apology for his boldness.

"I cannot bear your departure without knowing your name. Please grant me this lovely favor, lady whom the fates have graced me with your presence," he uttered.

Almah rolled her eyes, shrugged her shoulders, muttered, "What harm?" Bathshua then lowered her eyes and faintly whispered,"I am Bathshua."

Horite's face filled with glee, for he had uncovered a precious gem. Her name rang in his ear and then on his lips. "Bathshua, meaning daughter of wealth, your beauty is worth a king's ransom, and you glitter like a jewel. Your mysterious almond eyes and their promise of paradise leave me breathless." Horite stood erect and unyielding; his eyes were blazing in the flaming torchlight of passion. He brazenly continued, "Your stunning allure has captured my imagination. Bathshua, I beg of you, or I shall die for want of knowing you. The vision of you that stands before me has given me a reason for living."

Bathshua blushed, and her head turned, smitten by this tall, dark stranger's bold advances. Almah grabbed Bathshua by the wrist and tugged, trying to break the bubble of the moment's steamy ecstasy.

Bathshua pulled back and broke Almah's tightening grip, crushing her fierce determination to break the spiraling romantic spell. Frustrated, Almah yelled, "If you do not depart, I will go home alone and abandon you to whatever fate awaits you." Her voice seemed to be trailing off into the night.

Bathshua stood motionless, silent, and unmoved, remaining a willing slave and a prisoner to desire.

Horite was delighted, "Bathshua, let us go somewhere secluded away from this rowdy crowd. I know of a place nearby where we can see the moon and the stars and speak of our wishes and dreams, both big and small."

Bathshua was intrigued and then seductively agreed to be swept away to what he promised was a deserted outpost high atop the city's wall.

As Horite had promised, the view of the heavens was spectacular, more magnificent than she had ever remembered or imagined. Bathshua was starstruck, proclaiming, "Look at how all of God's creation lies before us. We are made small by His infinite grandeur."

Horite's whispering was tender and memorable. "Your beauty surpasses the heavens' vast wonder, and the pale moon blushes with envy at your presence. I would make you mine for all time—say 'Yes' to my longing embrace. I knew we should be together when I first laid eyes upon your wondrous loveliness, and my ears tingled from your delightful laughter. I wish to be your lover now and forever. Will you marry me?"

Bathshua was charmed, as if she were in a trance; her instincts overruled her common sense.

Horite laid her back down upon a cushion of straw. His lips crushed her mouth and subdued Bathshua's last faint murmurs of resistance. Horite's hand gently caressed her shivering body until gentle sparks ignited into a raging fire. He positioned himself to get to know her, and at the moment, Horite bit down upon her ear to distract her from the momentary pain of forbidden knowledge. The night of ecstasy passed with breathy whispers of undying devotion and feverish caresses from an ever-insatiable appetite for love.

The cock crowed, and the stable down below started to rouse with brays, neighs, and the shoveling of straw and dung from noisy grooms. Horite, still sleepy-eyed, looked around. But Bathshua had up and gone. A night of ecstasy had vanished like a perfect dream interrupted by stark reality. He was madly in love, but the object of his desire had all but disappeared, vanishing like mist into the bustling Jerusalem metropolis.

Horite searched Jerusalem, asking shopkeepers, merchants, beggars, and soldiers for the beautiful and mysterious Bathshua's whereabouts. He had no luck and was about to give up when he recalled her alluring scent, a mixture of jasmine, amber, and musk. He thought a perfume merchant; there were many, but only a few catered to the well-to-do. His description of the woman and her scent was greeted with blank stares and shaking heads. Even so, Horite was not discouraged but felt that the gods or the fates had decreed it. It was only a matter of time before being reunited and once again feasting at their lovers' banquet.

CHAPTER THIRTY
A Shameless Love

Two months had quickly passed, and Bathshua's disgrace had started to blossom. She was pregnant, retching every morning and pitching with raging emotions. Her momentary lapse of judgment was beginning to bear the fruit of a bitter harvest. "Almah, what am I to do? I will kill myself. I cannot endure telling my father and my grandfather. I am so ashamed, I have given myself to a Hittite, and now I am with his child," Bathshua tearfully moaned.

Almah attempted to console her mistress. "I should have insisted that you come with me, and worse than that, I should have never left you alone with that heathen. It is, even more, my fault than yours. Killing yourself is forbidden, and you would also cause the death of your innocent child, a crime greater than murder. We will go together to your grandfather Ahithophel, for he has the wisdom of the ages; he will know how to deal with this crisis, and we can let him be the one to break the news to your father."

The two braced themselves for the coming storm, walking slowly and silently, clutching each other's hand along the dark and gloomy corridors. The only light was coming from small openings in the granite stone walls. Ahithophel would be in his reading room and deep into the study of the Torah. As they approached his private retreat, a cold chill of reckoning came up from the floor. At the end of the hall, a fully lit menorah spilled out a warm, inviting glow. The lamp was as brilliant as Ahithophel's intellect. The entire room overflowed with ancient scrolls from all over the known world.

The rumor was that Ahithophel had manuscripts from the Euphrates to Egypt's lower kingdom and that he knew more than any man alive. Bathshua, seeing her grandfather, broke and rushed in. She knelt before him and lay her head in her grandfather's lap, sobbing and shaking with the fear of retribution. "What is so dire to make my beautiful granddaughter sorrow so?" Ahithophel lovingly stoked Bathshua's hair, attempting to soothe her outburst of obvious distress. Bathshua was still unable to overcome her grief and could not speak. Finally, Ahithophel looked up at Almah, still standing at the doorway, and inquired, "Almah, could you please tell me of what you know of Bathshua's remorseful condition?"

Almah looked down, for the old seer's eyes were piercing and warned of a severe reproach at the slightest hint of a lie. "It was all my doing," she began, and tears sprung from her eyes as well. "I had left Bathshua unattended knowingly in the company of a heathen ruffian. Her pregnancy would not have taken place if I had only stayed and remained her dutiful chaperone." Almah dropped to her knees and began weeping openly, "Please forgive me, my lord." Ahithophel's nature was not to dwell on blaming frail human weaknesses or harping on momentary lapses in judgment. On the contrary, the wisdom of the ages had taught him to use his energies in solving problems and untangling or lessening the consequences of difficult situations.

Bathshua stood up, lifted by her grandfather's gentle encouragement. "Grandfather," she began, "I am so ashamed for this disgrace that I have put upon you and our house."

"Who else knows of this, um, indiscretion?" Ahithophel hoarsely whispered. Both women shook their heads. Bathshua answered, "No one. I have not yet started to draw attention," she lamented in a sorrowful tone. I was hoping against hope that it was not so. Now I am convinced, with sickness every morning, and I have no doubt."

Ahithophel responded in a reassuring and soothing tone, "Well, young lady, it looks like we will have to find you a suitable husband, preferably the baby's natural father. What is the father's name?"

Bathshua sadly uttered, "His name is Horite, and he is a Hittite."

Ahithophel, saddened at her response, mumbled. "A Hittite?" He shook his head and then asked, "Do you love this man?"

Bathshua pressed, "I did lust at the moment of passion, Grandfather. But now only confusion and misgivings invade my every thought." But Ahithophel, thinking far ahead, as was his custom, asked, "Do you believe he would make a covenant to be circumcised and become a Hebrew so that he could marry you, Bathshua? But, most importantly, do you know where I might find him so that I might speak to him in earnest?"

Bashua, now visibly shaken, echoed remorse and embarrassment in her words. "After my seduction, my eyes opened to the grief and shame of it all. I felt dirty and alone and hurried off for home before the sun could witness my disgrace."

Ahithophel calmly attempted to console his beloved granddaughter. "You are only human and are subject to nature's whims and wiles. And so are we all, my precious granddaughter. Now calm yourself, my dear child; we together will find a way to make this unfortunate lapse in judgment come out right. Then, once again, you will be able to hold your head up in the light of day." Ahithophel now turned his wrath to Almah. "I cannot express my distress at you leaving Bathshua in the company of a stranger, at any point, and particularly in public. I have not decided who is to shoulder the greater harm and punishment. But as for your penance, and since you know what this man looks like, I will send you on a quest with two of my trusted household guards, Shemira and Lishmor. You are to scour the city, immediately and completely, both day and night, until you find this seducer. Do not return to my sight without Horite the Hittite in your presence." Almah bowed, agreeing to her master's wishes.

"Take this purse for food and to loosen the tongues of beggars, merchants, and liars. Be quick about it, for the seed he has planted grows by the hour."

Almah took the guards and quickly set out on their errand to lessen any further wrath from the master.

Exiting the mansion gate, Almah turned to the two burly men. "We need a plan. The city is large and teeming with new arrivals. If we keep on the move, we could easily keep missing him among all the scurrying faces. I believe the best chance for a speedy sighting is to go to where Bathshua and I first met the handsome Hittite. The Night Bazaar would give us our best starting place. We can find a place close to the main entrance, station ourselves at the busiest crossroad, and remain there for however long it takes. I am sure that, and in time, he will return to the scene of his seduction. I will get a room on the second floor with a balcony, and you two remain below for when he passes by. I will point him out so that you two may obtain his capture."

Three days and as many nights had passed with no success. Almah confided in her two escorts, "It seems that I have seen the whole population of Jerusalem, but to no avail. I am starting to see Horite's face in every passerby. The purse the master gave me is all but spent. I fear to return empty-handed only to suffer the master's vengeful wrath." Finally, Shemira spoke up. "We have no choice but to return. My belly growls, and I miss my bed. The master is the wisest of men. Tell him you will venture out again and that you will redouble your efforts." Lishmor quickly nodded in agreement. The three trudged back to the far side of Jerusalem and the house of Ahithophel, remorseful at their failed attempt.

Meanwhile, Horite's determined search bore fruit when he inquired of the very last perfumer nestled at the end of a long row of shops. Horite waited for the store to empty before making his inquiry, "Kind sir, I seek a beautiful young woman who smells of jasmine, amber, and musk. Her scent captured me, and she, in turn, captured my heart. Her name is Bathshua. Do you know of this woman and where I might find her?" The merchant, stooped with age, looked up, trying to gauge the man's measure who stood before him. "It is not proper to give out my patrons' names and their whereabouts just to any stranger, especially to a foreigner."

Horite, sensing a glimmer of hope, pleaded, "Sir, please take pity on me. I have spoken to her and have hopelessly fallen in love. I wish only to take the damsel's hand in marriage." The elder winked and exhaled love. "I know the vexation all too well. But, for your heartthrob's sake, I will relent and make an exception, for the woman you speak of is under excellent protection. Her father is Eliab, one of King David's thirty-seven Mighties, and her grandfather is Ahithophel, one of the king's chief counselors. So, I seriously doubt if you can get past her well-guarded gate. Besides, Bathshua, whom you so feverishly seek, had recently moved into the mansion adjacent to the king's castle."

Horite's face lit up, now overjoyed with the prospect of being reunited with his heart's desire.

CHAPTER THIRTY-ONE
The Cruelest Cut of All

The king's house was broad and grand; the smell of cedar increased as Horite drew near. Ahithophel's mansion was not quite as bold and was situated slightly to the rear of the king's stately home. Horite approached the lesser palace when he underwent a challenge by the gate guardian, "Who goes there and what is wanted?"

Horite showed himself behind a late-afternoon shadow and replied, "My name is Horite, and I wish to speak to Bathshua."

An alert guard whispered to his drowsy cohort, "Is that not the name of the man whom our master is eagerly seeking?"

The guard then called out, "Hold fast, stranger; I will inquire of Lord Ahithophel, my master." Then, hurrying down the passageway, he called back, "Keep your eyes fixed on this fellow, and do not let him escape your grasp or gaze."

Two menacing sentries suddenly appeared and escorted the detained stranger to Ahithophel's study chamber. Ahithophel rose and attempted to put the heathen seducer of his grand-daughter at ease.

"My name is Ahithophel; I am Bathshua's grandfather and chief counselor to the king." Then, with a soothing tone, he bade, "Have no fear or misgiving, and please enter and be seated, for we have an urgent matter to discuss. Can I offer you a cup of wine or something to eat?"

Horite was watchful of the two burly guardians standing at the room's only exit. "Thank you, lord, my mouth is dry, and I would be grateful for a drink to slake my parched throat." Ahithophel nodded to one of the sentries, who understood and quickly withdrew to provide a quenching vintage from his master's cellar.

Ahithophel inquired, "Your name is Horite, and you are a Hittite from the north and east, around the Syrian border."

"Yes, my lord, it is all correct. Have you had the occasion to visit my homeland?"

"I have traded there and am quite familiar with the Hittite people. Yours is a highly esteemed warrior race placed there by God since the beginning of time. So then, young man, what has brought you to Jerusalem?"

Horite was pleased to tell his tale, "My clan stood compelled to join forces with the Arameans to fight against David and Israel. I wished to have no part in such recruitment—for I revere David as a champion and Israel as a chosen people. I escaped at night and offered my sword to the chief captain, Joab. He promised me a regular place in the army and a passage back to Jerusalem as a hero. It was my first night in your magical city when I met

Bathshua. Please forgive me, lord, for it was love at first sight, and I did succumb to my base desires. I have searched for her as a man possessed ever since that night of reckless abandon. I would wish to honor Bathshua and so impart my offer of marriage if she would have me." Ahithophel was surprisingly impressed with Horite's forthright candor and said so. "As you have been searching out Bathshua, I have been searching for you."

"For me, lord?" Horite puzzled.

Ahithophel snapped, "Yes—and this because Bathshua is with child, and there is no doubt, apparently from your description, that the child is yours."

The blood rushed to Horite's face; his nostrils flared as if bracing himself for the next unexpected blow. But, instead, he stood up confident and secure, and in an accepting tone, uttered, "I am both happy and ashamed. I am happy because the woman I adore will give me our love child, and ashamed of myself for this turn of events. After all, I have brought disgrace and the poison seeds of scandal to your door. I am at your mercy, Lord Ahithophel. But, know this, lord, I have fallen in love with Bathshua and would see to her best growth and happiness both spiritual and temporal—that is, if you would allow me the honor to marry her."

Just then, Almah stood at the entrance. Her frustration turned into surprise not only that Horite was present in the room but that he also stood accountable for his actions.

"My lord, you have accomplished what I could not by securing this vagabond lover."

Ahithophel scolded, "That is enough name-calling, Almah; now, go fetch your mistress; this decidedly concerns her. I will address your part in this unfortunate incident when time allows.

Now be off with you. Bathshua's presence is required to resolve this unfolding drama."

Almah was pulling on her mistress's hand, who was dreading every step. Bathshua's head was down, filled with conflicting emotions. Bathshua entered and stepped into the spotlight of judgment in her grandfather's unwavering stare. Sensing his granddaughter's humiliation, Ahithophel arose, and hugged her and kissed her on the cheek. Then in a low and soothing tone, he attempted to comfort Bathshua, "My dear child, these failings of emotions and their far-reaching sorrows only tend to carve out a hollow space where joy later finds a place to fill at a later date. My dear, please sit here across from Horite, and be assured everything will eventually sort itself out. Now, please confirm or deny if this is the man that fathered your unborn child?" Bathshua, struggling to lift her sad eyes, nodded and, in a struggling voice, thinly uttered, "Yes, Grandfather, it is he."

"Well, then," Ahithophel, with a tightening chin that stiffened his upper lip into a grimace, began, "Horite has searched you out, my dear, desperate in love. He has pledged to marry you and has asked for your hand. But even though you are with his child, you still must make the final decision. Do you now agree to marry Horite and give your unborn child a father?" Bathshua, without pause or the slightest hesitation, snapped, "I do, and I must, Grandfather, for respectability's sake and my peace of mind." Then, Bathshua contritely added, "An unmarried woman with a child ranks less than a harlot."

Ahithophel whispered, "So be it. This marriage will be no easy task to perform. There are religious and cultural requirements that we must observe.

265

"First and foremost, Horite must become a Hebrew by undergoing the ritual covenant of circumcision and, at that time, take on a Hebrew name; do you agree to these conditions to marry a daughter of Zion?"

Horite was delighted and brimmed with excitement. "I do, lord, and with all my heart and devotion, I commit myself with a covenant to your granddaughter's happiness. What name will I be known by hereafter?"

Ahithophel pondered and then asked, "Do you know of our God Yahweh?" Horite hesitated. "I have heard the name, and I know the burning-bush story that was bright with fire but not consumed. So first, let me pray to this burning-bush god. I will pray to Him to receive the spirit of His non-consuming-firelight."

Ahithophel smiled with divine inspiration. "Perfect, and after your circumcision, you will be known as Uriah the Hittite, meaning the fire and light of Yahweh. Bathshua [meaning daughter of wealth], you, too, must take a new name, so this stain does not follow you, putting a dark shadow on you and your baby. Henceforth, you will be called Bathsheba [or the daughter of the covenant or the vow]. It would be best to covenant and vow that all your children are reared in our Hebrew traditions, forsaking other gods. From this day and always, you are no longer Bathshua but Bathsheba. Is that understood?"

"It is, my grandfather."

Ahithophel nodded and continued, "Very well, I suggest we keep these proceedings to the barest minimum of attendance, only family and clerical participants, lessening the chance of washwomen's gossip. Eliam, my son, and Bathshua's father must agree to this union and participate in rites, rituals, and observances. There is also a house, the former residence of Eliam and Bathshua. The house is on the other side of Jerusalem and now stands empty. If your father agrees, this will be our wedding present and your new home. You will depart immediately after the ceremony. For secrecy's sake, we will forgo the wedding feast."

Within a fortnight, Eliam returned from one of David's endless conflicts. The timing was better than perfect. Horite the Hittite was now Uriah the Hittite and had all but healed from his Hebrew covenant of circumcision. Eliam met with Uriah and his father, Ahithophel, to discuss the unfortunate misadventure and his pregnant daughter's future. Ahithophel took charge and addressed Eliam's concerns, "My son, take heart and know to accept God's will that it is both perfect and inevitable. Your future son-in-law has been circumcised and is studying the Torah. All wedding plans are in place, for time is of the essence. Bathshua, who is now known as Bathsheba, her belly will soon blossom, and her condition will become more than obvious. We were only waiting upon your return to obtain your consent and needed participation. If you agree, I will give the new couple your former residence as you have since moved in with me and next to the king: Eliam, Uriah, the Hittite, longs to be a soldier for Israel and King David. If you could see fit to place him under your command, I believe the benefit would be twofold. What say you, my son?"

Eliam's prolonged pause was uncomfortable as it was unnerving. Many emotions played across his face, mostly violation and vengeance. Finally, after a great length, he spoke. "Father, once again, you have proved resourceful as well as wise. If this Hittite seducer did not consent to become a Hebrew and pledge undying love and devotion to Bathshua—I mean to say, Bathsheba; that name change will take some time for it to become familiar! In any event, if he had not pledged undying devotion, I would have slaughtered him on the very spot where he stood. But Horite—I mean, Uriah—has, and will be the father of my grandchild, and having said that, so be it. I agree that he will be a family member. I will also recruit Uriah into my unit, so I can keep an eye on him. Chief Captain Joab will agree as I test his mettle and make him a skilled warrior or a dead hero."

The wedding went as planned, guided by Ahithophel. The ceremony was a private affair, with only a modest number of witnesses, just enough to satisfy the law. A small meal followed hard upon the celebration. Still, the mood remained subdued and passive, for Bathsheba's pregnancy was becoming apparent.

Eliam, the father of the bride, offered a fitting toast: "Thank you all for observing this covenant ritual, the wedding vows of Bathsheba the Israelite and Uriah the Hittite. The couple's first night as man and wife with privacy assured will be under the roof of their new home and my wedding present. It is far enough away to keep them safe from prying eyes and ensure them a fresh start. I wish for this, yet they will be close enough to afford a loving family's security and protection. Bathsheba has grown into a beautiful woman and will be a well-valued friend and helpful companion. Uriah has converted to Hebrew and has made it known that he will love and cherish Bathsheba. Uriah has pledged to raise their children and abide by the laws found in the Torah. He will strive to bring honor and glory to our house as a soldier of God and Israel. Finally, remember that two are better than one because they have a good reward for their labor. If one falls, the stronger one will lift the other: but woe to those alone when they fall, for they have no one to help them up. If two lie together, they have heat: but how can one be warm alone? And if one prevails against either, two together shall withstand the evil, and a threefold cord is not quickly broken. The third fold is Jehovah's holy spirit of promise. May you grow old together, happy and content, and surrounded by your posterity."

Loving cups filled to the brim and raised high, followed by a deep gulp from well-wishers, helped to wash down Eliam's great blessing.

The freshly wedded couple quietly departed to their new abode. Hoping the cover of night would hide their necessity of a loveless union, as viewed in the sunlight of respected convention.

Bathsheba, her shame smoothed over, then set about feathering her nest, hoping in time that love for her new husband would find a way to her heart. The strain of it all took its toll on both her body and soul.

"Husband," she cried one morning, "I am bleeding. A stream of blood is dripping down my thigh in gushes, and it will not stop. I feel dizzy and faint, and I have a belly filled with sharp daggers. I must lie down. Hurry, go, and fetch me the midwife!"

Uriah immediately dropped his burden and lit out for help. Returning in a rush, he pulled along the healer, forcing her to keep up with his furious pace. "Bathsheba!" Uriah anxiously yelled.

Bathsheba, sobbing and whimpering, choked, "I am here and alone, for the baby is no longer in my body." She then collapsed to the floor.

The practitioner and Uriah hoisted Bathsheba back onto her bed. The midwife exclaimed, "Boil me some water and soak some clean rags in the kettle. I think your wife will be all right. She is young, and the bleeding has stopped. What she needs now is some quiet and rest. After that, I will clean her up and dispose of the remains. By the law, it is considered a Nephilim; anything which does not live for thirty days we do not mourn, for it never knew life."

Bathsheba regained her strength, and life continued at its endless pace. Bathsheba could not shake the feeling that her illicit love affair and lapse of judgment caused God to curse her pregnancy. The strain of her miscarriage and forced marriage left a mood of resentment. Uriah did his utmost to seal the breach, for his love for Bathsheba only in time increased. Try as he might, the marriage bed often went cold, filled with seasoned excuses and tiresome backache complaints.

CHAPTER THIRTY-TWO
The Seduction of Plots and Plans

Ahithophel took pity on his granddaughter for her forced marriage and heartbreaking miscarriage. He sent Almah, her former loyal body servant, to help with day-to-day chores and provide a comforting sounding board. Bathsheba was glad for the company. When Uriah was in town and not training or deployed, his presence served only as a reminder of God's vengeance. Uriah, as a result, was spending more and more time volunteering for military campaigns.

Uriah had left on such an expedition one afternoon, and Bathsheba cried welcoming tears when she opened the door the following day. To her utter amazement, it was Almah. "My dear girl. It is a delight and a surprise to have some familiar company. You are a bright spot in my emotional wasteland."

"What do you mean by that?" Almah questioned.

Bathsheba dropped her head and quietly responded, "I remain guarded, for my heart remains shielded to my husband's romantic pleadings. I cannot seem to shake the feeling that my destiny was not to marry a simple soldier but a prince—or, at the very least, a favored son of nobility. I agreed to this wedlock only to avoid a family scandal and give my unborn child a name and a father's blessing. You know this. But now the child is gone, and I'm forbidden by the law even to mourn its passing. I am now caught here, and forever, in a trap of my own making!"

"Bathsheba," Almah whispered, sounding upbeat and cheery, "your face is elegant, and it does not fare well in a frown; allow me to give you pause for a smile."

"Speak on," Bathsheba said, curiously intrigued.

"King David has returned after a long absence, after battling and subduing many hostile nations. As you know, your grandfather Ahithophel's mansion is directly adjacent and slightly below the king's rooftop garden. I have witnessed David often engaged in his regular and predictable evening ritual. His maidservant—known for her gossip when she is in her cups, confided in me that David rests most days and arises just before sundown, the time of poets and philosophers. He goes up directly to his rooftop garden almost every evening when he is in attendance for quiet prayer and meditation. He finds solace in viewing heavenly bodies. Please excuse my impropriety, but I believe you might very well fit into the category." Bathsheba turned abruptly with a stern look and then smiled under a stifled giggle. "The king is known for staying up late and long into the night contemplating the wonders of God's creation, and you, madam, are surely that."

Bathsheba shook her head. "What are you getting at, Almah?"

Almah, with a wicked wink, laid out her plan of conspiracy and seduction. "Ahithophel's rooftop has a mikveh, the ceremonial bath that can collect rainwater and purify you from your uncleanness once your regular issue of blood has ended and then judged sanctified by the law. But not until after sundown. Luckily for us that this is the very same time that David will be on his rooftop retreat and in full view of your natural beauty, just like God made you."

"I am both puzzled and enchanted by your outrageous proposal, but he already has seven wives, does he not?"

"Yes, my lady, he does, but he also has a keen eye for comely women. Making him even more desirable, David is a handsome and renowned poet-musician. There is no prohibition in the Torah for the number of wives a man might marry, only if he can provide for their worldly needs. For a king, that would mean an unlimited number of consorts and concubines, depending on his stamina, imagination, and depth of purse. So, it is good to consider that David is king, and no one says no to the king—for such would be treason."

Bathsheba lamented, "There is a flaw in your cunning plan. For one, I have not had an issue of blood since the dreadful end of my pregnancy four months ago. Second, I believe God has sealed up my womb and has taken away my creative spark."

Almah was undaunted. "Your flow will begin again—I know it—and your health renewed. A new life will be your reward, for God blesses his faithful. When your blood issue ends, the ritual mikveh bath filled to the brim with warm rainwater will purify your contaminated blood. Then and only then, we will be ready to entice the unsuspecting prince on the roof top of your grandfather's mansion."

Just as Almah had predicted, within days, Bathsheba's natural monthly cycle reappeared with cramping, fatigue, and eruptions of anger. Her servant was delighted that her prophetic insight had so rapidly come to pass.

Almah insisted, "It is time to prepare. We will go to the mansion and help make ready for the mikveh bath. Your timing is crucial; you need to be exiting the tub just as David approaches the very edge of his overhead balcony. The sun is still emitting enough light so that he can feast his eyes on your youthful nakedness—glistening wet, vivid, and striking."

Early afternoon found the two plotters setting off for the house of Ahithophel. "If we are well-prepared, fate and luck will ensure our success." Almah quipped. "Will Uriah, your doting husband, miss you for a few days? Will he be curious as to your whereabouts?"

Bathsheba shook her head. "No, not at all; he is on a training mission in the desert. There is some invasion or big battle about to take place. Uriah is very closed-mouthed about such happenings."

The two women briskly approached the mansion; they entered freely, easily recognizable as family.

"Where is my grandfather?" Bathsheba inquired.

The head servant replied, "The master is away in a foreign land, as an ambassador promoting the goodwill of the king. I believe this time he is on a trading mission to Egypt."

The two women smiled at each other, for the timing of Ahithophel's absence could not have made things easier.

Almah addressed the head servant. "We need to prepare the mikveh for my lady's purification ritual. First, gather up the rainwater from the rooftop cisterns. Then, heat the water at the downstairs hearth and fill the tub until it is steaming hot. Most importantly, make sure everything stands ready so that my lady can enter the water immediately at twilight, while some of the light from the dying sun still lingers on the horizon."

All the needful things were in their proper place. The sun and the stage were both ready to set.

Bathsheba disrobed, her stunning figure brightening the dimming light. She slipped into the steamy, brazen tub and moaned with delight as the warm water lightly caressed her tingling flesh and heightened her senses.

Almah kept a watchful eye until she spotted David's long shadow approaching from his upper gallery. "He comes," she hissed.

Bathsheba stood up dripping wet, water droplets glistening in the freshly lit torchlight at the perfect moment. She refrained from looking up as she felt hungry eyes drinking in her naked beauty.

Almah approached with a warm towel and slowly circled the tub, squeezing out every desire-filled moment. Almah began by drying her mistress, shrewdly patting Bathsheba's shapely legs, rounded buttocks, and dabbing gently at upturned breasts. David became entranced as a raging storm of lust washed over him with every sensual gesture. His eyes strained against the fading light for one more fleeting glimpse of this mysterious vixen. Lastly, the two women hoisted the flaming torches and disappeared behind closed doors, leaving a void where only moments before David's exotic fantasy had been born.

David, still reeling from the hot sweat of passion, urgently inquired of his household servants, saying, "A strange woman has suddenly appeared like a water nymph bathing on Ahithophel's rooftop bath. Who is this bewitching creature?" Silence hung for only a moment when a servant girl, both bashful and private, uttered, "From your description and location, sire, it has to be Bathsheba, daughter of Eliam and so, too, the granddaughter of Ahithophel, sire, and the wife of Uriah, the converted Hittite. I know this, my lord, from the gossip of chambermaids and scullery wenches."

David pondered aloud, "So, why is it that I had never seen her before?"

The servant girl, anxious from her ongoing conversation with the king, looked around and then took a nervous breath. "She lives with her husband Uriah in Captain Eliam's former residence, located in the city's old Benjamite quarter."

David sought out two of his most loyal and trusted body-guards, Ahava and Saval. He commanded, "I need you two to go and deliver a message to the lady Bathsheba—who is at Ahithophel's adjacent mansion—with haste and discretion." David hurriedly set to work on a royal request with heartfelt words of love, desire, and ravenous passion. David procured a new clay writing tablet from his open cabinet and began pouring out his heart.

"Bathsheba, comely daughter of Eliam:

By chance, design, or by divine coincidence, my eyes have beheld the fullness of your loveliness. My breath catches, and my aching heart is filled and ready to burst at the mere mention of your name. Under every violation, the pursuit of you, my most ardent and aroused desire, and by everything holy, I should not be coveting another man's wife, no matter how beautiful. So, dear lady, please forgive me, for you have captured my mind, will, and emotions. I find myself adrift in a whirlwind of desire since the moment that my eyes beheld the very first sight of you. I beg and implore you for your company—if for nothing else but to talk so that I can hear the enticing tone of your voice and long to feel the personal comfort from your delightful company.

"If this earnest plea does not secure your willing conspiracy, then I command you, as your king and sovereign, for I will not take no for an answer.

"David, son of Jesse, king of Judah and Israel."

The two messengers hastily departed with David's fiery message of both command and desperate obsession.

David's guards had no trouble passing through Ahithophel's guarded and gated compound, for all bars and barriers quickly parted in the king's name. When questioned as to their errand, they demanded personal access to the lady Bathsheba. "We carry a private and personal letter from the king," Saval declared. "If I were you, I would not gossip about this occurrence. Discussing the private life of the king is treason—if you get my meaning."

Hearing the commotion, Bathsheba rushed into the parlor. "Did I understand you correctly that I have personal tidings from the king?"

Saval bowed, acknowledging Bathsheba's nobility. "Yes, my lady, and the king ordered me to put this, his private message, into your hands personally—and to no other."

Bathsheba paused as she read, relishing every potent and powerfully seductive word. Her throbbing heart began to flutter. Her pastel face flushed crimson, and her eyes rolled back in her head. Bathsheba fought to stave off a faint. Try as she might, her knees began to buckle, and the room started to spin. Almah ran in and caught Bathsheba by the arm, saving her mistress's unladylike fall to the floor.

Almah then guided Bathsheba to a nearby chair. "Please sit and try to relax, my lady; take three deep breaths, and focus on your whereabouts. Then, allow me the time to fetch a cup of red wine to calm your whirlwind of emotions and cool your fevered brow."

Bathsheba gulped down the potent tonic and felt the soothing burn steadying her nerves and giving life back to her legs.

Saval, already impatient, insisted, "Madam, the king is waiting and is anxious for your company; we must hurry."

Almah snapped back at the imposing brute: "My lady is just out of the bath, and her hair is still damp. I need to prepare her to meet the king. Your master needs to be a little patient. David can wait but a moment or two for this fine package to receive an elegant bow, and no less, if she is to be delivered straight away to the king's very doorstep."

Bathsheba, gloriously groomed, was made elegant with a perfectly combed and perfumed crown of hair. Almah made sure that Bathsheba was now richly adorned as a lady befitting her high station. "You are beautiful, my lady." Almah then turned to the guards and quipped, "For good or for ill, my mistress is ready to be presented to the king for his amusement and pleasure."

Bathsheba tightly grasped Almah's arm and commanded the guards, "I will not accompany you unless my maidservant remains in my attendance."

Ahava looked at Saval and shrugged, saying, "Whatever is necessary to fulfill the king's commission, then so be it."

Two sparking torches cast a dark shadow on the two trailing women. The foursome quickly crossed the hidden track that led to the side gate of David's castle.

David swiftly walked up and met his heart's desire as she carefully stepped out of the dark and onto his private terrace. His eyes were now irresistibly fixed on this stunning beauty about to cross over his welcoming threshold. He immediately dismissed both the guards and Almah, Bathsheba's maidservant, to avoid interruptions from prying eyes and wagging tongues.

David reached for the right words and finally voiced, "Bathsheba. Even your name has an enticing tone. Welcome to my home. I am both honored and pleased to be in your presence."

Bathsheba kept her eyes down to the ground; she felt a rush of desire, yet she was completely vulnerable, alone, and adrift in an uncharted sea of emotions.

David was beautiful, manly, and powerful as he attempted to quell Bathsheba's misgivings and put her concerns to rest. With a firm hand at the small of her back and an outstretched arm, he began, "My lady, please relax. You have nothing to fear. I have prepared a sumptuous feast in my private apartment. I hate eating alone, and your company will give me great comfort." David then escorted Bathsheba, arm in arm, across the great hall to his private suite, seeking love's intimacy. Once there, he softened her defenses with fine wines, rare delicacies, and the seduction of laughter.

The apartment was aglow in soft and intimate candlelight. Fresh-cut flowers added fragrance to the beguiling setting. David began, "Please sit in my plush chair and feel safe and adored, my lady. Our meal will be a delicious banquet, with many courses being served through a pass-through opening, allowing no servant to be seen or heard. I will not tolerate a moment's distraction from our conversation. Security and privacy will give us time for the two of us to bask in each other's company."

David attentively listened as Bathsheba started to relax. She eagerly answered his many probing questions. He treated her respectfully and expressed genuine interest in her point of view.

Bathsheba felt a warm glow and said so. "Thank you, sire, for valuing my thoughts and judgments. It is a rare thing for a man to honor a woman's mind in these troubled times."

With his most engaging smile, David replied, "Please, my dear lady, from now on, and for always, call me 'David.'" David moved subtly to capture her heart before he attempted to touch her body.

After many sips of red wine, Bathsheba's tongue untied. "Sire—I mean, David—I have a confession. I am a married woman. My husband's Hebrew name is Uriah, a converted Hittite."

David tried to look surprised but then admitted, "I am aware of your marriage and the name of your husband. I do not care, for my soul soars, and my breath catches at your presence. I would challenge heaven and hell itself and return again and again to know you—and to love you, whatever the cost, whatever the price. Do you protest, madam, and so diminish me to a pitiful lump?"

Bathsheba shook her head. "No, my David, for my marriage is neither happy nor fulfilling. I entered a loveless union to save my honor and the honor of my family. I have not known my husband, nor have we embraced in the marital bed for longer than I care to remember. I hunger for love and the touch of a man. Are you that man, my rescuer, and my champion?"

David lifted Bathsheba out of her seat and crushed her moist lips, his tongue delighting in the flavors of red wine, honey, and sweet raisins cakes. The room spun, and both collapsed, reeling on the nearby down-filled couch. The forbidden lovers' attempts failed miserably to maintain the slightest semblance of modesty as shirts and stays ripped away and landed askew on the floor.

The desperate embrace of love too long denied unearthed the treasure of Bathsheba's never-ending pleasure, lasting well beyond dawn's first light. Love and lust mixed with sweat, and the angels wept with envy at the tender intensity of their lovemaking.

The second crowing of the cock aroused David from his satisfied slumber. He turned slightly to gaze upon Bathsheba's gleaming pink complexion. Their sweaty all-night lovemaking had dampened all the bedding. Her breathing came short and shallow, almost panting. David gently touched her cheek. Her eyes glazed with desire and began to flutter and slowly opened to an enchanted vision of her new, skillful lover.

"Good morning, my darling Bathsheba. Even saying your name brings pleasure to my lips. Did you sleep well, my darling love nymph?"

Bathsheba playfully replied, "What little of it I managed, it was more than satisfying; it was if I had died and gone to heaven."

They both smiled and laughed as if coming from one voice. David inquired, "Are you hungry, my adorable sprite? I am starving and have taken the liberty of ordering breakfast for the two of us. I pray you can linger without causing suspicion or cause an alarm from your being absent too long. I cannot entertain the thought of you departing from my sight and longing embrace. Either far or near, you will always be in my heart and my mind, and I will always be your obedient servant."

David, on a more somber note, questioned, "Where is your husband? Does he not get suspicious as to your whereabouts?"

Bathsheba's rapture melted into reality. "He is a soldier in your army and away at training for some coming battle. That is all he would tell me. My father is Eliam, one of your thirty-seven Mighties, and my grandfather is Ahithophel, your next-door neighbor, and chief counselor. As you know, he is currently on a trade mission in Egypt for your and Israel's benefit. Our timing could not have been better or made this perfect without fate's intervention."

David pondered his good fortune and cheerfully responded, "I was about to take the army to Ammon and engage in a very time-consuming siege of Rabbah, a heavily fortified fortress. I need to redress a dreadful insult to my person by way of ridiculing my emissaries. But I think my nephew Joab is more than capable of victory, and I would prefer to stay in Jerusalem and give my undivided attention to you, Bathsheba, my beautiful and alluring affair of state." The two whiled away the morning with a lavish breakfast, light conversation, and another delightful romp lasting through that blissful day and long into the night.

CHAPTER THIRTY-THREE

The Last Piece in the Empire Puzzle

The year had expired, and it was the time when kings went forth to war. The harvest season finally concluded, freeing up men for recruitment and providing provisions to fill the empty bellies of marching soldiers.

David summoned Joab, "Nephew, you are my most loyal and seasoned chief captain, and I have a mission that awaits your hard won experience."

"So much praise, Uncle—I fear a daunting task lies behind your next command."

David smiled and continued, "Yes, Joab. This mission will undoubtedly test your mettle both as a fighter and a leader. We have left Ammon idle too long. It is the last piece in our puzzle to secure our eastern borders. The king's highway is still in jeopardy, and our nation's vital trade remains vulnerable. Our most northern trade route is often preyed upon by Ammonite raiders.

Rabbah, the Royal city of King Hanun, is the key to our region's long-awaited supremacy. Hanun's cruel insult to my messengers still goes unanswered. Let us make plans and keep in mind the lay of the land and all possible hazards.

"As you already know, Rabbah lies in the narrow valley of the upper Jabbok, nestled securely between the two streams. It makes their water supply plentiful, ensuring your siege to be a long and costly one.

"Once the City of Waters has fallen, we will have to contend with the elevated and highly fortified royal citadel. King Hanun's impregnable retreat sits on a commanding bluff on the royal city's upper north side. It will take many fearless men to breach its bulwarks and its many formidable barriers. I tell you this to make you aware of all the challenges you must overcome.

"As you know, the Arameans are no longer a threat. All the Syrian chariots are either captured or crushed. But luckily, there is none to come to the aid of those Ammonite jackals. Although some Ammonite tribes chafe under our heel and only lack a uniting leader. Nephew, it would be best to remain ever vigilant and wary of intrusion from northern Syrian renegade chieftains.

"I need you to lead Israel's forces fording the shallows at the Beth-barah Jordan river crossing. I will send supplies in abundance, including food and a generous supply of wine, from Jerusalem, until victory is assured.

"Do you have any questions, Joab?"

Joab looked baffled. "You are not coming, Uncle?"

David shook his head, "No," sheepishly grinning.

"The walls of Rabbah are high and formidable. Their battlements brim with deadly arrows. It might be a very long siege—unless, of course, a desperate hunger forces them outside their protective walls and compels them to engage you in the open to ward off starvation. But, to answer your question, I have already been away too long, and my husbandly duties have gone wanting."

David winked. "Affairs of state are also taxing, some are demanding, and some are more pleasant than others.

"Besides, as the chief captain, you do not need me. Without the Arameans to contend with, this campaign is a sure victory. Do you remember what happened in your last encounter? You barely made it back with your skin intact. A decisive victory at Rabbah will restore Israel's confidence in your leadership abilities. Of course, it will take time, and patience will count as much as courage. But, without a speck of misgiving, I have every confidence in your will to succeed. Now, make me and all Israel proud of you, my courageous warrior nephew."

The king's messengers swiftly dispatched their timely call to war to every town, village, and hamlet.

Both Uriah and Bathsheba were back in their house the following afternoon. Eliam, Bathsheba's father, came bearing gifts and news:

"My dear daughter, Bathsheba, prepare yourself for your husband's extended absence. Then, we depart at dawn for the siege and conquer of Hanun's Ammonite kingdom. With its massive walls and deadly archers, Rabbah could prove to be a very long encounter before the enemy succumbs to either storm or starvation. So, prepare, Uriah—our time is at hand, my newly minted son-in-law, for we leave directly for Ammon."

David, God's Chosen Crucible

"The recent wars to claim our northern borders have taken their toll on both men and resources. Israel's boundaries now extend north to the Euphrates and south to Egypt, thus ensuring the king's highway of trade, materials, and information is free from disruption. The sticking point is the Ammon pirates and King Hanun's walled-in city of Rabbah. Besides, King Hanun's insult to King David's comforting messengers continues to fester.

"Uriah: It is time for you to say farewell to Bathsheba, your warm bed, and home-cooked meals. These are the things that will occupy your mind on restless nights and in the long pauses between fierce enemy clashes."

Uriah made his painful way to say goodbye to his beloved. The marriage bed remained cold despite his many attempts at romance. Many a night, Uriah had found warmth only next to the dying embers of the cooking pots. "My darling Bathsheba," Uriah began, "the call to war is at our door, and at first light, I depart for the glory of King David in the redress of a grievous insult to him and Israel. My heart aches for the love of you, and I wish that our marriage bed would taste of my longing for your beauty. Tonight is our last night together until the war is over, or I die in the fighting."

Bathsheba had her seasoned excuses and said, "I cannot consent—for my heart is not open to your advances. But I wish you well in the service of God and the king." Bathsheba slyly hid a smile of relief, knowing full well she would soon be in her lover's arms.

Uriah slipped out into the deepest dark before dawn, for his heart could not stand another rejection. As of late, Bathsheba had become even more distant and withdrawn, even if that were possible. Bathsheba avoided the very sight of him, and his slightest touch brought recoil and a look of disgust to her face.

Uriah faded into the regular army, and he sought the solace of discipline. The army grew more prominent by the addition of farmers, merchants, and herders. The provisional militias from all outlying tribes traded their hoes, plows, and scythes for swords, spears, bows, and deadly iron-tipped arrows.

Joab called forth Abishai. "My warrior brother, and most capable second commander. I have considered the best route for the army to reach Rabbah, and David agrees, but I would like your thoughts on this matter. I propose we take our forces and your cross over at the south shallow waters of the Beth-bara; it is the shortest path through the plains."

Abishai leaned in and asked, "What about the use of the militia that David left at Sukkot to protect the Jabbok River crossing?"

Joab nodded in agreement. "That is the same question I asked David. He said, and I quote, 'I am concerned that some of the Aramean vassal states chafe under Israeli rule. If given the right opportunity, they could organize and launch a surprise attack on our northern flank. Such an action would genuinely hamper our blockade of Rabbah. Leaving the militia force at Sukkot would discourage all such ventures." Then he concluded, preventing any further discussion, 'Besides, nephew, you have more than ample men that I must feed—and weapons enough to carry the day. Enough said.'"

With a mischievous smile, Abishai voiced, "Well, then, it seems our uncle, as usual, has thought of every possibility. We must travel in haste, and before King Hanun knows of our invasion plans and prepares his fortress city with fresh food and stores, guaranteeing an endless war of equal losses. I am sure we will get more advice and directions from our esteemed uncle, for his eyes and ears are everywhere, even on the battlefield. Messengers from Jerusalem and needed supplies will frequently crisscross our encampment. The passion pit that is David's private apartments will be a far more comfortable command post for our distracted king."

Joab grunted at his brother's offhanded remark. "Let us not idly speculate, brother, or demean the king; after all, he is our mother's favorite brother. Remember, brother, that we had to withdraw from the field of battle on our last encounter with the walls of Rabbah. We barely made it out alive, and by God's will, we were able to keep the bulk of the army intact, as well as our skins! This time, to salve that sting of that retreat, we must conquer that same impregnable fortress, no matter the cost or the sacrifice. It is forty miles to Rabbah as the crow flies, but men seldom fly like crows. It is an uphill trek with every step, a challenging forced march at best. We shall spend three days on those pitted and rutted paths, not considering injuries, accidents, and unavoidable mishaps in the river crossing. Four days, if we would spare the men from fatigue. The longer we spend on our approach, the more time Hanun and his chief captain Nemun—a most resilient and cunning foe—will have enough time to reinforce their position with food from the threshing floor, men, and weaponry. But, of course, we have one obvious choice to cover the distance in two days, with a forced march. Naturally, we will dull our men's fighting edge, and some may even drop from fatigue.

But the army will have plenty of time to rest from their fatigue once we encircle the city of waters and so deprive Hanun of the grain from his threshing floor and meats from sheep, goats, and cattle. A bounty that we will deny the enemy and, in turn, sustain us against a long siege."

Abishai agreed to the aggressive double-time sprint.

As predicted, the forced march was a grueling affair. The nights were cold, and no campfires were allowed—a precaution taken to avoid detection. Men grumbled as they huddled for the sake of warmth. The provisions were no better—salted meat and unleavened bread—but the double portion of red wine was the bright spot in many an evening retreat.

"Uriah," a fellow soldier challenged, "could the Hittites cover as much ground as the army of God had done this day?"

Uriah, avoiding any conflict from this subtle slight, responded, "I don't think there is an army anywhere that could travel as fast and as far as we did today."

The soldier grunted his approval and slipped back into the shadows.

The second day was twice as demanding, and the second night even colder. The men's grumbling and chatter were reduced to whispers, for Ammonite patrols had been alerted and were now on the lookout for intruders.

In the moments before dawn, men quietly roused from their slumber to make the final stretch to the capital of Rabbah. Upon reaching Rabbah's massive stone walls, Joab and his army spied trains of loaded carts and wagons crossing over small bridges and into the vast gated threshold. Joab immediately started giving orders to his captains, "Abishai, does the place look familiar?

Abishai stuck out his chest and proudly confessed, "It does, brother; it is the place where we found ourselves in the jaws of a trap, and you brilliantly split the army in half, and we attacked in two directions. I do remember your brilliant strategy. We had God on our side to make it out alive. For now, the horizon is empty, and the Arameans are now no longer a threat. David remains cautious, even though there is not a ghost of a chance of their involvement."

Joab growled at his brother and, with iron in his voice, said, "That was then, and this is now! God has granted us a second chance to set things right. I need you to put men in between the streams. We can cover three sides of the city. On the cliff above rests Hanun's fortress compound. It commands the high ground and overlooks the city. The bluffs there are sheer. There is no ready access from either side, behind, or below. Position men regularly spaced to cover as much of the wall as possible so that no one comes in or goes out. Tonight, we shall prevent the arrival of King Hanun's feast and eat it ourselves!

"When faced with starvation, men will lower themselves by ropes and forage for their families. Also, be aware that some of the more desperate of the king's men may try to escape our vengeance."

Abishai saluted his brother and then slowly turned, and expressed in a frustrated tone, "It seems our rush to confine these swine has been in vain. The last of their supplies were passing through the gate as we arrived. I am afraid this will be a long wait. It will try our patience; determination and persistence is our greatest challenge and our defining moment."

Joab quickly responded, "We arrived in time to deny another twenty-four hours worth of supplies from reaching the city. So, whatever it takes, brother, no matter how long the wait or how high the wall. In the meantime, keep the men busy with guard duty, patrols, and building assault ladders to breach the walls. If starvation does not loosen the hinged gate, we will have to storm the barricades. But let us prepare for an extended stay and give time for disease and famine to do their grisly work first."

Nightfall found the city of waters surrounded and tightly guarded on every side. One hundred evenly spaced companies covered the killing ground, ensuring no passage in or out of the besieged enemy compound. The army hastily erected tents, and the nearly exhausted men found rest and warmth in the brotherhood of arms and crackling campfires.

At the beginning of the middle watch, the army was sound asleep on or about midnight, recognized by the occasional cough, grunt, and non-stop snoring. The sentries were hard-pressed to keep from dozing off after their final day's push to the Ammonite city capital.

The dark city walls all at once blazed from cauldrons of fire that ringed the upper balconies. At that very moment, a downpour of flaming arrows lit up the night sky. Tents were set ablaze, and some men fatally struck dead as they lay at peace and rest in the dark. The shrieks of the wounded shook some into a panic. A few of the men ran, burning into the shadows. The companies feverishly withdrew out of range of the deadly darts, taking only whatever essentials they could salvage. Joab was now guarding the front gate safely, just far enough out of reach, but surprisingly only by a few cubits. A steep natural rise afforded Joab both a good view and ample protection. Abishai was not so lucky and came within inches of being struck down. He ordered all his captains to withdraw their men to a safe distance and forgo this night's campfires.

Once the flames subsided and some semblance of order restored, Abishai sought out his brother's condition. Keeping a safe distance, he made his way through the commotion to his brother's location. Abishai nervously recounted, "Joab, we have underestimated the distance and accuracy of their deadly marksmen. The walls' height extends their reach, much more than I had expected. They used our warming fires to gauge our location. I have ordered no more campfires, not for this night, in any event. We have nearly fifty men dead, and the wounded are twice that again. What are we to do, Chief Captain?"

Joab sensed his brother's distress and voiced calming words to ease his misgivings. "Now we know the exact distance of their bow shots. This discovery is important and tells us how far we can approach without encountering their deadly shafts. Moreover, the range and design of their weapons are crucial knowledge for when we finally storm their ramparts—unless they give way to starvation and pestilence."

CHAPTER THIRTY-FOUR
Causalities of Love and War

The siege was proving difficult and dangerous: every approach to the city walls at once became a killing zone. Seven weeks passed, then eight. Messengers from David were hot with the scalding words from the king: "Attack, attack, attack," he demanded. "It is costly to feed and resupply such a large army in the field. You, my dear nephew, are bleeding my coffers dry." Yet, Joab held his ground and measured his reply. "Sire, it is only a matter of time, for the shell of this egg is about to crack—a little more patience and pressure, my dear uncle, and Rabbah's street will run red with blood."

The only reprieve from the stalemate and routine of tiresome guard duty was the occasional supply wagons from Jerusalem. Carts filled to the brim with tasty meats, wine, and ever juicier gossip. The drivers and their escorts were ready to share the latest rumors of washwomen, chambermaids, and the muck raked up by stablehands.

Nirgan, a tall, wire-thin drover who could talk without pause or even taking a breath, was one such; a "delicious poison" gossipmonger and a nonstop blabbermouth. The words of his stories were like sweet venom. They would go down to the darker chambers of the human heart. The tale bearer's reward is a captivated audience and their undivided attention. The anxious gathering hung on to his every word and gesture, giving him a moment's pleasure from the heightened state of self-importance. The evening meal, hastily consumed, left time to share several seasoned skins of dark red wine generously provided by Nirgan. The allure of spirits aided in recruiting eager listeners. The soothing potion gave the sense of ease and comfort that greased wagging tongues and set the stage for spicy insider news from the home front. The firelight and smoldering laughter attracted Uriah to the noisy gathering. He found a seat just within the outside ring of shifting shadows, just close enough to hear the grumbling of men and the crackle of the fire.

"Tell us of the king's adventures," one excited soldier prodded. "The rumor is that he does not join us because he is obsessed with a sizzling hot enchantress."

"Tell us everything, and do not leave out any of the more lurid details!"

Nirgan took a greedy swig from a swollen wineskin, quickly followed by another dripping mouthful. Before he could grab a third jolt, the wineskin abruptly slipped from his greasy fingertips, yanked gingerly by the next man in line until the last of the dregs emptied as it got pulled down by the rowdy crowd. A hunger for wine, entertainment, and news from home helps relieve the stark terror of certain death followed by weeks of mind-numbing boredom. Nirgan stretched himself to his full height and stature. He began by sweeping a pointed finger around the circle of boisterous men. Then, heightening a dramatic effect and signaling, he was about to reveal insider information. He took in a deep breath that produced a guttural belch, and in a low whisper, he blurted out, "Men, I speak of things that are confidential, which you must keep in the strictest confidence." All went silent, as every man leaned in so as not to miss a single utterance.

"I speak of the king's torrid love affair; the current rumor, is that it is a married woman." A collective "Aha!" of excitement rose from the tickled gathering.

"The king never, or rarely, appears in public. Instead, he wakes just before sundown and whiles away the night, held captive by his wanton pleasures in the belly of this seductress."

"What is the name of this alluring beauty?" The frustrated listener, unable to hold his peace, voiced, "Speak up—I can barely hear you." Nirgan squinted in the direction of his heckler, who again repeated, "What is her name?"

Nirgan warily looked around and then blurted out, "Bathsheba? Bath-Shua? A married woman. I heard her name from a stable boy, who heard it from his lady friend, who is one of the king's chambermaids. If word gets out that I have spoken such gossip, it could mean my life for slandering the dignity of the king partaking in an adulterous affair."

"Well, then," a thirsty soldier chuckled, "we will keep your state secret, and you can keep your head on your shoulders, but it will cost you another skin of your delightful vintage."

Back in the dancing shadows, Uriah groaned, pierced by the likely twin horns of adultery and humiliation. He doubled over with shame, a cuckold spewing bile and regret. He shrank down inside and held back the anger of betrayal, remorse, and despair. Uriah loved and admired David and would have given his life in his service. The loss of his beloved wife, Bathsheba, stabbed him through the heart, even though his desperate love stayed rejected and painfully denied. Uriah would have climbed the highest mountain or fought any battle to rekindle her affection. She was now in the passionate throes of forbidden love and under the king's absolute power.

Uriah went off into the dark underbrush to seek the solace of prayer and salvation. He first prayed to the Hittite god Šauška – goddess of fertility, war, and healing. His heartfelt pleas felt empty as if falling upon deaf ears. Uriah then called upon the Hebrew God—a God with so many names that no one could know them all. He prayed, "God, with many names, I have suffered Your circumcision rites, confirmed my pledge of loyalty and esteem, and suffered the cruelest cut with pain and blood. Please hear my sorrows. My heart breaks, and my fate is uncertain. I beg for peace and acceptance. Make my paths straight, so that hate and the spirit of self-loathing will fade away. So that once again, I can reunite with you and be in harmony with all of creation. Lord God, please forgive me, my king, and my wife, so that I may regain my self-respect."

He was immediately impressed with words that were heard but not spoken. "Be not dismayed or broken, and this trial is but a moment. I turn a man's weakness into his greatest strength. Your name will be voiced and enshrined through all generations and for all eternity. Be of good cheer; your sorrow and pain will carve out the hollow space filled later with peace and joy." Uriah felt serenity and the grace that comes from forgiveness—both from God and himself. He would press on as one of the king's trusted warriors and a soldier in the service of the great Hebrew God, Jehovah.

CHAPTER THIRTY-FIVE
Drawn to the Killing Zone

King Hanun gathered his ministers, noblemen, and all his chief captains. The anxious counselors sat uncomfortably packed around a massive banquet table. The great hall stood lavishly decked out in red banners and polished weaponry. King Hanun began, "Gentlemen, the current siege of Rabbah, our beloved capital city, as of late, has become perilous. Food stores are thinning, and famine will, in the end, cause the onset of disease and pestilence. David's army is safely rooted in its measured distance. Their position lessens our longest bows' killing range, our most potent weapon against this Hebrew aggression. We need to break this stalemate before it is too late. If we surrender, our slaughter is inescapable. We must make a way or find one. The floor is open for ideas, plans, and hard-line discussion on how we are to proceed to break this endless conflict." Captain Batun, a young firebrand, stood up and eagerly began, "Your majesty and all the great men seated at this gathering—I believe our best protection is a daring attack. The longer we wait, the weaker we get. The season favors our enemy camped outside our gate and out of range of our deadly darts. If given enough time, David will gather a still greater army and easily overwhelm our weakened resolve from the lack of food and supplies. Even our wine stores are quickly evaporating. We could not hold back such a storm of overpowering numbers of determined men. I propose we make an all-out assault; either it will drive them away, or we will die in the attempt. It is better than perishing slowly from starvation while waiting for the bitter end."

The room went still; everyone was trying to digest this grand strategy, including the king.

Nemun, the chief captain, took a hard swallow and cleared his throat, "I admire young captain Batun's zeal and commitment to glory, and much that he said is thought-provoking. But, first of all, we do not know if David could muster any more soldiers. What we face might be his entire fighting force that encircles our city. So, I propose we start with a measured response, weakening the enemy by chipping away at their infantry and assaulting their morale with fear and frustration."

"Speak on," King Hanun insisted.

Chief Captain Nemun bowed in respect and pointed beyond the walls. "Our enemy stays well out of range, and we inflict no significant damage. We have tried increasing the reach of the arrows' arc forcefully launched by our strongest archers. But we still fall far short of the enemy's setback position. So, I propose that we lure them in closer and within range of our most deadly and accurate marksmen. In this way, we can start crushing their will to fight and reduce their superior numbers."

"Well, Nemun, that all sounds well and good. But how do you propose to bait your trap and bring them in close enough for our shafts to do their killing work? And please get on with it! I starve, and my head grows dull from pressing hunger." King Hanun demanded answers.

Chief Captain Nemun bowed his head and continued. "Please excuse my long-winded explanation, Your Majesty. I am sorry for taking up so much of your precious time." Nemun cleared his throat to hide his disdain for pampered royalty and promptly continued. "We will open the gate just before first light and stack the army in battle formation, drawing the Israelites into battle and in range of our stinging deadly barbs. We used this tactic once before luring Israel into battle right outside our doors, and then at the perfect moment, Syrian chariots surprised them. They barely escaped, slithering away like a wounded snake back over the Jordan and to safety. We have no allies to assist us, and we need cunning and patience."

Hanun pondered the suggestion and questioned, "What if our forces are overwhelmed before we can close the gates?"

Nemun had considered that possibility and was quick to answer, "I will train the men to retreat at my signal. Then, each man will swiftly file back through the narrowing opening, leaving only enough space for the last man to pass through. Meanwhile, the archers will cover their withdrawal by raining death and destruction from the battlements."

King Hanun roared, "Make it so," and briskly hurried off, a slave to his appetites and passions.

The crowing of the morning cock foreshadowed the coming of menacing events. The moment's quiet peace was abruptly shattered by the shofar horns' bone-chilling blast summoning Israel into the fray of battle.

Joab summoned Abishai, saying, "Gather up your men, leaving only the fewest as possible to secure the outer walls of the city; come swiftly, and be ready for combat."

Abishai came running, turning toward the open field to witness the Ammonite army protecting the central causeway in full array. "What...do...we...have...here?" Abishai, now gulping for air, spoke out to Joab. "It looks like our patient wait has borne fruit, low hanging, and ripe for the plucking. What say you, brother?"

"Well said, brother. It does appear that our tiresome stalemate is over. None too soon, I might add! Our dear uncle, the king, has been pressing hard for a swift end to this conflict. David's complaint is the rising cost of maintaining an army in the field, and he grows weary of failure and excuses. The deadly quills of the Ammonite bowmen give me pause, but we must assault and prevail, whatever the cost."

"Whatever the cost, brother?" Abishai questioned.

"Yes, whatever the cost," Joab said, echoing Abishai's words.

"Let us form ranks, with every spearman having a shield-bearing swordsman at his shoulder, and, lastly, our bowmen countering the enemy archers high on top of the parapets. We must engage fiercely, so have ladders and scaling ropes at the ready, and pray that our shields shelter us from the iron rain. We will attack in waves."

A great blast from a chorus of shofar horns echoed back with a booming drumbeat from the Ammonite high corridors. Israel advanced, swords drawn, spears leveled, and bowmen at the ready.

Uriah stepped up to the very forefront and positioned himself to be the point of the column. The Ammonite archers let loose of their tight sinew bowstrings the moment Israel was in range. A swarm of arrows blackened the blue morning sky, raining down death and destruction with each barrage. The shields afforded little or no protection against the falling barbs until a resounding clash of iron weapons and determined men formed a swirling melee of kicked-up dust and dark spurting blood. The yells and screams of fighting men so close as to obscure friend from foe quelled the deadly darts in hesitant restraint. Joab's bowmen covered the walls with shafts of their own, opposing the sureness of the enemy's stinging strikes.

The shofar sounded the withdrawal signal; the Israelite losses were substantial, but the enemy was also bloodied. The Ammonite army quickly slipped behind their protective red-granite walls as their massive gate shut with the groan of men and a thud from the locking bolt.

After retreating beyond the range of archers, Joab called forth his brother and co-captain Abishai for a tally of their losses and to decide their next best course of action. "Well, brother, I think our losses are acceptable, and we have drawn the enemy out of their stronghold. But, to our good fortune, I believe their resolve is starting to waver."

Abishai countered, "Perhaps, brother, but as we have drawn them out, they have drawn us in. We will need some success to report back to our impatient uncle. His confidence weakens with our dubious stalemate. So let us try a new ploy. We can send in a smaller force and have them hastily retreat, drawing out the enemy. We can hide our main body in the underbrush and out of reach and range of their killer flying spikes."

Joab keenly agreed. "Yes, yes—the very next time they show themselves, we will put your plan into action.

"Let us prepare the men immediately after retrieving and burying our dead. By the way, brother, I was much impressed with one of the men. He led the first assault and was the last to leave the field, covered in dust and blood. He fought to the very final thrust of the sword."

Abishai nodded. "Yes, I, too, witnessed this hero's feat of courage. He is Uriah the Hittite."

"So be it. David is looking for any good news from this long siege. I will send him a dispatch and tell him of our headway— and that, soon, we will be celebrating victory over the City of Waters. I will include the name of Uriah the Hittite as a mighty man of valor, and this will give David some assurance that we are doing our utmost to end this costly invasion."

CHAPTER THIRTY-SIX

Adultery, Twice Wise, Once Removed

Bathsheba and her maidservant Almah appeared unexpectedly at the king's private entrance, a rear portion of the palace shrouded in shadows purposely obscured from the general view. It was a discreet portal, neatly hidden away from prying eyes and public inspection.

The posted guards instantly pulled in their crossed spears, welcoming the regular and familiar callers. The senior guard bowed his head in recognition and said, "Ladies, please follow me, and allow me to escort you to the king's apartments."

David was made aware of the instant of Bathsheba's arrival, per his standing order. But, when learning of his illicit mistress's presence, David abruptly dismissed all in attendance and rushed as only a man in love would do.

David gave Almah a sharp look upon entering the room, indicating her presence was neither needed nor welcomed. Bathsheba, taking the cue from her lover's obvious displeasure, gently directed her faithful maidservant: "Almah, please leave us;

go to the scullery, eat your fill, and then retreat to the servants' quarters; rest there until summoned." Almah lowered her eyes, bowed in respect to the king, and then quickly departed into the dimly lit corridor.

David swept across the room, attempting to embrace his current obsession, only to encounter the back of her displeasure. Then, sensing a chill in the air, David inquired as to Bathsheba's apparent displeasure.

"My most adored and coveted lover, what seems to be the problem? Have I done or said something that has made me lose favor in your eyes? Please confide in me, and by all that is holy, I will make it right and so that, once again, we can be carried away in love's tender embraces."

Bathsheba blushed, as if still an innocent virgin, and whispered, "My loving prince, your words reach deep down to my essence, and my womanhood cries out that my soul has found its other half. I would rather kill myself than cause you harm or foul distress. But I do not know any other way to cushion the blow, my love, so I will just come out and say it. I'm with child, your child, and of this, there is no question nor room for doubt."

David grew brooding and silent; he stepped away to fix his gaze on a sprawling vista afforded to him by an open window. The room became heavy with words unspoken. David pondered the fate of four souls pushing hard against the walls of his mind. The wrestling subsided, and finally, David took a deep breath and exhaled a sigh of decision, his head nodding in agreement from an inner and unsettling conversation.

He walked over purposely to where Bathsheba was sitting silently on the bed. She was anxiously biting her lip and battling her inner demons. David lovingly took her hand and began, "My dearest lady, a new life is precious in the sight of God, and for that, I'm glad that you are carrying my seed. I must confess that I should not be all that surprised, accounting for our frequent lovemaking and the tender depths of our desire. Our chances have now become a certainty. The rub is that your husband has been away too long from both Jerusalem and your marital bed. When your conception begins to blossom, the finger-pointing and month-counting will commence in earnest. First, the wagging tongues of washwomen will hang in the marketplace of gossipmongers. Then, in a single day, it will fill the ears of commoners, priests, and prophets alike throughout Israel. The speed of spread will astound you, for the only thing that travels faster than bad news is good gossip.

"As the king, I am accountable only to God and God's punishments. Nathan, the prophet, has the power to scorn me and bring terrible anguish to my soul with the sword of his mouth and the fierceness of his scorn, But you, my endangered love sprite, are subject to Israel's laws, or rather the law of Moses. That would mean a stoning. Nathan, in time, may become well aware of our illicit affair. He will indeed demand a stoning and put the evil out of Israel. Your pregnancy will not dismiss the sentence of death. On the contrary, it will only help to confirm our infidelity. I will not be able to extend a wing of protection to shield you from his judgment, for Nathan is God's appointed messenger on earth, and to oppose or to bar him would be a sacrilege."

Bathsheba, fearful and troubled, questioned, "What now, my love? My life and your integrity hang in the balance, and it all rests on your next decision. Are you as wise as you are cunning? Are you then twice blessed to rise above this challenge?"

David stood poised and regal, silent, and pleased to have the support of his mistress. "My dear Bathsheba, you know me too well, for we will face this battle together, and with your needed and vital assistance, our successful collaboration is inevitable. You will be my sling, and I will be your rock."

"Sometimes, the fates are kind and right on time. Luckily, I have recently received a dispatch from Joab, my nephew and chief captain, about his progress—or should I say *lack of it*—the siege of Rabbah, Ammon's capital city.

"In Joab's message, your absentee husband Uriah has distinguished himself as a fierce and tenacious warrior, the first to enter the battle and the last to leave; it is almost as if he has a death wish."

Bathsheba, bothered and bewildered, was burning red at the mention of her lawful husband; it was a stinging reminder of her current dilemma and the mounting burden of guilt and shame that she now must carry. She pondered the second crisis of her life brought on by the only two men she had ever known carnally.

She snapped back, "Why tell me all this?"

David acknowledged her distress with a gentle caress of her cheek and explained, "Please, my dear, bear with me. I believe I have a kernel of a plan. Firstly, I can invite Uriah back to Jerusalem and reward him for his courage in battle. I can also bestow upon him the title of a fearless warrior of Israel and install him as one of my esteemed 'Mighties.' I will then honor him with a feast of meats and an abundance of wine. Then, at the proper time, I will give him my approval and a whole bushel of delicacies to share with you when he spends the night under your roof and in the intimate comfort of your bed."

David's speaking slowed, and he stood behind her, speaking in quiet and measured tones. "My dear, this is where your heart's sacrifice finds its place upon the altar of motherhood and in the avoidance of your certain execution. I will give Uriah leave to spend the night with you, his alluring and beautiful wife. I am reluctant even to suggest this desperate request. I do so only to save your life and the life of our unborn child—notwithstanding the ill repute that will be inevitably cast upon me, the nation's beloved sovereign."

Everything came in a sudden rush. Bathsheba saw that David, as the king, had nothing to fear—no matter what—but she would have to lie, cheat, and seduce a man who was almost a stranger, and be unfaithful to the man she knew as her ardent lover. She turned to face him. David looked away from Bathsheba's grimaced face, which displayed that she was sullen, haunted, and unbearably saddened.

In a strained groan, he uttered, "I need you to seduce Uriah and consummate your night together in love's sweet surrender. For in doing so, it will belie any doubts as to who sired your child—avoiding scandal, retribution, and death."

Bathsheba pondered on the grave and deadly backlash of her refusal to play the legal harlot. She then decided that, if she denied Uriah or rejected David's proposal, her life and the life of her unborn child would be forfeited. She sobbed in tearful regret—and then suddenly raged with a defiant yell. "What kind of man are you that would ask for such a thing—from a woman for whom he supposedly confessed of having an undying and eternal love?" She screamed in a way that could be heard in many quarters of the palace, beating her fists upon his steadfast chest and inflicting angry bruises.

David patiently bided his time, allowing Bathsheba's emotions to run wild and giving her ample time to exhaust her fire, praying that her unbridled passions would give way to logic, reason, and an overwhelming instinct for survival.

Bathsheba, thoroughly drained from her ordeal of conflicting desires, made her judgment and struck her bargain. At that moment, the weight of the world seemed to lift up and off of her shoulders. She threw back her head and dug down deep into a reservoir of resolve. Then, in a matter-of-fact voice, she declared, "I will, and I must engage in this deception for the well-being of my innocent baby. If for nothing else, my peace of mind and your sake, my beloved David, I will participate in this charade for good or for ill. Let us cast our fates together upon the grounds of dire necessity."

David was both pleased and relieved that a bridge of decision now cleared the way over troubled waters. He swiftly covered the distance between their two souls with the passion of action and took Bathsheba, still quivering, in his manly embrace. David eased her down, pliant and limp as a ragdoll, onto a goose-down couch. He gently began whispering sweetly in her ear, "My most perfect and beautiful angel, I know that we will be together forever, for I cannot live without you. You, Bathsheba, are the storm that fuels my desire for pleasure, happiness, and bliss. I am nothing without you and will protect you and nourish you for as long as I have breath in my lungs and eyes to see. I love you, my most darling Bathsheba."

Bathsheba swooned, and at once, their lovemaking commenced, angry, forceful, and soon glistening with sweat. Dawn found them still entwined, having exhausted the entire moonlit night in punishing and desperate lovemaking.

CHAPTER
THIRTY-SEVEN
Unlikely Travel Companions

David called forth his scribe and began dictating a dispatch calculated to achieve its intended effects of military pressure and crushing a personal scandal.

Chief Captain Joab,

Your siege of Rabbah remains much longer than I would have expected, as the Syrian chariots are no longer a threat. I was counting on your zeal for revenge from your prior and near-disastrous encounter. You and your brother Abishai barely made it out alive against the combined Ammonite and Syrian forces. I'd hoped that your memory of that sting would have spurred you on to greater resolve for a quick and decisive victory. I need not remind you that keeping an army in the field is a costly and troublesome affair. My advice to you, my two valued nephews, is to redouble your efforts and bring this episode to a timely end, with King Hanun's head passing through the brick kiln on a fitting plate.

On a lighter note, Israel needs some good news coming from the front. You had mentioned a hero in your ranks. A recently converted Hittite named Uriah—I believe that is his name. I would have you send him back to Jerusalem, so I can reward him for his courage in the nation's cause with a title of recognition, with a feast and some rest at home, in his honor. Then, I shall prepare for his homecoming into the capital. I will await his arrival a week after your receipt of this order.

David Ben Jesse

King of Judah and Israel.

A panting runner, covered in dust and known for his speed, barreled headlong into the Israeli camp with pressing news from Jerusalem. After passing through the outer guards, he began shouting, "An urgent message from the king to Chief Captain Joab." The command tent's flap carefully parted as Joab's head peered out to view the rousing crier. Joab stepped out of the shadows, closely followed by Abishai, his brother. "Here, Malak," Joab called out and reached out for the dispatch. The courier bent a knee in respect and handed off the king's urgent message.

"Shall I wait for your reply?" Malak, the king's runner, dutifully inquired.

Joab, not looking up, said, "Yes, yes. Go and rest in the mess tent. Get some food and wine and be at the ready for my summons." Then, raising his voice, he turned to the captain of the guard and commanded, "See to it." Joab slipped back into the privacy of the tent, with Abishai close behind him.

Abishai, looking over Joab's shoulder, probed, "What does it say, brother? Is it the same demand that we finish up this unending invasion because it drains his coffers and lessens his treasure?"

"Yes, that, too,' Joab replied after reading, "but this time, he has also made an unusual request. He wants Uriah, the Hittite, sent back to Jerusalem to reward him and promote his gallantry in battle.

"I do not recollect such a request before, do you, brother?"

Abishai shook his head "No," shrugged his shoulders, and questioned, "I know our uncle's cunning, and so there is some other reason for this ploy."

"Yes, to take a man out of the field of battle before its conclusion is most unusual, and it is very unlike him." Joab rightly defended. "But we have never had a siege this long, not like this, and perhaps Uriah is needed to improve morale or encourage the miserly princes to pledge money to keep us in the field. But be that as it may, he sounded most insistent. Call Uriah, and make him ready for travel. He can leave in the morning with the king's messenger. Uriah can tell David in person about the challenges we face."

Uriah regarded the summons and reported immediately to Joab. Joab, direct as usual, began, "I have a special mission for you, Uriah. The king has commanded your presence in Jerusalem."

Uriah, surprised and puzzled, uttered, "Me, lord? Why me? I do not wish to leave the siege. Besides, the men expect me to be at the very forefront of battle."

Joab sternly replied, "This is not a request. Your name and exploits stood expressly mentioned in the king's dispatch. Your fearlessness and courage have not gone unnoticed. The king will also inquire how I am doing as your leader. For instance, he will ask if the army thrives in its resolve and does the war proceed to ensure a certain victory? The king also wants to honor you and, by doing so, inspire the people, for they grow weary of this lingering deadlock, and they need to rally around a hero, and the hero of the moment is you!

"The king will question you as to our performance and successes. Be forthright and decisive. Tell him we are making progress and that it's just a matter of time and more supplies of food, wine, shafts, and spears. Press the need for more men. Heroes are always well received, and it persuades the people to invest in the king's coming victory."

Uriah bowed, resigned to his fate, and went off to prepare an uncertain homecoming.

Uriah had a sleepless night, searching for the depths of humility and understanding; he reported as ordered at Joab's command tent. The king's messenger already stood ready and eager to depart.

Joab, warding off the morning chill from the embers of a steaming porridge cooking pot, rose to greet Uriah. "Uriah the Hittite, this is Malak ben Irmia, your guide." Both men nodded their greeting.

Joab went on, "Malak will escort you to the house of the king—where you need to be presented by week's end. Time is pressing, so all possible speed is necessary. Malak, you escort him along the best and fastest route to avoid bandits, liars, wolves, and lions. Uriah, King David did not say how long your visit was to be, so I was hoping you would return as soon as the king gives you leave, for you are the point of my spear and the edge of my sword. Your hunger for the struggle stirs the men to greater feats of daring and courage. May God bless your travels."

Both men offered a salute of respect, and with that, they were off in a fast-paced gait.

Malak, with lungs like bellows and legs like iron bands, kept up a feverish tempo. He slowed only long enough for Uriah to catch his second wind. Uriah doggedly attempted to match Malak's breakneck pace, but to no avail; he continued to lose ground to the king's fleet messenger. Not a breath was squandered or wasted in idle chatter. Rounding a rise and trying to outrun sundown, Malak luckily spotted a rocky outcropping on the top of a nearby hill. He breathed out, "This would be a safe stopover with partial relief from the wind and a promise of a good night's shelter."

Malak at once began scouring the landscape for wood, brush, and branches. Meanwhile, Uriah sat panting, attempting to retrieve his breath and strength. Dry kindling quickly took Malak's spark as the two men gathered stones for encircling the blaze; the stones helped the fire radiate warmth and lessen the night's cloudless chilling invasion. Rocks and sharp pebbles were then carefully removed, clearing a place to spread ground-covering branches. Rations of dried meat and unleavened bread quickly eased the pangs of hunger.

"I will take the first watch, and you, Uriah, the second, and so on until sunup," Malak declared. "We must keep alert and watchful. The crackle of burning timber and its flickering embers will keep beasts in the shadows, and only the most desperate of starving animals will approach men with fire. But, on the other hand, robbers and cutthroats perceive a small campfire as an opportunity for murder and plunder."

Malak questioned, "Uriah is a Hebrew name meaning, 'Yahweh is my light,' yes? But you are a Hittite of Canaan, which is a warrior tribe, at that. So how is that name even possible for a heathen? If you cared to confide, I would listen and keep your secret."

At first, Uriah hesitated but needed the ear of another and began in earnest. "I converted because I fell in love with a Hebrew maiden. I have suffered the cruelest cut, circumcised as an adult, to become a consecrated Hebrew. I had to make a vow to raise our unborn child by the law of Moses. I made a covenant with your Hebrew God and did so on my honor."

Malak questioned, "Boy or girl?

Uriah mournfully uttered, "It died too soon to tell, and the marriage has since become a fit of anger and despair, filled with rage and resentment. My father-in-law is Eliam, one of King David's Mighties. He is also a vested warrior, and so my recruitment into the army of God became fitting, proper, and certain. There are rumors and gossip close to home—and I dare not repeat them for fear that they might be true. My homecoming is fraught with suspicion and misgiving. But I accept myself to be a faithful follower of the almighty Hebrew God and remain the obedient servant to the anointed king of Israel, his servant, and my lord."

Uriah, needing to change the subject, inquired, "Malak, your name means Messenger of God. Is that true?"

"You are correct." Malak affirmed his proud name by throwing back his head and puffing up his chest. "I am the king's most trusted courier. I can crisscross the realm in a sprint without resting. It matters not whether in the heat of battle or heated political exchanges. When lives hang in the balance, I am he that the king seeks out to deliver his most critical and urgent messages."

A lone wolf howled in the distance at the rising of the moon. Malak answered with a "growl" of his own that echoed off the valley walls. "That will alert the pack that this territory is marked," he said casually. "I piddled on shrubs and bushes while gathering fuel for the fire. That will help to confuse the pack. The night wears on, and it is your time to rest. Tomorrow will be another test of your resolve and stamina. I will rouse you at the beginning of the second watch. So, have no doubt it is all God's will; however, it turns out, be at peace and sleep sound. Goodnight."

Uriah returned the "goodnight" and was asleep almost as fast as his head touched the ground.

Uriah pondered the vastness of creation at witnessing a shower of shooting stars in the quiet moments before sunrise. Smoldering embers reduced to smoke gave up the last of its warm glow just before dawn. Malak squinted the sleep from his eyes just as the sun revealed their remaining travel to Jerusalem and, for Uriah, a view to an uncertain homecoming.

The two men hungrily broke their fast with the meager rations of travel. Salted meat and thin, dry crackers washed down with a deep swig from a new wineskin. Malak pointed off to the horizon and said, "There is a brook a day's journey from here. If we can keep the same pace as yesterday, we will reach it before nightfall. We can clean up there and wash off the dust and the dirt of the wilderness. Then, on the next morrow, we will see the Milo spires of Jerusalem reaching the heavens. Our efforts will ensure a timely entrance and make your meeting with King David as expected. So let us be off and waste not a moment in idle chatter."

CHAPTER THIRTY-EIGHT

An Unfaithful Homecoming

Malak's travel strategy proved to be effective. All went well as both men ran stride for stride in perfect harmony. Uriah gained additional stamina and strength from his relentless struggle to keep up with Malak's grueling tempo. The effort to compete rewarded them with a timely arrival. As they approached the holy Hebrew capital, Uriah grumbled and murmured as if speaking to an inner demon. Then, sensing a conflict, Malak suggested, "Let us cool down before entering the king's presence, all breathless and dripping of sweat. Uriah, I must confess, I have noticed that the closer to our destination, the more you slip into distress. If you need to talk to someone, now is the time, and on my honor, what you confide in me will never darken my lips with poisonous gossip."

Uriah stopped dead in his tracks, and face to face with Malak, he started to unburden his pain and anguish. Downcast, he began,

"A vicious rumor from Jerusalem has pierced through to my heart." He stuttered, paused, and swallowed hard. "A man of great power and wealth is rumored to have bedded my wife in my absence. My beloved shuns me, but my love for her has only grown desperate during my absence. I dare not mention this great man's name, for I fear that the charge is true, and my life and the life of my wife will surely be forfeited if I tingle this adulterer's name in the wrong ears. I cannot face my wife—and pray this gray farce will be short-lived, so I can speedily get back to combat, where the black and white of life and death still makes perfect sense."

Malak stood quiet and unmoved, and, at length an uplifting nod. "You have spoken well, Uriah, no names mentioned. I pray that your burden lies lessened for the confession. All acclaim the glory of God, and our part is to fear him and keep his com-mandments. We are all part and parcel of a grand design, so let us proceed with awe and respect and keep the faith come what may, glory or trouble: God's will be done."

Their journey nearly completed, the king's messenger and his prized escort approached the seven hills of Jerusalem. The outer rim ushered in a magnificent view of the ancient city of prophets. David's prominent citadel of protection reflected high above Mount Zion. The morning sun rose high over the horizon and gave the capital a gleaming golden halo, confirming God's chosen people a place of power and protection.

Sentries, tax collectors, and a horde of lame, blind, and rag-wearing beggars swarmed the Jerusalem entrance. The two travelers recoiled from the discord of competing noises. Babies were crying and barkers yelling, and all were vying for attention over the deafening din of a bustling urban trade metropolis. The sweet smell of exotic perfumes mixed with the burning fat from roasting lambs, and camel dung's pungent odor mingled with the Bedouin caravans' encrusted sweat.

The fierce-looking sentinels discouraged the likes of liars, thieves, and any suspicious characters. They also helped collect levies on all goods coming in or out of the city, especially when a strong arm was required to pick clean deep pockets of hidden shekels. Lastly, the ever-present open palms of the poor, sick, and afflicted sought the charity of pious alms to eke out the barest threads of living.

Malak saluted the chief guard, who at once recognized him as the king's special courier. "Malak, always good to see you. What business brings you to my gateway?"

Malak pointed, "This is Uriah the Hittite, and he has received a royal summons as befitting a champion. He is an esteemed warrior of Israel currently at the siege of Rabbah. I am to take him to the imperial residence immediately upon arrival to meet with the king so that he might receive a hero's welcome, abounding with glory and honor."

The supervisor stiffened in the presence of someone so highly regarded; he turned and commanded, in his most official voice, "You two men escort the king's emissary and his valued companion straight away to the king's mansion—and be quick about it!"

Through the teeming streets and back alleyways, the four men briskly stepped. All obstructions and crowds quickly parted in the name of the king's men on an urgent mission.

Crossed spears quickly straightened at the approach of familiar Hebrew uniforms. Malak shouted out, "I am the king's emissary escorting Uriah, the Hittite—expressly ordered to meet with

King David. I demand to be presented to our lord and deliver this hero, fulfilling my royal commission."

Malak dismissed their two attendants with a simple, "Thank you for making our way; now return to your essential inspections at the Golden gate."

Malak turned at once and spied a familiar servant, Ebed, beckoning them to the mansion's porch. The spirited fellow motioned with a sweeping arm gesture to follow him through the aromatic cedar-planked and winding corridors. Finally, the trio stopped at the king's receiving anteroom.

"Gentlemen," touted the head servant, "Please, take your rest and make yourself comfortable; it might be a wait before the king becomes available. I will have some of our best vintage wine to quench your thirst and goat cheese and unleavened bread to satisfy your hunger. Malak, who shall I say your companion is so that I can notify the king directly?"

Malak replied, with a nod and a wink, "This is none other than Uriah the Hittite, the hero of the siege of Rabbah, invited by the king to bestow upon him title and homage. I have escorted him to the king's house as ordered."

Ebed respectfully nodded, "I will go at once and try to locate the king. The mansion is vast, and it might take some time to find him. Please, if you gentlemen require anything, anything at all, please ring the bell located on the mantle." Saying that, the royal retainer disappeared into a maze of passageways.

An exhaustive search of the entire grounds commenced in earnest, and even other servants assisted in the hunt, but with no apparent success. The only possible place left was the king's private apartments, and it was forbidden to trespass there. *Malak did say it was urgent,* Ebed thought to himself as he tapped ever so lightly on the secluded bed-chamber entrance. No answer. *Perhaps the king does not abide.* Ebed, swallowing hard, increased the urgency and power of his strikes, but still no response. Half relieved, he turned to walk away.

In his most threatening voice, David questioned, "Who goes there and dares to disturb the king and risk his anger?"

The blood drained from Ebed's head, his knees buckled, and a cold chill brought on a shiver. "It is I, Ebed, your faithful servant."

The door slightly cracked open, revealing a squinting eye adjusting to the light. David, in a menacing tone, barked, "I know who you are—speak up, man, and get on with it before I lose my patience and run you through with a curtain rod." The threat met with a faint and barely audible giggle discreetly nestled in dark shadows.

Ebed, weak from stress, begged, "Your majesty, please forgive this unpardonable but unavoidable interruption."

"Yes, yes, go on," David said, growling his irritation.

Fearfully, Ebed cleared his throat and choked out, "Malak has returned with Uriah the Hittite in his care and custody. They now await you in the anteroom for an audience." A shrill gasp of a woman's voice was met with a powerful, "Shhhh." The small opening vanished with a loud snap followed by some muffled arguing and then a long silence. Ebed, fearful of speaking out of turn, waited dutifully for his master's voice.

Finally, after a long pause, David forcefully voiced through the slightly parted leaden door in a composed tone, his words sounding full and assured.

"Ebed!"

"Yes, I am here, my lord, waiting on your orders."

David, with renewed vigor, exclaimed, "Excellent! First, tell Uriah I am delighted at his safe return from the war, and I wish to speak to him privately about the conflict. So, on that note, inform Malak to depart from Uriah's company and make himself available until summoned. He can shelter in the adjoining servants' quarters. Lastly, I need a mess of fine-cut meats, a basket full, I think—no, make it two, and two helpers to follow Uriah to his home. Go make it so."

Ebed bowed to his sovereign's calculated message, slowly backing away and then scurrying off to inform the king's honored guest of his majesty's generosity.

"Don't you shush me," Bathsheba snipped. "You act as if nobody has ever noticed me. Am I not practically a fixture here, spending some days and most nights in your apartments? Our late-night feasts are provided by serving wenches: all the chambermaids that change our soiled bedding, butlers, guards, and the like. I imagine even the gardener has taken note of us rollicking in the flower beds. Do you think they all are blind to the ways of the world? Do you believe that they don't know what is going on? Please!" Bathsheba, bold as ever, demanded an answer.

David, the ever-cunning tactician, gently responded to her outburst. "My darling girl, I know you are upset for the moment because love's cruel sacrifice has arrived in the guise of your long-absent husband. We had discussed all the possible lethal consequences of adultery in Israel. Your death and the death of our unborn child hang in the balance if Nathan, the prophet, discovers our illicit affair. It would be your ending and my disgraceful humiliation in the sight of all Israel. If caught spreading gossip or malicious rumors about the king's private business, I would not be too concerned about the servant's wagging tongues. To speak of the king's intimate life is considered a treasonous act, at once met with execution, no questions asked. The servants look, but do not see; they hear, but do not listen."

David dressed and then confessed, "I must go and meet with Uriah, at least, to make the pretense of interest in how the war progresses."

Bathsheba was downcast but resigned herself to the part she must play in this deadly deception. David, in a gesture of kindness, encircled his arms all around her in tender support. He held her long and ever so tightly until she started to quake with passion. Their parting moments lingered, as they had often begun their days, as of late, with angry and desperate lovemaking.

David finally had met a woman who matched his unquenchable appetite for life and living; Uriah could wait a little longer.

CHAPTER THIRTY-NINE
A Reclusive Reunion

David basked in Bathsheba's loving embrace just as long as he dared—for time stands still when Venus's muse sings her beguiling song of forbidden love. He quickly rose to touch up with cloaking perfume and lightly brushed hair—all in a vain attempt to mask lovemaking's unkempt look and revealing telltale sweat.

David would lull this cuckolded dupe, Uriah, for the unwitting acceptance of fatherhood of his and Bathsheba's unborn child. He would accomplish this by employing practical questions on "how best to capture Rabbah" over a relaxed and disarming conversation.

The recruitment of Bathsheba's captivating charms would make the deception a certainty. "Bathsheba, my love, now go and prepare for your painful and needful seduction." David gently whispered, "I will encourage Uriah to deliver a plentiful supply of sweetmeats for your indulgent pleasure. The tasty aroma of the king's bounty will subtly increase his appetite, hastening his steps to home and hearth while heightening his hunger to feast in your bed. I do this also in the hopes of reminding you of my love for you and that it might soften the blow to your splintered emotions. I pray that this will help lessen your disdain for your artificial abandon to another man's lust—husband or not."

David confidently navigated the cedar-planked corridors to his courtly anteroom to pacify his prey and do honor to his guest. He stood silently at the opening, witnessing Uriah, who had finally surrendered to the day's stressful events. But consequently, David's calculated abandonment only heightened the weary hours of waiting, proved by Uriah's deep breathing and uneasy snoring.

David thundered, "Uriah," and again, he shouted even louder.

Uriah roused as if struck by lightning. He sat straight up with a start and inhaled a short and shallow gulp of air. His blurry eyes fought against the bright light coming from a nearby window. The weary traveler strained to focus on the imposing figure silhouetted and filling the archway opening.

Then, in a regal tone, David announced himself: "I am David Ben Jesse, king of Judah and Israel. You are Uriah, a converted Hebrew from the Hittite clan, and from birth to dirt a Canaanite."

Uriah, only half-awake and with a frog in his throat, bowed, swallowed hard, and nodded in agreement.

David continued without a pause. "I understand you are a married man, and your wife's name is Bathsheba, daughter of Eliam, and granddaughter of Ahithophel, the oracle. You are currently engaged in the deadly siege of the City of Waters, or Rabbah, the secure capital Royal City of Ammon. A recent dispatch from my nephew Joab, my chief captain, and Abishai, his brother, the co-commander, have cited you as a fearless hero of Israel. Have I spoken correctly, Uriah, the Hittite?"

Uriah, finding his voice, replied, "All is as you have said, my lord king, except my portion of being a hero. I do my duty to the best of my abilities. When I focus on the moment's conflict in the midst of raging combat, as strange as it might sound, I find a heightened state of awareness. The struggle puts my mind at ease, for all other thoughts vanish when living on the edge of life and death."

Inwardly surprised, David confessed, "Well spoken. You are a man after my own heart, cut from a similar bolt of cloth. You are a soldier that has no fear and so lacks the crutch of courage. Courage is the temporary backbone for a struggling coward in need to show his heart to himself, proven in the eyes of his fellows." David now thought better of the man, and his soul pinched at his evil design. Nevertheless, there was no going back, for the arrow of deceit was in flight, and the double-dealing dog was about to bite.

Continuing his charade, David inquired, "Tell me, Hittite, warrior of Israel, how do you perceive my nephew Joab's abilities in his efforts and strategies in the prosecution of this costly and seemingly endless conflict? Do you see an end to it? How do the people fare? Is their morale unflagging, or do the men lack solidarity? Speak up and speak plainly; your words will not pass my inspection unattended." David was cleverly attempting to cross a bridge of intimacy and trust.

Uriah paused, collecting his thoughts. What could he say to the king about his favored nephew and Israel's chief captain? Surely nothing critical or disparaging.

Uriah looked David straight in the eye and confidently began, "Joab is a highly resourceful general and always considers the best strategy before committing men to battle. Chief Captain

Joab attempts to seize the moment and exploit every advantage. The problem, lord king, is the enemy's wealth of arrows. Every time we storm the fortified entrance, the deadly shafts blacken the sky. When we slice through their first rank of steadfast warriors protecting the gate, their sharp barbs descend in a blinding hailstorm of death. Once halted, our attacks provide the remaining defenders time enough to hurry back behind their fortified walls. We are making progress, but what persists is a gnawing conflict of attrition.

"Well, as far as the men are concerned, soldiers always like to grumble. It relieves tension and boredom. After all, their chosen lot in life is to court death in faraway places.

"Although, the wine, food, and sundries ease their suffering of living in an open field. The men praise your name for your support and remain unwavering in their resolve to win the day for God, king, and country."

Uriah's insights fascinated David, and he said as much. "Well done—you are indeed a fellow man of war. You have given me much to ponder.

"I have a fitting reward for your service. It has come to my understanding that you have an extremely appealing wife and that her beauty is so alluring that it drives men mad with passion. The story is that she possesses the body of a goddess, the face of an angel, and the most delightful and elegant turned ankles. You are a lucky man, Uriah." David could feel a stirring just from describing his lustful mistress. David thought quickly and absentmindedly continued,

"What was her name, again?" he uttered, with as much pretended innocence as he could muster.

Uriah's brow lifted, witnessing the intimate details of his wife exciting the teller. "Her name is Bathsheba," Uriah whispered guardedly.

"Yes, yes, that's right. I almost forgot." David's face flushed, just a tinge of being an inexperienced liar. He took a deep, uncomfortable breath to regain his thoughts and maintain a more regal composure. Then, he continued, "Uriah, you will not dine with me this night or here in the mansion. Go down to your house, wash your feet, relieve the dust and sweat of stress, and relax." David rang the servant's bell located on the mantle. Ebed, the head servant, appeared as if by magic.

"Ebed, have you prepared the mess of meat and the exquisite delicacies that will follow Uriah back to his home?" David inquired.

"Yes, your majesty, even the ashishot, or sweet cake; all is as you commanded. The servants and their aromatic steaming pots await Uriah's departure."

Ebed bowed low.

David gave a knowing wink to Uriah and coyly said, "Take this feast home to your beautiful wife with my compliments, from the king, and with my good wishes. Ah, yes, and it almost slipped my mind. Tomorrow at sundown, I have planned a banquet in your honor. I was hoping you could share your heroism and so flatter my visiting dignitaries of wealth and station. Your prominent presence will help me to raise shekels for my ever-emptying war chest.

"Bring your wife if you have a mind to—or leave her at home, longing for your swift and safe return. Now go and enjoy a night in your warm marital bed far from biting snakes, stinging scorpions, and the unforgiving cold, hard rocky ground. Farewell until then." David departed, smiling confidently at the future success of his gambit.

Ebed guided Uriah through the maze of passageways, followed closely by the two feast-bearing porters. Passing the door of the servants' quarters, Uriah felt a cold chill, and his feet began to freeze in place.

Ebed pointed to the outlet at the end of the corridor. He firmly addressed the two overloaded custodians: "Follow this gentleman, and deliver the foodstuffs to the place of his choosing. Then return in haste to help prepare for the upcoming royal banquet." Ebed bowed and asked, "Is there anything else, honored guest?"

Uriah turned his face and hoarsely whispered a thin, "No."

Ebed then rushed off to organize tomorrow evening's festivities.

"Uriah," a familiar voice echoed from deep within the servants' quarters.

Uriah, at once, recognized the raspy voice and said so, "Is that you, Malak?"

At once, Malak's head pushed out from behind the shadows. Malak, squinting his eyes in surprise, declared, "What are you doing down here?"

Uriah turned to his two baggage handlers and instructed, "Put your burdens down, and wait here for my return." Uriah stepped inside the vacant servants' quarters, motioning Malak to follow him to a shielded alcove and so quieting his fears of being overheard. Uriah, feeling hopeless, questioned, "I require an experienced ear and some expert advice. Sadly, I do not have anyone else to help me navigate my dilemma of clashing emotions.

Malak peered around for any unwitting ears and eyes of spies. Malak assured Uriah, "I am the king's man, first and foremost, but I never have and will never divulge a confidence even on pain of death; speak on."

Uriah began, spilling out a torrent of emotions. "While on our journey, do you remember me speaking of a hateful rumor that a powerful man was bedding my wife, but I refrained from mentioning his name for lack of evidence?"

"Yes, I do so recall," Malak said, affirming his recollection.

Uriah looked around once again to ensure that no errant eavesdroppers lurked in the shadows and whispered, "I know now and without a doubt that the potent usurper of my wife's bed is David, the king himself."

Malak stepped back, shocked and dismayed, needing a moment for the accusation of betrayal to digest.

Malak stepped in, getting even closer to Uriah's ear and, in scarcely a whisper, warned, "Be more than careful of such an allegation. It is treasonous and quickly met with a beheading. It will be a strike so decisive that your head would hit the ground before your last words finished their sounding. How do you know for a certainty that it is David? What have you seen precisely with your own eyes?"

Uriah, his ire kindled, testily responded, "I have not walked in on the lovers in the act, if that is what you mean. Allow me to lay out my suspicions and see if you agree with me. First, the appalling camp gossip was my first hint of wrongdoing. Our long separation for these many mouths added weight to the possibility. But I did not know for sure until today.

"Not until after I spoke to the king personally. He described my wife in lurid details and became physically aroused by his mischievous telling. He then caught himself feigning innocence by asking, 'What is her name again?' Then he tried tempting me to bed my wife and provided me a feast of meats and delicacies. He specifically ordered Bathsheba's favorite ashishot, or sweet cake, to be delivered by me to help in her seduction, and I fear to signal his complicity. I fear that all this grand deception is more than a simple adulterous affair and that there very well may be something hidden in my wife's belly, God forbid." Uriah choked, sweat and tears mingled on his cheek. "I cannot face my wife, for my spirit is broken into a thousand pieces, and my soul wavers on the precipice.

"I love King David, and I feel torn between duty, love, and country. I cannot and will not cross my wife's threshold, let alone dally in her arms. I look to you, Malak, to guide me once again on this, my most perilous journey of the heart. Yet, I am unable to think or act. As if my feet freeze to this very spot while an emotional whirlwind buffets my every action."

Malak listened intently and pondered all the details gushing forth like a pent-up torrent. Then, after a long pause, he concluded, "If what you say is correct and the king has all but ordered you to go home and sleep with your wife—if you refrain and disobey, what possible excuse could you use to justify your refusal? Suppose you accuse the king of infidelity, a capital offense. In that case, you will immediately suffer the king's wrath, and you would also put your wife under the killing stones of adulterous betrayal. Allow me a moment of reflection before I make such a life-and-death proposal." Malak paced around the edges of the servants' quarters in ever-tightening circles. He then confided, "Walking helps me to think." Then like a spark igniting a fire, he uttered, "Aha, try this—say this: 'The ark, and Israel, and Judah, abide in tents; my lord Joab and the servants of my lord are encamped in the open fields; shall I then go into my house, to eat and to drink, and to lie with my wife? As you live, and as your soul lives, I will not do this thing.'"

Uriah, completely dumbfounded, replied, "Who would believe such a thing?"

Malak further justified, "If you say it with passion and confidence, as if your life depended upon it, it will ring true enough. After all, it matters not what you say but how you say it; Uriah, anytime you do not want to do something, any excuse will do, no matter how absurd."

Uriah sighed in relief, grasping at the straws of a credible ruse that might even stretch for the truth. Malak's hollow alibi spared him from an inevitable clash with his unfaithful wife and the likely unfolding of a disastrous truth.

He then asked, "Where shall I sleep? I am exhausted from all this intrigue, and what shall I do with the king's mess of meats?

Malak, always one step ahead, quickly replied, "You will find rest right here in the servants' quarters. I will get you some fresh straw and a clean quilted comforter. You will enjoy the cushion of warmth and the security of having a roof over your head. So go and dismiss your porters. We will enjoy the sweetmeats right here. What we do not eat, the servants can feast on when they return from their labors. Except for the ashishot—it is also my favorite sweet cake; consider it a bounty for my help and advice."

Uriah agreed to the fee, exhaling, "So be it."

CHAPTER FORTY
A Seasoned Excuse

Farts, snores, and coughing bouts were routinely interrupted by the relief of yellow streams splashing into overflowing chamber pots. Uriah, restless nonetheless, tried to wrestle some peace out of his pallet. But awkwardly, the unbounded straw bunched up into lumps, leaving him unprotected on the cold stone floor.

Dawn found the servants well-fed and well-rested. Ebed was making his daily morning rounds, setting his charges with duties and chores. He barged through the open door, yelling orders and rousing the shirkers out of their featherbeds. To his utter surprise, he viewed Uriah in the very back of the room, dressing. The meat pots that he had so masterfully prepared now were emptied and overturned. The king's well-laid plans had gone astray, and there would be hell to pay.

Ebed went at once, scurrying to the king's private apartments. Fearful of disturbing the king yet a second time, he feared for his position and the inevitable tongue-lashing. Ebed gave a heavy rap of alarm, hard enough to skin his knuckles.

A voice, half in a yawn and half in anger, yelled out, "Who goes there, and it better be news of war or a fire!" David, in his nightshirt, gingerly swung open the door. "Oh, it is you, Ebed. No, not again. What is it this time?"

Ebed bowed low, filled with fear and trembling, and sheepishly uttered, "Your majesty, please excuse the disturbance. I have witnessed an unexpected guest whose presence needs to come to your attention. I would not have disturbed you, sire, unless I thought it both critical and urgent that you knew the whereabouts of this familiar but lingering lodger."

David snapped back, "Get on with it, old man, before I freeze to death."

Ebed blurted out. "Uriah, the Hittite did not go home last night. Instead, he fed the servants with your gift of bounty and then sheltered in their quarters."

David's morning chill quickly smoldered with the insult of a subtle plan gone awry. The bitter pill of failure and the sour grape of defeat are hard swallows for the lowly beggar and twice hard for the noble prince. Ebed waited patiently for the slap of misplaced outrage, but David checked his emotions.

Finally, the king composed himself and calmly instructed Ebed, "Go and find me a warm cloak and sandals. I will go down and question the cause of this disrespect and delay. Then, I would know Uriah's reasoning for upsetting my leave and generosity."

David entered through the back door of his house. Ebed was trailing far behind, unable to match the determined strides of the king's smoldering anxiety. Ebed doubled his pace and hurried ahead, and began directing the day's workflow, clearing the room of eavesdroppers and ensuring a private conversation.

335

David, God's Chosen Crucible

David sternly began, "Uriah, did you not just journey from a raging battle, and while engaged, were asked to eat small portions of tasteless food? Did you not sleep in the open field on barren dirt, roofless, and subject to rain, fog, and chill? Did you not have to fend off flying, slithering, and creeping creatures that bite in the night? Then tell me, Uriah, why did you not go to your house and feast on the mess of meats and delicacies I generously provided? Why did you not take a rest in your familiar bed, gathering warmth and comfort from your beautiful wife?"

Uriah stood his ground, mustering his nerve to satisfy the king's critical inquiry, and countered, "All is as you have described, sire. But does not the ark, the soldiers of Israel, and Judah shelter in tents? Does not my lord Joab, the host's chief captain, and all the king's servants remain encamped and exposed in the open field? Then how can I go into my house to eat, drink, and lie with my wife in good conscience? As my sovereign lives and breathes, and as my soul is alive in me, I will not—and cannot—do this thing."

David could not and would not challenge Uriah's heartfelt plea but instead attempted a slight consolation, "Well said, and I now completely understand your reluctance. But remember, you have only a day or so before I permit you to depart back to the conflict. So, Uriah, at least try to relax enough to reconsider your self-defeating behavior. It is a special occasion. Your needs surely outweigh your mistaken sense of duty and your empathy for the lack and misery of your comrades.

"Do I need to remind you, Uriah, that this evening's planned banquet is in your honor? I require you to stay close and remain within the borders of the compound. I do not want to take the chance that you might get it into your head to go wandering off.

Your absence would leave me looking foolish, trying to explain to my honored guests that my promised hero has gone astray. Malak can show you around the grounds and be your guide for the day." David gave the slightest nod, making eye contact with Malak, and enticed, "The garden pond is quite beautiful this time of year; it is still, deep, and peacefully reflective. So, Ebed, please see to our honored guests' breakfast. After you see to their needs, report back at once to my private study. I have a pressing matter requiring your swiftness and discretion. Gentlemen, until tonight, enjoy your day. I am off to the never-ending affairs of state. She is a relentless taskmistress and a demanding wench at best."

All bowed in respect as David left hastily, craving to get back to his writing desk to compose a private message of explanation.

Dearest Bathsheba,

I cannot imagine your confusion and distress at Uriah's unexplained absence. A loveliness such as yours is certainly not accustomed to being left waiting by the wayside. Any man in his right mind and has eyes to see could not refrain from savoring the nearness of your company. Please allow me, my darling girl, to put your concerns to rest. I had not fed him during my rigorous questioning as to the prosecution of the war. Instead, I had a mess of meats and delicious delicacies made ready to deliver, along with your long-separated husband. I thought this would help speed Uriah on his way to hearth and home and eventually to your sacrificial bed. He was on his way as far as I knew, and everything we had planned was falling into place.

This morning, I was alerted that he had gifted the feast to the servants and slept at the king's door. I confronted Uriah, still in my nightshirt. I said, "Why have you insulted my gifts of a generous feast and leave to find comfort in the arms of your wife?"

He replied, "But does not the Ark, the soldiers of Israel, and Judah shelter in tents? Does not my lord Joab, the host's chief captain, and all the king servants remain encamped and exposed in the open field? Can I go into my house to eat and drink and lie with my wife in good conscience? As my sovereign lives and breathes, and as my soul is alive in me, I will not and cannot do this thing."

I had no choice but to suppose that his words were sincere. But please allow me, my darling girl, to put your fears to rest.

Tonight, I am hosting a banquet in Uriah's honor. I will sway him with dark red wine and lessen his reluctance to seek delight in your enticing charms. I will whisper in his ear of a husband's duty and the fulfilling pleasures of women. So, as much as it pains me, my almond-eyed beauty, prepare yourself for a late-night caller this very night. If perchance, Uriah remains stubborn and doggedly refuses my promptings, either way, he will leave Jerusalem tomorrow. Uriah will depart, first light, and he will no longer be our vexing problem.

I hunger for your swift return to our well-appointed love nest and will not wait a moment longer. But, instead, I plan to send him back to combat, where life and death hang by a thread. Enough said.

Inform the messenger of your receipt and agreement.

Your loving prince, David

Ebed lightly knocked at the door just as David placed his final stroke to his message of comfort and warning.

David called out, "Ebed, come in. I would know your soft tapping anywhere." David pressed his royal seal on the rolled papyrus. "Ebed, I realize you are already aware that the king's seal means for the receiver's eyes only. In this instance, it is Lady

Bathsheba. Her home is in the old Benjamite quarter. You had accompanied me there one night. Do you recall its exact location? Things look different in the daylight."

Ebed confidently replied, "Yes, your majesty. I know the house, and I am well aware of your need for complete discretion."

David exclaimed, "Excellent, my good and faithful servant. Take the backstreets, blend in, and move quickly. Once you have entered the house, give the message only to Bathsheba, and tell her that you will stand ready for her answer. Do you have any questions?"

Ebed firmly responded, "No, your majesty, all is understood, and consider it undertaken just as you have instructed." He put the king's message in his pouch and bowed slowly, backing out. Ebed quickly vanished, a devoted agent on a secret mission.

Ebed, heavily hooded, stepped hurriedly through the crowded streets, focusing on his feet and avoiding eye contact.

Bathsheba entered her home, followed by two servant girls loaded down with foodstuffs from the market. Ebed, catching his breath, called out just before the door locked both him and his alarming words, "Lady Bathsheba!

"Please kind lady; excuse my intrusion; I have an urgent message for your eyes only from the highest authority!" Ebed patted his dispatch pouch. "I know you—Ebed, isn't it?" Bathsheba asked.

"Yes, madam, it is I." Ebed bowed. "Then you know who sent me, and if we could have total privacy so that I may deliver my master's intimate reflections."

Next, Bathsheba addressed the two maids, "Ladies, please give us a moment, and close the door behind you." Both women curtsied and quickly departed.

"All right, we are alone. What would you have for me?"

Ebed drew out David's personal and sealed post and handed it to Bathsheba, saying, "I am to stand by for your reply, as commanded."

Bathsheba broke the seal and unfurled the scroll; she began carefully studying the tone and intent of the message. Before concluding, she shook her head and, under her breath, whispered, "Who would believe such a thing? So, Uriah prefers to suffer and not seek comfort in the arms of a lover. All because the Ark of the Covenant lies under a flimsy cover, and his comrades live in a tent?"

Bathsheba completed her reading and conceded, "Tell your master I agree and will prepare for this evening's repulsive encounter, once again. Please convey my displeasure to the king, and do not mince my words with honey to sweeten the poison."

Ebed bowed and agreed, "Yes, madam, entirely as you have spoken. Thank you, my lady, and if I might say for the king, thank you for your gracious understanding." He bowed and exited smartly, hurrying back to the mansion, mission accomplished.

She then took the scroll into the scullery and threw it in the fire.

David had just finished his noonday meal, his belly satisfied. He headed up to his apartments for a nap to refresh himself for tonight's celebration.

Ebed, suddenly turning a corner, almost collided with the king. Ebed was panting and trying to catch his breath from his frantic dash through the back alleys of Jerusalem. He came up short, "A thousand pardons, your majesty. I sprinted back just as fast as my legs would carry me. I have completed my task, and I am ready to report."

David was pleased with the swiftness and praised Ebed's diligence. "Outstanding—come in, and close the door. Now tell me, what was her reply to my promptings?"

Ebed breathed out, "I will attempt an exact word-for-word repetition, as I had promised, and my lady insisted. 'Tell your master that I agree and will prepare for this evening's revolting encounter, once again.'"

"Ebed—think, man: Did she say anything else?"

Ebed shook his head "No," and then he paused, "Well, not directly to me anyway, but she did murmur something to herself, and it was faint, barely a whisper."

David's curiosity was piqued. "Speak up, man—what did you hear?"

Ebed said, "As best as I can recollect, she shook her head in puzzlement and mocked, 'Who would believe such a thing, and something about a flimsy covered Ark?' That is all I know."

Of course, David knew what she meant at once. Uriah had given him a flimsy excuse to cover the truth, but he kept that thought to himself.

David's driving concern was tonight's extravagant banquet. He expected that he could press Uriah into finding his way back home and to the comfort of his estranged wife's reluctant bed.

David directed, "Ebed, go see to the preparations for this evening's festivities. I am counting on you to make it a well-appointed affair with an abundance of dark red wine, sweetmeats, and exotic delicacies. Now I tire and need my rest—go, and do your magic. Ebed bowed and sped off, submitting to the king's every need, want, and desire.

CHAPTER FORTY-ONE
A Love or Death Conspiracy

The king's great hall overflowed with lively chatter from a crowd of Israeli and Judean nobles. Many wealthy merchants who could fill empty coffers were also in attendance. Dignitaries came from all over the realm to celebrate a hero's homecoming.

A banquet was a needed distraction from the everyday struggle for power and money. It also provided for the liberal solicitation of discreet royal favors. Moreover, it was a perfect excuse to eat and drink in excess on the king's tight-fisted shekel.

David, well-rested, arose from his bed at eventide as it was his custom. Ebed was busy laying out the king's formal attire when David inquired, "Is all prepared for my gala?"

"Yes, Your Majesty. You will be well pleased, with the careful attention to detail befitting your exalted station."

"I remind you, Ebed, that the devil might be in the cracks and crevices, but God is certainly in the details, and this is because, from small things, great beginnings come to pass."

David adjusted his finely polished crown and slipped his wrist through his bejeweled bracelet of authority—the very same trappings of power that had adorned Saul, the former king of Israel. David had one nagging doubt that his guest of honor would not appear as promised.

"Ebed, before making my entrance, I need to know Uriah is present; go and ensure his appearance!"

The head servant, wielding a knowing grin, cheerfully replied, "Uriah and Malak were among the first to arrive, and they seem to be enjoying deep cups of your dark red wine."

"Excellent—it is time to make my appearance. I need you to arrange that Uriah is seated next to me at the head of the table and has no other ears within hearing of my whispering. Most importantly, remember always to keep his cup full to the brim with my choicest vintage. Ebed, I also need you to fend off all intruders seeking my attention. I do not want to be disturbed or to have my private conversation interrupted. Go now—prepare all things as instructed, and make ready to herald my entrance. I will be along presently."

David perfumed himself and smoothed out all the wrinkles in his royal trappings. He then adjusted his crown for one last time before making his regal entrance.

David always felt like a man of destiny, ever since he was a child protecting the sheep in the wilderness. He defended them against the constant threat of lions, bears, and hungry wolves. He would suffer attacks by liars, poachers, and even other shepherds trying to replenish their thinning flocks during the dark of the night. David mused how these experiences had prepared him for the political intrigues of his fledgling nation's struggle for greatness. He saw himself as a man close to the heart of God and filled with His grace, mercy, and endless bounty. David had learned that his appearance was everything, especially in politics, and that he must always be ready to play the game, show up, and do his part. God was the director, and he, His player. But when it came to Bathsheba, his love compelled him to take a darker route. The life of his soulmate and their unborn child hung on the delicate threads of a spider's web.

The chamberlain pounded his stout wooden staff three times on the pitiless stone floors.

The alarming thuds echoed through the winding corridors. These attention-grabbing vibrations announced that David, the king of Israel and Judah, had just entered the bustling ballroom. All went silent as men bowed and women curtsied; all stood their ground waiting for the monarch's customary leave to sit back down.

David took his time greeting and thanking one and all for their turnout. The prince caught a glimpse of Uriah, standing to the right of his great seat of authority and in the place of honor, exactly where he wanted him. The closer to the king, the higher your rank, wealth, or influence.

After a second call to order, and after all whispering had ceased, David addressed the diverse gentry. "Ladies and gentlemen of rank and station, welcome to my home to share in this joyous occasion. We are gathered here for a twofold purpose.

"First and foremost, we gather here to pay tribute to Uriah the Hittite, a converted Canaanite who is now a fellow Hebrew soldier in the army of God. Uriah has proven himself on the field of battle to be a mighty man of valor." David directed Uriah to kneel. He then regally proclaimed, "Uriah. from this night forward, you stand promoted to my inner circle of 'Mighties.'" David's sword lightly tapped Uriah's shoulder. The prince hoisted his goblet and heartily announced, "I propose a toast in honor of Uriah the Hittite, our newest, fearless 'Mighty.'" The guests' cups quickly drained, and even before they emptied, David raised another round. "I proclaim that we are very near to the capture of the City of Waters. The royal citadel's riches will be ours for the taking. Please, all take your seats, and this brings me to my second reason for our gathering." Once everyone had found their place, David picked up the pace. "The long siege of Rabbah has significantly drained Israel's treasury, hampering our chances for victory.

"Need I remind you that we together have conquered Edom and Moab, which lie to our east and south, and have defeated Syria's threatening chariots from the north and east? The only kingdom that hampers the security of our entire eastern border is our old adversary, Ammon. Once their capital, the royal city succumbs, and King Hanun finds death under an iron plow. Then and only then will the king's trade route extend unmolested from the Euphrates to the Egyptian border. Therefore, we together will have conquered all the lands known now and forever as the empire of Israel.

"A new age of prosperity will pour through Jerusalem. All my friends present are to be the most important benefactors. But, regrettably, taxes are required to ensure our victory at Rabbah. It is a small price to pay for regional and commercial domination. My tax collectors have assessed each subject accordingly. They soon will be collecting either voluntarily or by force of arms and prison time for any shirking their responsibility to the nation." David afforded himself a long and uncomfortable pause, making eye contact, and assuring all present that he was deadly serious about any shirkers' penalties and punishments.

On a lighter note, David re-engaged a sullener audience. "Enough business—let us return to eating and drinking, and basking in our assured bright future as God's chosen people." There was some polite clapping. Still, most were not pleased with the prospect of yet another levy of taxes.

Uriah sat in the honored seat nearest to the right hand of the king. David placed his hand on Uriah's shoulder and praised, "Let me be the first to applaud your rise into the ranks of one of my highly esteemed 'Mighties.' Well done, sir." Uriah seemed numb to the compliment but replied, "Thank you, Your Majesty."

David deftly sliced through a succulent rib of a fatted calf dripping with gravy. He generously filled Uriah's plate to overflowing, saying, "Eat your fill. I am sure this feast is a tasty reprieve from the dry and cold army rations." David watched Uriah drain his wine goblet empty and then cast a threatening eye in Ebed's direction as if to say, "Uriah's cup is empty; keep it filled if you know what's good for you." Ebed took the hint and upended the wineskin, continually filling Uriah's wine bowl to the brim.

Leaning in, David attempted to invade Uriah's private thoughts and gently scolded, "Uriah, celebrate your acclaim and revel in your applause. For life is filled with pain and sorrow, so reap the moment's rewards against the usual troubles of a doubtful tomorrow. Although, I must admit that I was greatly disappointed at your unwillingness to feast at your home table with the mess of meats I had provided. I suffered an even greater insult at your refusal to find comfort in your warm, familiar bed. Let alone your heartless rejection of the passionate arms of your beautiful wife in favor of the hard, cold ground of the servants' quarters." Uriah attempted a thinly veiled protest, but David's refusal to listen to any excuses ended their debates. David continued his rebuke. "I know what you are going to say, an intense but misplaced effort to justify your desire to honor the misery of others.

"Lest you forget, my Hittite friend, I am a man of war. I have learned that life is a conflict where each man must face two adversaries—his demons within and his deadly opponents from without, and oftentimes both are vicious and hell-bent on his very destruction.

"We band together as brothers, not because of friendship or devotion, but that camaraderie enhances our chances of survival. Yet, each man must cross that naked bridge of understanding alone and unaided. I say this to you as a reminder to embrace the fleeting pleasures of life and love, for, on the morrow, you will return to the battle and so an uncertain future. The enemy's blade makes no distinction between good man or evil intent.

"On a lighter note, did you know that I have seven wives, and I try at all times to keep them satisfied? However, I did have to put Princess Michal away for ridicule and defiance. A woman is one of God's most pleasing treasures, and a husband's duty is to keep the home fires burning, if you get my meaning."

After draining many skins, Uriah could barely stand. David was now at his wits' end, for it was his last attempt to launch his reluctant cuckolded hero to Bathsheba's well practiced, but unwilling charms.

"So, Uriah, the hour grows late, and one last toast to send you on your way back to your loving home. I hope the words of wisdom that I had imparted will speed your steps to do your husbandly duty in your wife's inviting bed."

David banged his vessel on the table until the room fell silent; he rose to his feet, for the wine had loosed his tongue and thundered, "One last toast to Uriah the Hittite, our esteemed hero of Rabbah: May fate find a way to serve God's purpose in you."

Uriah raised and bowed down to the king and departed the great hall, still echoing with applause.

Uriah, completely drunk on the king's deceptive wisdom and generosity of wine, still could not and would not be seduced to abandon his sense of justice. David's relentless insistence that Uriah bed his neglected wife only served to heighten his suspicions and resolve. All of David's hidden deceptions just helped confirm his fear that the king was, in fact, Bathsheba's secret lover.

Eventually, Uriah stumbled his way back to his resting place on the servants' quarters floor.

His consolation was that, on the morrow, he would be returning to the black-and-white struggle of conflict, where life and death hang by a hair, and all worldly concerns paled in comparison.

CHAPTER FORTY-TWO

A Warrant Most Cunning

Ebed swung open the door to the servants' quarters and spotted Uriah retching into a chamber pot. Uriah squinted back through bloodshot eyes and appeared to be suffering from a miserable hangover. Remarkably Malak was already dressed and making his way to the scullery to partake of last night's leftovers for breakfast. Ebed's eyes widened, and he hurried off to alert the king that his previous night's efforts to entice Uriah to sleep with his wife had once again failed miserably.

The late-night gaiety and the drinking bout with Uriah had left David sleeping off an alcohol-induced stupor. Ebed, gathering all his courage, banged furiously on the king's chamber door. David roused and threw his sandal at the door, and growled, "Who goes there? Fair warning, it had better be a matter of life and death, or you will suffer the cutting sting of a scorpion whip."

"It is I—Ebed. Please pardon my disturbance, great king, as you have always instructed me—lord—bad news first."

Scuffling to the door, David scolded, "Get on with it! My head is throbbing, and my eyes have sand under the lids."

Ebed blurted out, "Uriah has slept once again at the king's door. I am obeying your standing order to know of his comings and goings."

"All right, Ebed, again, you have done your commission as directed. Now fetch me three raw eggs and some bitter herbs, and then fill my roof bath with cold rainwater." Once dressed and revived, he addressed Ebed. "I need you to summon Uriah and Malak to my writing table. I have a personal message for my nephew Joab at Rabbah."

David's blood was up as if going into battle, both tense and determined as he set about composing a note of conspiracy and infamy.

— For Your Eyes Only—
Chief Captain Joab,
To my loyal nephew and Israel's chief captain,
I speak to you in the confidence of our family's pledge to hold sacred our communications. The bearer of this dispatch, Uriah, the Hittite, is well known to you. He has shown willful neglect causing me grief and embarrassment. Uriah's continued existence can ultimately bring about the destruction of lives that I hold near and dear to my person. I need him skillfully eliminated. I cannot do the deed openly and so staining my hands forever with his blood. Neither can I order his death by using a liar or cunning assassin, for even that will deliver a lingering suspicion to my doorstep. Secretly, I have devised a plan to distance myself

and you, my creative nephew, from even the slightest hint of any wrongdoing.

Set Uriah in the forefront of the hottest battle. When he is in the thick of the fight, subtly signal all about him to withdraw their support. He will be quickly overwhelmed by the enemy—but he will fight every challenger to a glorious end and die a hero's death, and that will be your report.

If Uriah dies in combat, then it leaves neither of us accountable in the eyes of man or of God. I know that you will make sure that Uriah does not leave the field alive and help restore my peace of mind in any event. With all earnestness at my command, I implore you to keep these thoughts to yourself and avoid a multitude of troubles.

Your Sovereign,

David Ben Jesse, King of Judah and Israel

Burn after reading.

David pressed folded the warrant—and with that uneasy crease, he sealed both his and Uriah's fates permanently.

A stout rap at the alcove door announced the arrival of Malak, the messenger, and Uriah, the Hittite. Something evil was in the air, but neither dared to mention the ominous chill sweeping through the dimly lit room. David rose from his writing table as the two men bowed in respect. David pinched out a forced smile of welcome and began, "Uriah, I hope you have revived from last night's excesses and are fit to travel back to the battle. I was hoping that you would have taken my advice and enjoyed all the pleasures afforded you at hearth and home. But, instead, I learned that once again, you slept at the king's door. I must admit to my disappointment with the rejection of my hospitality. But no matter, things will right themselves soon enough.

"Uriah, I have a private and personal dispatch for Chief Captain Joab, and it is for his eyes only." David then placed the note into a courier pouch, tightly pressed the latch closed with the royal seal, and handed it to Uriah for delivery.

"Because you have proven yourself a man of honor, I trust you to deliver this dispatch personally into the hands of the commanding general."

David then turned his attention to Malak. "I need you to accompany Uriah back to Rabbah. It remains a hostile wilderness, and two are better than one. For if one falls, the other will lift his fellow traveler. Besides, Uriah could get robbed, and my document could fall into the enemy's clutches. Then again, for any man left alone in the wilderness, curiosity could arouse too great a temptation to lay bare its secret contents. Lastly, Malak, I will need you to bring back news on how the siege progresses and confirm that my orders were understood and executed perfectly to the letter.

"You both have my leave to depart before the sun reaches its noonday zenith and the desert heat parches the throat and blisters the feet. Godspeed."

Uriah and Malak bowed in relief and were glad to depart from Jerusalem and leave far behind all of David's suspicious scheming.

Malak and Uriah quickly packed their necessary provisions for their journey back to Rabbah. Uriah never attempted to inquire about his wife Bathsheba's well-being or even cross the threshold of his former hearth and home.

The two men hurriedly passed through the main gate, and after several grueling hours, Uriah took a deep breath and looked back from the last hilltop vantage. He watched the imposing spires of Jerusalem's high towers disappear into the hazy distance. He reflectively turned to Malak. "I have a dark shadow of foreboding that lingers in my heart. I cannot dismiss the feeling that this is the last time I will view the holy city. That my wife's love is gone forever, plucked up, root and branch by another."

Malak halted only long enough to respond, "Do not focus on yesterday's troubles, for it only gives strength to the three specters—remorse, rage, and regret. The morning sun will rise and grant to all the promise of an unspoiled tomorrow. So, take heart, Uriah, and help your destiny to overcome adversity. Meanwhile, we are squandering daylight. I want to make it to the Beth-Barah or the fording place of the Jordan before sundown."

The two men approached the crossover just as the sun, now a massive, brilliant orange ball, majestically paused, declaring its fiery splendor. The darkening orb began its descent below the horizon, inviting the night of cover and rest. The babbling shallows of the life-giving Jordan would soon silently enter into the desolate eastern wilderness beyond Moab.

Malak found a secure and elevated position on the riverbank to recover from a robust run. Both men had fled Jerusalem as if leaving the scene of a crime. Malak began, "We can see both sides of the river from here and all the other travelers' campfires. None dare cross at night, east or west, except cutthroats and liars. No one can easily approach us without being spotted. We will make haste in the morning, for this night's red sky promises the perfect delight of a cloudless tomorrow. Let us gather God's bounty of cured driftwood and the abundant dry camel droppings, and build us a campfire to ward off the night's desert chill. It is always colder by the water's edge." The two men worked well as a team. Both men sat relaxed, enjoying the king's life-sustaining rations and enjoying the first lick of fire and its crackling wave of warmth. Malak mused, "I feel most at home when I am on the road. I feel anxious standing still, cooped up like fowl denied his winged freedom, and you, Uriah, a man of one wife, a house, and home—is that your ideal life?" A shooting star brilliantly streaked across the heavens and just as quickly flared out of sight.

Uriah replied, "It was, in fact, my dream, but now my heart breaks beyond repair. The two people I love most in life—David, my king, and Bathsheba, my wife—have conspired against me. I find my only solace in the life-and-death conflict of man-to-man combat. It is the only time I feel awake and alive. I desire to get back to where my life makes sense."

After a long pause, Malak said in a matter-of-fact voice, "I will take the first watch. We will cross the shallows in the morning and turn north and east with the sun on our cheek. We will reach the walls of Rabbah the second day after tomorrow. So, take your sleep and put away today's evils, and do not worry about tomorrow's woes, for today's troubles are sufficient unto themselves.

"Joy comes in the morning, even more so than you can imagine patiently waiting upon the dawn.

"But, there is always another challenge to overcome or fall by the wayside.

"So, let go, and let God, for, in the end, all purpose will unfold like an ancient scroll. The best that we can do is play our allotted roles in this grand scheme of life.

"So, I keep on the move and never look back, fearful that the devil stalks my tracks.

"Sleep now. For all thoughts rest in the sleep of the dead.

"I will wake you at the beginning of the second watch. Keep your eyes on the horizon; pirates prowl the banks looking for unwary prey."

Uriah, long gone, snored his response.

CHAPTER FORTY-THREE

The Sure Blade of Treachery

Swiftness and endurance energized the two hardy travelers—the king's secret message delivered in record time, driven in part by Malak's passion, to outpace his previous route. The outpost guards recognized Malak and Uriah's speedy approach. Two short blasts from the shofar horn alerted that two familiar comrades had just entered the camp.

Uriah and Malak presented themselves at the tent of Joab; the chief captain, hearing the shrill trumpet call, pulled back the flap and exited into the sun. The fresh arrivals beheld their warrior commander, dark and intense. He strapped on his sword that was stained black with blood from a multitude of enemy kills.

Joab at once questioned: "Uriah, I did not expect you back so soon. Did you tire so quickly of Jerusalem?" Then, not waiting for an answer but continuing in the same breath, "What is this? You now wear the mark of one of David's 'Mighties,' a distinguished honor—an acknowledged warrior of courage and standing. Well done! I see that you are also carrying the king's dispatch—you and not Malak; that is unusual. Give it here." Joab at once broke the seal with his dagger, lifted out the folded letter, and began reading. His eyes narrowed, and his brow furrowed. He glanced up at Uriah several times and back to the message before crumpling it with his fist and then tossing it into the fire. Then, with a sterner tone, Joab addressed Malak. "I take it you are here acting as the royal babysitter. Speak up, man."

Malak chafed at the sarcastic remark—but responded respectfully. "Chief Captain, the king ordered me to escort Uriah for security and safety's sake, ensuring that the king's seal remained intact and that his message was placed in the commander's hands—and for his eyes only.

"I am also to report back as to the progress of the siege and that the king's instructions contained therein was understood and carried out to the letter."

Joab, still in a foul mood, grumbled, "The king's spy, you say. Very well—the king is entitled to his battlefield updates. After all, he has the most to gain or to lose. So that you are aware, Malak, I have no room for deadwood. I will assign you to a combat group. I will call for you when I have something for you to report to the king. I will then send you on your way back to my uncle with the news that he craves so desperately to hear. Is that understood?"

Malak nodded in submission, not daring to engage in any further thorny discussion. An aide led him off to his new assignment.

Joab turned his attention back to Uriah, stating, "I have a hardened group of courageous men known for taking the fight to the enemy. I will add you to their ranks for testing in the very belly of the battle. Take your rest, and have a good meal. Report back here for your posting at the beginning of the third watch."

Uriah so, too, nodded in agreement, avoiding Joab's troubling and unjustified anger. Uriah promptly departed to search for food and shelter. A night's rest for a combat soldier is often fitful and fleeting. But for Uriah, it felt more like being back home.

David's request only served to unsettle Joab's moral sense of right and wrong. Joab went back inside his tent, unstrapped his sword, tossed it on the floor, and thought this was more the work for liars with daggers, not generals.

It was one thing to kill a foreign enemy in man-to-man combat, which was an expected result of his profession. However, the killing of General Abner was in retribution for killing their brother Asahel, and it demanded a blood-feud retribution.

Joab thought, "But now I am to conspire with the king, our uncle, in the murder of a 'Mighty,' a man of courage who had served under my command with distinction and honor, and the only explanation is a vague insult." Joab began questioning his role in this deadly and unholy drama. "Did this despicable act cross the bounds of duty to family, king, and country? Was this not a treacherous scheme to murder? Have I been reduced to an unwitting tool of infamy?"

Finally, Joab's moral wrestle relented, and he considered, "Was it not my sworn duty to serve and protect the king and further the interests of God's chosen people, Israel, without hesitation or misgiving?"

Joab now gave this cloaked killing of Uriah by Ammonite sword a deep and abiding consideration. But, first, he needed to confide in his brother Abishai, for the sheer weight of conspiracy was too heavy to bear alone. Needing a confidant, Joab summoned Abishai to his command tent. In a somber tone, he addressed his older brother, "I have received a sealed dispatch from our uncle directing me to arrange for the death of Uriah the Hittite. I am to make it look like an unfortunate but all-too-regular result of this armed conflict."

Abishai questioned, "Did he give you the reason for Uriah's death sentence?"

Joab, in a frustrated tone, shook his head. "No, he was very guarded and weighed every word carefully. All he said was that it was necessary to save lives and for his peace of mind.

"David secretly suggested that we put Uriah in the forefront of battle and then signal the gallant men around him to withdraw, leaving him alone and vulnerable to the onrushing rampage of enemy vengeance."

Abishai, outraged by the king's proposal, grumbled, "The only reason David asks such a thing is that we are family and would not betray his confidence. Instead, it seems that our vaunted uncle asks you to cover up his love affair by demanding warriors to become liars and assassins in a seedy plot to kill his rival."

"I agree with you, my brother, but a mandate from an anointed king is sacred. So, it seems that we need to put our feelings aside and get on with it and trust in God, even in the dark. How do you suggest that we proceed?"

Abishai considered several options and then shook his head at each discarded scheme. Then in an instant, his head snapped back, and he uttered, "Yes, yes. Right," as if his inner self had devised a plan of action. He began, "We need seven men to form the leading edge of a fast-moving wedge. Just think of it like when flocks fly in formation, and they resemble the tip of a spear slicing through the sky above. The unexpected advance of a seven-man force will draw a hail of arrows. Of course, you will require a tight roof of overhead shields to afford some protection. Joab, it will be necessary that you accompany the selected five that will go forth with Uriah. You will position yourself in the rear to keep a fixed eye on the action. You will summon Uriah just before you step off into the fray and assign him the place of honor at the point of the spear. Instruct the five to silently withdraw from their positions after hearing a single blast from the shofar horn, leaving Uriah unaware and vulnerable to the enemy onslaught. The signal is to notify that it is every man for himself or face certain death. You must make it clear that their survival depends on their ability to disengage and withdraw to safety when hearing the Shofar horn's ear-piercing blast."

Joab was impressed with his brother's strategy and said so. "Brilliant planning, Abishai—and I have five men in mind, the five Suleiman brothers. I will summon them presently. The brothers are never more than a stone's throw distance away from each other."

Joab called forth the Suleimans, all brave warriors from the same esteemed father, each with a different mother. Joab sent a sentry to gather them up and present them at his shelter for a private council. Abishai parted the flap and invited them into the dark and secretive confines of the command pavilion.

General Joab entreated, "Gentleman, I have a special mission needful of discretion, courage, and faithful obedience to every needful detail. We will together engage in a head-on diversion. When the Ammonite army deploys to draw us into battle, we will be ready for them this time. We will form a seven-man point-of-the-spear formation. Let me explain. Uriah, the Hittite, recently honored as one of David's Mighties, will be the point. Then two brothers will flank him on either side and one step back at arm's length, and so forth. I will be the last man on the right, and Ahiah, the oldest brother, the very last man on the left. You can decide your position in line by casting lots.

"We will be the first to cross over the stream and attack the center of the Ammonite army. We will mesh our shields together and so create a roof of protection. Our advance will blind all enemy eyes. They will then launch a barrage of arrows that will darken the sky. However, our diversion will give our people a short reprieve from the deadly darts. We will be taking the brunt of the storm, but not for long. If we can get in close enough, it will limit their archers' accuracy as we tangle man to man, kicking up dust and obscuring their vision, unable to tell friend from foe. If we are successful, our army will overwhelm the Ammonite foe before they can scurry behind their massive walls. If they engage our forces, we will push through and take the gate—heroes to the last.

"Now listen up—if the enemy is disciplined and more determined than expected, and our deaths seem to be unavoidable, I will sound one extended blast from the shofar, which is your signal to retire from the maelstrom of battle. Do this without thought or hesitation. For it is a life-or-death decision, and then it is every man for himself. I cannot stress enough each man's importance to withdraw, and it is a direct order. No heroics. Does anyone have any questions? Ask them now."

Bahur, the youngest brother, questioned, "If we are the first men into the city, do we get the pick of the women?"

A laugh broke the tension, and even the straight-faced Joab cracked a smile. Then, Joab righted himself and quipped, "If there are no serious questions, you are all dismissed until dawn tomorrow to wait upon the opening of the gate and the fielding of the Ammonite army. After that, I will see you on the killing field."

Returning to the command tent, Abishai inquired of his brother, "When were you planning on explaining to Uriah his role in this charade?"

Joab covertly proposed, "Just before we depart and not a moment sooner. I do not want the Suleiman brothers to form an attachment or reveal the shofar horn's warning to withdraw. So, it is best Uriah is kept in the dark and unaware of his coming downfall as long as possible."

CHAPTER FORTY-FOUR
A Broken-Hearted Suicide

It was the darkest hour, for the sun had not yet found its crown. Abishai and Joab prepared in the gloom for the execution of their royal ruse, ensuring the destruction of Uriah. Abishai questioned Joab, "What if, by some miracle, your hoax works, and Uriah and the Sulieman brothers make it to the opened gate? If we can flood in, will you still sound your secret signal and ensure the end of Uriah at the cost of victory?"

Joab smiled and, without a second thought, scolded his brother. "As you very well know, battles are fluid, and advantages are gained or lost like a shifting tide in a storm. A good commander, to prevail, must anticipate and react to all possibilities. I will make that decision if or when it presents itself. But, the likelihood of capturing the entrance to the city by storm has been doubtful from the onset. So, dear brother, I need you to order Uriah to my tent for a private council. In the meantime, I need you to conceal the army behind rocks, ravines, and trees, ready to spring. I want our men to be out of sight of the Ammonite

Chief Captain Nemun. Again, he will position his men to draw us in and within range of their fanged flying shafts. This time, we will attack the open gate when only half of his men fill the entranceway. We will not allow Nemun enough time to field the whole of his army. I, with my seven-man wedge, will hurl at the enemy position with all due haste. You and the rest of our forces will emerge from cover. All will follow briskly, hanging back the length of a bow shot. If or when I decide that we are being overwhelmed and death is inescapable, then I will tickle the ears of the Suleiman brothers to withdraw, leaving Uriah prey to his deadly but glorious fate. The horn blast will also signal for you to stall your advance and for all to fall back."

Abishai countered, "A grand design. But what if Uriah catches sight of your deception and attempts to return to safety?"

Joab sternly replied, "In the confusion that is the fog of battle, his heart will succumb to my obedient dagger. Our loving uncle has made it clear, by fair means or foul, Uriah is not to leave the field alive."

Abishai returned to organizing his command behind rocks, ravines, trees, and boulders, waiting for the perfect moment to uncover and attack in force.

Uriah reported to Joab as ordered. Joab explained, "Uriah, you have earned great honor, and you are to lead the attack. You are now one of King David's 'Mighties,' so you will be the first man in a seven-man force—you, me, and the five Suleiman brothers in a staggered formation resembling the point of a spear. We will draw down the enemy arrows, allowing our main force to close in and fill the breach that we create. The enemy, not yet fully fielded, will stumble at the swiftness of our attack. We will make all haste for the gate." For the first time in days, Uriah felt welcomed and prized. He snapped to attention and smartly replied, "It would be my honor, chief captain, to lead the charge."

Joab responded, "Very well. It is time to find your place at the point of the spear and the leading edge of the sword." Joab escorted Uriah to the rally point. The five Suleimans had settled down behind a rise and out of sight of enemy observation. They were joking and stroking their weapons with rough polishing stones coaxing a cutting edge with the sarcasm of brothers. Joab began, "Men, this is Uriah the Hittite and the newest member of King David's vaunted Mighties, and he is the man who will lead our bold thrust into the heart of the inferno. For protection, we have great shields that will cover us like a brass roof once hoisted up and over our heads.

"The sun will be up soon, and all are eager to run this race. I count on the Ammonite Chief Captain Nemun to field his garrison at the gate and tempt us within killing range of his flying spikes. The plan is to wait until only half his men are in position because it would take again as long for them to retreat through the crowded opening. The order to reverse their path will cause confusion and a temporary blockage. Nemun's brief uncertainty will give us a temporary but needed advantage. We will be charging right at them, drawing their deadly darts upon our heads. Abishai and our concealed army will rise and follow us carefully, filling our breach and punching through to the city's soft underbelly. If there are no questions, then we wait on the rising of the sun for our trap to be sprung."

Uriah took hold of his new shield and sat in the very front, preparing his mind to do battle.

Bahur, the youngest brother, crossed over the split, curious to interview this last-minute arrival. "My name is Bahur, and you are Uriah the Hittite, and recently acclaimed as one of King David's esteemed Mighties, and so a man of daring courage and honor. You have the privilege this day of being the first man into battle. I will be a step behind and just over your right shoulder. Today and together, we will taste the sweet nectar of glory."

Uriah took pleasure in the young man's daring and counseled, "I seek no glory or acclaim. I know that when I am in the midst of conflict, all my troubles, worries, and sadness seem to vanish with a heightened sense of focused tension. I experience reality to the fullest when challenging the life-or-death struggle of mortal combat."

Bahur nodded with respect and admiration. "I think I like you, Uriah the Hittite, and you, the newest member of the select circle of King David's invincible Mighties. I feel it a privilege to fight at your side."

The dim gray morning light slowly peeked over the horizon, marking the parting of Rabbah's massive gates. The army of Nemun began filing through the opening, covering the distance of a bowshot from the deadly Ammonite marksmen.

The time was at hand. Joab positioned his eager crew in their rare spearhead formation. He signaled Abishai and his army silently with the launch of a fire arrow that streaked across the last of the night's dark gray sky, signaling all to engage. As Joab had planned, less than half of the Ammonite fighting men had left the protection of the city gate. Joab's spearhead of men and shields picked up their pace in a life-or-death-race gamble. Joab's boldness and audacity tickled the fingers of fate. Luckily, the expected rain of arrows was not forthcoming, as the bowmen were late in their postings. Chief Captain Nemun viewed the strange attack formation from the heights of the city battlements. His men would be at the mercy of Israel if his archers delayed a moment longer. Recalling his troops was no longer an option; it would cause mass confusion and result in a deadly blockage. Nemun shouted at the top of his lungs, piercing the din of battle. Hearing their master's scream, his bowmen rallied, coming to the rescue of the disorganized Ammonite garrison, evidenced by the high-pitched whistling hum from a dark cloud of inflight arrows. The first volley rained down upon the fast-approaching spearhead formation. All seven men knelt, holding fast to their overhead shields, and endured a merciless striking. The intentional misdirection gave ample time for the army charging close behind to cross over the wadi stream and enter the killing zone unopposed.

Uriah slammed into the enemy's disorganized front line, followed closely by the Suleiman clan. Joab veered off and hung back, watching intently from a nearby ravine. The archers were now concentrating on the screaming and whooping war cries of Israeli storm troopers fast approaching.

The six-man advance party battled ferociously, slicing, cutting, and stabbing their way to the still partially open gate, and now only a hair's breadth away. The charging army speedily closed the distance nonstop while being savagely stung by a swarm of Ammonite arrows.

Then, suddenly, a fresh pour of Ammonite warriors battled through the one-sided opening. Uriah and the five Suleiman brothers were making a valiant attempt, but an overwhelming and certain death proved inescapable. As fresh troops joined the fray, Joab hefted his shofar horn, sounding an ordered retreat, but it came out flat until he forced out several forced spits and wetted his lips. The lone single blast was easily recognizable to all but Uriah. The brothers separated and fought their way back out of danger. Uriah was being surrounded and took a backward glance, and there he viewed the unexpected desertion. His wife's abandonment, his king's dismissal, and now his comrades in arms. It was more crushing than any man could fathom, let alone withstand. Uriah's rage shifted to his blade and became a whirlwind of vengeance. Young Bahur sought to discover Uriah's whereabouts and spied him alone, surrounded, fearless, and fighting. He doubled back to aid his newfound friend. Ahiah, the oldest brother, called Bahur to return, but the brashness of youth could not turn away. Ahiah lived by the family motto: "We live and prevail or die in the struggle, together and forever." Then Ahiah and his three siblings charged back into the cauldron. Joab was momentarily stirred by glory to join in but thought better as to the apparent suicide.

Bahur returned, slashing and stabbing, bracing himself back-to-back with Uriah. He then laughed out loud, saying, "I could not let you take all the glory for yourself, for there is more than enough to go around." Ahiah and the other three brothers joined the fight, and together they fought as men possessed. The bowmen no longer focused on the retreating army but turned their piercing shafts on the six raging man tigers below. The arrows found their mark one by one, and finally, the brothers succumbed to the overwhelming odds. Bahur endured cuts from his crotch to his crown and, releasing his last breath, lunged out and took his killer with him to the grave. Uriah clawed and snarled until stabbed through to his broken heart. He welcomed death, for he died with glory and honor and not as the king's gullible cuckold.

CHAPTER FORTY-FIVE
The Sword Devours One As Well As Another

The siege was nearly won, but the cost of men was ever mounting. The recent action was the closest that Joab had come to breaking the deadlock. He was confident that it was just a matter of time because both sides were wearing down. It was a war of slow destruction—and, at this pace, Joab would soon need more men to ensure victory and end the conflict. Chief Captain Nemun, on the other hand, had to make do with what he had, an ever-dwindling food supply and fewer men, making his hold on the city slippery and worsening with every passing hour.

Joab had fulfilled his commission with the destruction of Uriah. He understood politics better than most, chiefly the dark side in concealing scandals and turmoil from the view of ordinary people. Besides, a command from his uncle, the anointed king, was the same as if coming from God. Joab was grateful not to have stained his blade with the blood of a hero and, worse, a warrior under his command.

Joab summoned Malak, the messenger, who was always quick and agile, coming through the battle without a scratch. Joab, in his most commanding voice, stressed the need for unerring accuracy, "You are to report to the king all that went on in our recent encounter. I need you to listen intently, so my exact words are not wasted or squandered with opinions, mistakes, or wild guesses.

"Tell David that the Ammonite men prevailed against us. They came out of the walled city and lured us into the killing field, and we were upon them even to the entering of the gate. The Ammonite archers shot from off the wall and rained death and destruction down upon us all. Many of the king's men died in the storm. I know my uncle; the king's anger will rage at this failing. When David has finished railing, say to him that Uriah, the Hittite, is dead and also that he was fearless and died a glorious death."

Malak was visibly shaken with the unsettling report, as it was the first he had heard of his fast friend's sacrifice on the field of honor. But, Joab persisted, "Keep in mind that the news of Uriah's passing and his courageous last stand will quell my uncle's fury and belay any further tongue-lashing."

Malak made quick work of his journey back to Jerusalem. Running gave him clarity of thought and purpose. In his heart, he knew that there was evil afoot, but he was, after all, the king's man and political intrigues he left to those better suited for the shadows.

Malak soon viewed the seven hills of Jerusalem and rushed through the king's gate. Two stout guards handily escorted Malak to the king's porch, having urgent news from the front.

Malak presented himself to David, who anxiously paced in his private waiting room far away from prying eyes and eavesdroppers. Malak did his customary bow of homage and said, "Your Majesty, I have come from Rabbah with all due haste knowing that the king is eager to hear the details of the ongoing struggle at the forefront of battle. So, I will not waste a moment in relaying the words given to me by Chief Captain Joab. "The Ammonite men prevailed against us. They came out of the walled city and lured us into the killing field, and we were upon them even to the entering of the gate. The Ammonite archers shot from off the wall and rained death and destruction down upon us, and many of the king's men died gallantly in the failed attempt."

David's ire was rising, and he began questioning Malak. "When Joab approached the city walls and fought, did he not know they would shoot from the walls? When you return to Rabbah, I want you to tell Joab a telling story from our recent history and ask him, who killed Abimelech, the first king of Israel and Canaan? So that you know the answer, he was the blended son of Jerubbaal or Gideon. Abimelech met his end from the dainty hand of a woman. The woman cast a piece of a millstone upon his head from high above the tower wall. Abimelech died there in the city of Thebez. Ask Joab why he would go so close to the wall knowing full well it is the very place where danger befalls us all without exception or restraint."

Malak nodded in agreement and uttered, "Yes, my lord, I will inquire word for word, each matter in question." The messenger gave a hard swallow and, screwing up his courage, blurted out, "I have some more bad news, sire."

371

David's jaw tightened, his brow furrowed, and his hearing sharpened, waiting on Malak's next statement—"Uriah the Hittite also died in a valiant action as befitting one of the king's Mighties."

David's once scowling face relaxed, he breathed a long sigh of relief, and his notorious temper melted like candle wax. A weighty burden seemed to have lifted from off his shoulders. David, now upbeat and consoling, started leveling with Malak. "Tell Joab not to let the death of Uriah press down on him or upend his peace of mind. For in the conflict of causes, the sword devours one as well as another. After all, it is by blind luck, erratic fate, or the will of God that the arrow of destiny finds its mark.

"Malak, you say that you were upon them, the Ammonite defenders, even unto entering the gate. Is that not so?"

Malak agreed. "It is like you say, my lord: Joab and his soldiers were a hair's breadth away from a total breach of the city. The bowmen then focused their aim and tipped the balance, all but blunting our advance. The Ammonite warriors took courage surrounding and crushing our advanced spearhead fighters. Then, gauging the enemy's overwhelming strength, Joab signaled the withdrawal, saving lives and narrowly surviving the onslaught himself."

David listened intently and pondered, replying with sage advice. "I see an opportunity here. For Joab's forces to get that close to storming the gate, it can only mean one thing—that the enemy's resolve is weakening. You need to tell my nephew, Chief Captain Joab, that he needs to make the battle more ferocious and determined. Explain to him that an exerted push with confidence and daring will see the walls fall and the gates parting, proclaiming him a mighty man of valor.

"Ask my nephew if he still feels the sting from when last he went up against the children of Ammon, and he had to retreat with his tail between his legs. Unfortunately, that loss remains a glaring embarrassment. So, I wanted to give him this opportunity to redeem himself by providing a second chance to conquer a former adversary. That is why I did not go—all the glory would be his, and songs will be sung, 'Joab, the conqueror of Ammon.'

"Lastly, and annoyingly so, King Hanun's insult and ridicule of me and Israel have gone unanswered, and Joab will loudly rectify that complaint in the king's name.

"Inform my nephew that Ammon is the last piece in my empire of Israel.

"The destruction of Ammon will secure the king's trade route against our final disrupter. When you are victorious, it will make Jerusalem the exclusive trade hub for the entire region. We will then broker all commerce between the Euphrates River to the fertile Egyptian delta. Thus, our nation will flourish and commence a golden age. Moreover, we will have secured our eastern borders against any invasion, and will dare to intrude, molest, or make afraid.

"Encourage Joab with these words, that I know with absolute certainty that, when he puts his mind to a task, he is unstoppable and that I have no doubt about his ultimate victory. I fully expect that he will have a glowing account of his successful capture of the City of Waters in his next dispatch. Now be off with you, Malak, and Godspeed."

CHAPTER FORTY-SIX
A Required Grief and a Marriage Delayed

D avid summoned Ebed, his loyal body servant, and found him waiting eagerly to serve outside his master's apartments. "Yes, your kingship. What is your pleasure? I am ready to serve."

David, attempting to hide his pleasure, spoke in a flat, dispassionate tone, "Uriah, the Hittite, died in battle, and before the rumor mills start churning, I need to message his wife—I mean to say, his recent widow, Lady Bathsheba. She needs to get the bad news from a caring friend before hearing it from a washwoman or a passing stranger.

Ebed, eager to please, gulped hard and uttered, "Your Majesty: if I might be so bold as to make a suggestion?"

"Yes, yes, go on, and make it brief, for the Devil is forever on the prowl, and his crier is scandalous gossip. A well-placed rumor can strike down a kingdom with barely a whisper in the ears of the powerful."

Ebed began to sweat, being unsure in the soundness of his proposal, but meekly suggested, "Perhaps it would best serve the king to break the news to Bathsheba personally. Then, you can summon her to the king's house, or you can go in person to her dwelling—a befitting gesture for royalty in the consoling of a war hero's widow.

"I am confident that your presence would lessen the crushing blow of her sorrow, and she would find comfort in your company."

David snapped back, furious at the idea. "Do you think that I had not considered all those possibilities? I have to follow the proper religious procedures; after all, I am the king. There are rumors that I am having an illicit affair with a married woman of breeding and standing. Remember, Bathsheba is the daughter of Eliam, one of my Mighties, and her grandfather is Ahithophel, a trusted minister and an Oracle of God. If I were to go out of my way to console her, a freshly widowed woman, who, I might add, was married to the very same fellow that I had commanded to abandon his post at the siege of Rabbah and then had him report here to me in Jerusalem. The man who had refused to visit his wife when given the opportunity—not once, but twice. Suppose I now approach this recently widowed woman or summon her to me. In that case, it will only increase the speed of pointing fingers and wagging tongues, enflaming already smoldering suspicions. Lady Bathsheba needs to begin her thirty-day mourning ritual as soon as possible, and I need to keep my distance, alone and unseen.

"I will now attempt to compose a heartfelt letter; echoing my words would only sound contrived and shallow. Therefore,

Ebed, wait outside, and allow me to collect my thoughts and make yourself ready to dash to my beloved's private home."

Dearest Bathsheba,

Precious daughter of Israel:

Our parting churns my soul with longing and sorrow. The vision of your beauty fills my waking hours. My lonely bed remains unwashed and unkempt so that I can fill my nights with your captivating scent. The expectation of your presence remains too long denied with seemingly endless tomorrows and downcast skies. Soon, my beloved Bathsheba, we will never have to part. The fates have conspired and decreed that our joining aligns with the stars. A way made in the death of your husband, Uriah, who died boldly in battle. My heartfelt sympathies for your loss are eclipsed only by the unplanned and fortunate event that will bring you back to my loving arms and legally back into my bed. I knew I had met my match, my soul mate with an insatiable appetite for love and life. It was only a matter of time until we arrived at this very moment. You are my diamond and my pearl, a priceless ruby of a girl. How it turns out is all in your and God's hands. Will you marry me and be my queen? Our unborn child will have all the advantages of royalty and, perhaps—someday, and if a boy, even becoming a king himself. We will have to wait the customary thirty days of mourning. If you say "Yes" to my proposal of an everlasting, love-filled marriage, I will come and fetch you away to your new home. I will have Abiathar, the high priest, seal us in the eyes of God and man.

I overflow with love, excitement, and expectation.

Your servant, David ben Jesse, King of Judah and Israel

My darling, please destroy this message, blinding spying eyes, and and silencing errant tongues.

David, once satisfied with his intent, sealed it in an official royal pouch.

He then shouted, "Ebed, come here! You are to deliver this message to Lady Bathsheba without being seen or heard by smartly navigating the back alleys of Jerusalem. I need you to inform the lady that you are not to leave without an answer. Is that clear? You will stay there as long as it is necessary. Even if it means standing outside of her door until the cock crows or the moon glows."

Ebed puffed up his chest and dutifully confessed, "Yes, Your Majesty—as you command. I will return with my lady's reply in my hand—of this, you can be certain." Ebed pulled his heavy hood over his head and, without further ado, was off in a rush.

A short time later, Ebed, with his face hidden, arrived at his destination. He briskly knocked, giving a sense of urgency. A young maidservant answered the door. "What is wanted?" Ebed answered in a gruff, hoarse voice, acting his authority, and demanded, "I need to see your mistress immediately!" The girl was taken back with Ebed's stern order, "Who should I say is calling?" she meekly uttered. Almah, Bathsheba's body servant, called out. "Let him in; it is Ebed, the king's lackey. Wait here, Ebed, and I will fetch my mistress."

Bathsheba, hearing the commotion, entered the foyer. "Ebed, I thought I heard your troublesome voice. The greetings you carry from the king—are they good tidings or foul?"

Ebed looked puzzled. "I know not, madam. I am only here by the king's command to deliver his personal and private message. I am to wait for your reply, notwithstanding the length of time."

Ebed handed Bathsheba the sealed pouch. She hastily broke the seal and began reading. He studied her every gesture, expecting a thorough questioning upon his return to the king's mansion. Instead, Bathsheba first grimaced and sighed, and then she smiled and reread it all a second time.

Then, subtly, and not wanting to break the spell of David's muse, Ebed waited for the perfect moment and questioned, "My lady, do you have an answer? I know the king is particularly eager to get your response."

Bathsheba pondered, but only for a moment, rejecting Ebed's veiled prodding with a wave of her hand and countered, "I need to collect my thoughts so I can mindfully respond in the same like and manner with a written note of my own. Ebed, giving you my deepest thoughts to be offhandedly repeated would be uncomfortable and inappropriate. Almah, take Ebed to the pantry and slake his thirst and fill his belly. I will return when my message to the king accurately conveys my innermost thoughts and feelings, and not a moment sooner."

Bathsheba retired to her secretary to gather her writing instruments and fresh skin of parchment.

To David, king of Israel, and sire to our unborn child:

Uriah's death is a disturbing event, even though no love remained between us. No, just the opposite is accurate ever since I met you. I met my destiny. The barriers we have overcome by defying the laws of God and man have forged our souls together in a bonded and steadfast pledge.

My spirit was adrift in an endless sea of discontent until fate whispered to me from your lofty rooftop battlements. From the very first, our lovemaking was both sacred and profane. Our hearts entwine in the furnace of desire. I could hear angels weeping, their envious tears cooling our burning flesh disguised as dripping sweat. When I look upon your face, I long to know your thoughts and so enmesh our lives together. There is no other perfect partner for me but you, my Prince. You are the captain of my emotions and a compass to my passions. Writing these words, I pant in short breaths, my heart refuses to be still, and my head spins bewildered in love. Yes, I do want to marry you and make our love story both sublime and eternal.

Living without you another thirty days and thirty nights will seem like an endless torment locked in the crucible of obsession. It is much too long, my darling winged stallion, before we can seek the bliss of heaven's caresses. Instead, I chafe with anticipation of love and longing.

Soon, my beloved, I will begin to blossom, and wagging tongues and gossipmongers will start finger counting with self-righteous judgment. Then, no one will dare to accuse or even hint at any sin-laden transgression after marriage.

I will be prepared on the thirty-first day to enter a legally and lawfully covenant of marriage to you, my soon-to-be husband.

Custom, culture, and the eyes of the world will evaluate my sincerity and diligent observance during the thirty days of our separation. I will adhere to the three phases of the mourning death ritual, starting with the Aninut, followed by Aveilut, and lastly, Sheloshim—thirty days and not a moment more, my darling. I extend my patience for propriety's sake and anticipate our joyous reunion and our promise never to to part again.

Bathsheba bat Eliam

"Almah," Bathsheba called.

Almah quickly made herself known. "Yes, madam, what is your wish?" Bathsheba flushed with her heart's desire, finished her writing, and continued, "I have placed my reply to David's proposal of marriage in the king's pouch with a lock of my perfumed hair."

Almah looked puzzled. "But, madam—you are a married woman. How is that even possible?"

"Oh, yes. I forgot to mention that your master Uriah died in battle, and I am now officially a widow. We must now prepare with all due diligence the thirty days of mourning. I have accepted the king's marriage proposal after my mourning period and before the unmistakable childbearing swell."

Almah let go of a long low whistle and uttered, "Madam, my condolences and congratulations—whatever is fitting for the situation. I must say that is a lot to digest in one sitting."

Bathsheba replied, "Thank you, and thank you. Now be off with you. Give the pouch to Ebed, as it needs to be delivered before the sun goes down. It is the time when David rises from his afternoon nap, refreshed, and often waxes poetic as he ponders the dying sun battling the rising moon for supremacy of the dark. I want his thought to be about me and me alone this night. Now, go!"

CHAPTER FORTY-SEVEN
Gutters, Dams, and Invasion Plans

M alak challenged himself, increasing his speed with every trek between Jerusalem and Rabbah. In time he became so familiar with the route that he could run at night, avoiding low spots and hidden pitfalls in the dark.

Malak's recognizable face gave him a security pass through the outpost guards, gaining ready access to Joab's command tent.

"Oh, it is you, Malak. What news from my uncle, the king?" Joab questioned, briskly stepping out from behind the shadows.

Malak looked around to make sure there were no delinquent eavesdroppers. "It was just like you said, my lord. The king's ire quickly subsided once the knowledge of Uriah's death passed my lips. The king's behavior became almost cheerful, as if a great burden lifted from off his shoulders." Joab breathed easy and questioned, "Yes, yes, go on—it was just the reaction that I had expected. What else?"

"He also said to tell Joab, 'Not to let this thing trouble him, for the sword devours one as well as another.' By your leave, my lord, if I may continue, the king did chastise you for going too close to the walls and becoming prey to the waiting bowmen. Furthermore, the king ordered me to relate the story of Abimelech exactly as told to me."

Joab chided, "No, not on your life, Malak. I have heard that story more times than I could count. Whenever my uncle is in his cups, his go-to story is Gideon, Abimelech, and the millstone that crushed Abimelech's head."

"Forgive me, but the king has ordered me to ask the Chief Captain, 'Why did he go so close to the wall knowing that it was ripe with danger?'"

Joab, clearly annoyed, bellowed, "I dare to go close to the wall because that is where the enemy is caught, it is where the battle is fought, and it is where victory is sought, close to the wall."

Malak, taken aback by the stern reply, choked, "Please, Chief Captain, excuse my boldness. I am only the messenger trying to relay a word-for-word warning from the king.

"My lord, the king, was aware of you nearly conquering the gate, and so, on a more encouraging note. He thinks that one more all-out attack will gain you entrance to the city. The king has great confidence in you and began by praising your abilities, saying, 'I know with absolute certainty that, when my nephew puts his mind to a task, he is unstoppable, and that I have no doubt as to his ultimate victory. I fully expect that he will have a glowing account of his successful capture of the City of Waters in his next dispatch.'"

Joab was pleased with the extended confidence and grounded compliments and stated as much. "That is high praise, indeed, coming from a warrior king, and a cunning man of war himself.

Malak, go and locate commander Abishai, my brother, and tell him I require his presence. Tell him that I need to discuss an attack strategy. I have an unusual and creative tactic that needs his experienced reflection. So, you stay close, messenger, for I feel David will get his victory declaration sooner than he expected."

Abishai was alerted and reluctantly made his way to Joab's location. "Brother, I hoped this is important. I was enjoying a rarely afforded afternoon nap," he said, stifling a yawn. "What is this? I hear you have had a moment of discovery to end this endless stalemate of attrition. I pray you to enlighten me, my brother, and make known to me your military genius."

The good-natured chiding of brothers was more than typical, for they had shared the murder of Abner, close combat, and a cunning king for an uncle. Joab, with the vision, laid out his reasoning. "The grinding down of men that we have suffered cannot go on much longer, certainly not for another month. Then, with one more push and little deception, we can open the gate and capture the City of Waters. Our losses will be many, for they will fight like wounded tigers. I believe, once we have captured the lower city, the citadel or the crown of the royal city that rests securely on the bluffs will remain out of reach until David provides us with more men and so, another army."

Abishai questioned, "First of all, brother, you have aroused my interest as to your deception, and secondly, how will you dislodge our uncle from his ongoing love affair with that spell-binding enchantress, Bathsheba?"

Joab scowled, "Abishai, I had put that thread of intrigue together, and you are never to repeat that implication. But, blood or no, David will not abide that accusation and will quietly dispatch a stealthy assassin or have us conveniently slaughtered in battle. Do not doubt that I have suffered our uncle's fury on more than one occasion. His wrath is boundless." Abishai, repentant and sullen, nodded and said, "My tongue retracts, and my lips are stuck together forever on this matter."

"Now, let us get on with the business of war. As you can see from this drawing, Rabbah lies between two streams—the wadi Suwaylih on the right and the wadi Dhulayl on the left. Both flow from the wadi Ammon. The flow of the wadi Dhulayl is Rabbah's primary source of fresh water. The central gutter is below the surface of the river. I propose that we dam the Ammon wadi, emptying the Dhulayl wadi and exposing an entrance to the underground reservoir, giving a choice crew of men access to the inner city. We can then open the main gate, ushering in our waiting army and capturing the town too long denied. The damming of the Ammon and the lowering of the two wadis will enable our underground invasion. The draining of the Suwaylih will also afford an empty trench, concealing a striking force ready to spring into action. It must be all done in one night and well before the sun rises."

Abishai, impressed and astonished, responded, "Brother, that is a brilliant strategy. It is so outrageous that it has all the makings of a great victory—or a great tragedy. How did you come to the knowledge of this underground watercourse?"

"I was with David at Jericho when he met the downcast emissaries that he had appointed to console Prince Hanun and attend the funeral of his recently passed father, King Nahash. The sight of half-bearded and half-naked men of consequence bruised the eye and tightened the jaw. Their garments parted, and their back parts naked to the sun—one of those self-same envoys related that he had stopped at a well to slake his thirst. There, a washwoman, while hoisting a bucket, bragged about Rabbah's freshwater supply provided by their underground aqueduct. A river that filled the city's bottomless reservoir gave life to the city of waters. I have since surveyed the whole of the city walls. I have found the place where the stream flows into a lightly concealed tunnel. It is on the left and drains from the wadi Dhulayl. After all, it is the swiftest flow—and it reaches as far north to Succoth's fertile plain.

"As you already know, that it is where David has stationed his militia to guard the Jabbok River water crossing against rogue Syrian tribes that chafe under Israeli domination. David believes he is protecting our flank against the possibility of an attack. By the way, and so you know, the said loyal militia will not move unless led by the king personally."

"By the way, brother, what gave you the idea to use the gutter?"

Joab took a moment in reflection. "Now that you ask, it was back when David wanted Jebus to be officially named Jerusalem and make the city his capital. The Jebusites faced David with a challenge and said, 'Except you take away the blind and the lame, you shalt not come in here to the city.' They were referring to a brazen idol engraved with Abraham's promise that read that 'Abraham's posterity would never conquer Jebus by force of arms.' Taking that oath was part of the purchase price of his resting place, the cave of Machpelah. On the idol were two men with their mouths forever opened, as if reciting Abraham's ancient pledge. They were confirming that, in the mouth of the second witness, it establishes the matter. One was lame, and one was

385

blind. Jacob was lame, and Isaac was blind. Wherefore they said, because of the blind and the lame representing the solemn vow of Abraham, you shall not come into this house.

"On that day, David challenged every man in his presence, loudly voicing, 'Whosoever goes up to the gutter and destroys the Jebusite's lame and blind idol, that grieves my soul in the breaking of Abraham's oath, he shall be chief and captain of the host.' I accepted the challenge. I took a small crew and went up the gutter and climbed out of a well. We found the idol in the center of town, close to the bazaar. The statue remained guarded both day and night. We quickly dispatched the few sentries to the afterlife. Then, with sparks flying, we hacked the image until it was scrap metal. David captured Jerusalem, and the Jebusites' claim after that fell on deaf ears. David kept his promise, and I have been chief captain from that day to now.

"Well, Abishai, your thoughts on my strategy to break the deadlock?"

Abishai, grateful for the recollection, countered, "I had forgotten that incident; now your plan makes perfect sense. After that telling, I am confident that we can, and we will come up thru the gutter.

"But when do we dam the Ammon wadi flow?"

"Three nights hence, brother, is the new moon, and we will attack then.

"Remember, it must be all accomplished in one night, damming and draining, to blind the all-seeing eye of Rabbah's high tower lookouts.

"You will take twenty men and silently invade the then emptied Suwaylih trench. The rest of the army will be rallied and prepared for invasion far enough away to avoid detection. Watch and wait until I secure an opening to the stronghold. Then, I will signal with a long blast from my shofar horn, signaling all to attack—hold nothing back!"

CHAPTER FORTY-EIGHT
The Royal City of Waters Falls

The sound of breaking rocks in the distance confirmed that Joab's plan was in progress. Boulders that were too large to wrestle were handily pounded into smaller pieces and placed onto the Ammon wadi embankment. Joab questioned his brother, "Are all preparations in place? Have you chosen the twenty men who will join you below cover in the emptied Suwaylih wadi? Have the captains of hundreds been advised to wait for the Shofar blast and then engage in an all-out charge? Can you dam the river by the beginning of the second watch or, say, midnight? If so, will we go forth with vigor and confidence?"

Abishai agreed, "Yes, chief captain, all these needful things proceed as we speak. I am curious, brother—how many men are you taking with you through the gutter to secure the gate?"

Joab briskly replied, "Ten, of course—was it not for the sake of ten righteous men that Sodom and Gomorrah would have found relief from God's wrath? A minyan is needed, my dear brother, the perfect number, small enough to conceal and large enough to overpower the guards at the gate. This brief breach will allow you and your crew enough time to storm the opening and hold until the full army floods into the city. Let us get on with it. We have a man's work to undertake this night—and feel assured, brother, victory will come with the dawn, so help us, God."

Joab enlisted the fearless force of ten of his most valiant warriors. The night campfires cast menacing shadows on all the men seated around his inner circle. Joab began speaking barely above a whisper, taking heed that his voice would not carry beyond the dry wood's sputtering crackle.

"Men, I have picked you to accompany me on a dangerous mission to gain admission to the City of Waters. Tonight, with daring and planning, we will overcome every obstacle. We will, and we must, open the enemy gate to the city and our victory too long denied. We will follow the path of the emptied trench of the Dhulayl wadi. It is critical that every man ties down his weapon. Silence is the handmaiden of stealth—no talking, whispers, coughing, or sounds of any kind. We must remain out of sight from the upper balcony sentries. We will be crawling most of the way on our hands and knees, keeping our heads down below the ridge. The outpost guards, I expect, will be few in number and half-asleep or chatting to relieve the boredom of staring into the endless darkness. Let us not arouse those sleeping dogs with a misplaced sneeze.

"When we reach the exposed tunnel access to Rabbah's underground water supply, we can secretly gain admission to the city. I will have a prepared torch and a pitcher of live coals to light our way after entering the void. We will rise through the city's shallow wells. I have a knotted rope attached to a hook that should suffice very nicely, lifting ourselves out of the underground reservoir. The late hour will help to ensure the success of our covert—if not culvert—raid." Joab stirred up a rare light-hearted chuckle with his wordplay, breaking the intensity of the coming struggle.

Midnight came early in the Ammon Valley. The new moon was a distant, silvery-horned crescent when Abishai ordered, "Men, our time is at hand; fill in the stream with the rocks piled high on the banks. The flow will back up, making a small lake in the lower valley. Once the wadis empty, gather your weapons, and strap them to your thigh. Secure any jangle, clap, or slap. Take caution, for each footfall must be deliberate and focused. The wet ground we tread will be slick and slippery. We travel below the rim of the drained Suwaylih wadi. Then in the shadows, and with perfect silence, we will patiently wait opposite the gate for the shofar's blast to launch our attack. We will support Joab and his ten men securing the gateway opening, allowing the entire army to invade."

As Joab had predicted, the two streams emptied late into the night. There was a constant trickle spilling over the makeshift dam, so each wadi echoed a thinner sound of running water.

Joab and his cadre entered the Dhulayl wadi when Joab and his twenty sappers made their descent into the emptied Suwaylih trench. Joab and his ten men groped their way through to the access tunnel. Crouching down on all fours, they entered the city's watercourse. The gloom was made worse by the stale, dank air. In the deepest dark, Joab lit his torch from the still-burning embers hidden inside his earthen pot. The firelight pierced the blackness, projecting eerie shadows—the slightest sound echoing off the hollow walls. Joab peered through the thick gloom, trying to gain a view of a possible underground exit. Then, looking down into a puddle at his feet, a reflection, a silvery sliver. The new moon had reached its zenith. Slowly moving closer to the overhead opening, he brushed up against a rope and a bucket. Joab hissed, "Our way is before us. I will scale this line up to the well's mouth and drop down my knotted cord for the rest to easily gain a handhold. Remember, not a word or whisper. We will then proceed to the gate together, vanishing into the shadows."

The streets were deserted and eerily quiet. The guards on watch were either half-asleep or staring out into the night, watching the distant Israeli campfires that dotted the horizon. Joab and his men, unseen and unheard, approached the unprotected inner gate. Joab gathered his men in a dark corner, and with the still small voice and, using his hands, relayed his commands. "Men, you six will climb the staircase and silence the sentinels. Once you reach the top, it is three to the right and three to the left. Do your utmost to dispatch the sentries silently to the afterlife. A fully cut throat will arrest any shouting. We need to delay the alarm as long as humanly possible. If they remain alive, they will hurl death down upon our heads as we attempt to remove the locking pin." Joab stooped down and picked up a small stone. "When you have silenced the watch, drop the rock from above, and we will begin the removal of the weighty crossbar. I will stay on the ground and press mightily against the center with the other three men. When you hear my shofar horn ushering in a conflict of demons, make ready for all of Hell's fury."

The six men lightly stepped up the winding staircase and, with guile and cunning, cut down the unsuspecting lookouts. Joab felt the stone dropping at his feet, signaling the all-clear to proceed.

Joab and his three men wrestled the unwilling beam to the ground with a fearsome strain and near-superhuman effort. All four panting from the exertion, lay their strong backs to the weighty gate, again, and again, but to no advantage; it remained steadfast. Joab was about to call his six men down from high above the ramparts. The slayers had already sensed that something was wrong and were chafing at the long pause. They flew down the stairs like birds of prey. A quick survey revealed the dilemma; it was a lack of power. All ten with their collective might groaned in unison as the massive hinges creaked and then gave way, screeching their reluctance. Joab sounded his shofar horn that broke the still of the night. He was inviting heaven and hell to converge on his hard-fought breakthrough opening. The City of Waters lay open and ripe for invasion.

Abishai and his twenty men waited crouched down in their muddy trench. Then, hearing the agreed signal, they rose and sprinted at a blistering pace to aid in Joab's calculated gamble.

Meanwhile, the army of Israel charged out of the gloom, surprising the unprepared Ammonite bowmen. No archer had yet climbed to the vantage of the battlements.

A seasoned crew of Ammonite warriors appeared and struggled valiantly to regain the gateway. Joab and his ten men fearlessly fought in a life-and-death battle, holding fast and protecting the narrow opening, even to the surrendering of their own lives. Then, with great passion, Abishai and his twenty sappers stormed the open doorway at the last desperate moment and stemmed the first tide of ferocious enemy reinforcements.

The Ammonite alarm pierced the night. Men yelled, and the woman shrieked. Children huddled in terror; starving infants cried in the dark, demanding the comfort of their mother's breast.

Twenty bows snapped, then a hundred; barbed Ammonite arrows took flight in the night as the whole army of Israel joined the fight. Ammonite warriors pressed the gate. Then, finally, the gate slowly began inching open and then pulled back again and again, nearly shutting. It was the Ammonites' last desperate attempt to rescue their formidable and impenetrable barricade.

The conflict was fiercest at its parting and rapidly shrinking corridor. One man, then two, then five passed through, barely gaining a foothold for the Israelis inside the walls. To stay out in the open was to die, for death came down from the sky. But the trickle turned into a flood of angry men wielding swords and scimitars, killing anything that breathed or looked them in the eye.

Nemun, chief captain of the Ammonite defenses, could not believe his senses. Israel had broken through to the inner city! His acclaimed bowmen, who were his best protection, were utterly neutralized and forced off the ramparts. Nemun retired to his house and adorned himself with rank, shield, and armor. He said goodbye to his wife and joined his men with courage and honor. He rallied his forces for one grand gesture, but in the end, it proved futile. The City of Waters had fallen.

Perched high above in his castle stronghold, King Hanun's crown of the royal city witnessed the carnage of his once beautiful capital.

Pillage, plunder, and rape were the order of the day. Israel was drunk on the bloodlust of their fallen prey. The stalwart Ammonite defenders regrouped as best they could, choosing a house-to-house strategy, forcing the enemy to pay dearly for every inch of sacred ground. The fighting fierce and unyielding warriors on both sides gave no quarter and rejected mercy. The city center was still in turmoil, with fires roasting fallen soldiers. The wells were dry, and the air was acrid and pungent. Men choked on smoke—dying screams begging for compassion went unheeded like a scene in a macabre pageant.

Booty and pleasure are the wages most coveted by both regular soldiers and recruited militia alike.

Joab and Abishai came upon each other at the rising of the sun. Both men were bloodied and bruised but proud and satisfied with themselves for their seemingly impossible conquest. Abishai embraced his younger brother. "You are a hero, brother; your exploits are the stuff of legend. We have prevailed mightily and have rescued our honor from being tarnished. Do you recall when we found ourselves between the Rabbah army in our face and the Syrian chariot horde at our backs? We were doomed, but for God's will, your resolve, and a brilliant, improvised strategy. We separated into two armies and fought our way out through a narrow corridor. Then, fleeing back across the Jordan with our tails between our legs."

Joab looked up, rallying from his near exhaustion. "I do, brother. Indeed, I do, and now we have righted that dubious loss with a resounding victory.

"We have taken the City of Waters with fire and fury. But we still have a formidable challenge that may prove overwhelming and lies directly over our heads."

Abishai looked up and faintly nodded, saying, "King Hanun and his impregnable citadel above us on the cliffs, of course, the glittering jewel of the royal city."

Joab looked skyward at the gleaming towers reflecting in the morning sun, its spires pointed and sharp like the spikes on a king's golden crown.

Joab thinly insisted, "We have lost too many men on this hard-fought campaign to assault, let alone prevail against Hanun's castle stronghold, for it is a city unto itself. No, brother, what we have here is only but a partial victory. Not until the king is defeated and his fortress conquered will total victory be ours."

Abishai questioned, "Do you have another inspired ruse, ploy, or plot so that a few can vault over those perilous walls and smite that despot?"

Joab winked and, with a mischievous smile, agreed, "I do have some ideas, but it will require more men than what we now have at arms. We must engage our uncle's services and his recruitment strength. He is currently nesting with his temptress back in Jerusalem."

"How do you propose we lure him away from his luxurious comforts and back to this unforgiving carnage and slaughter?"

Quick on his feet, Joab replied, "There is only one thing that will entice David back into the conflict. We must pander to his vanity and inflate his ego with the promise of acclaim. Lest we need yet another reminder, Ammon is the last gem in David's crown securing the empire of Israel, his legend, and legacy. Knowing our uncle as I do, he would move mountains and heaven itself to watch the final endings of a hated enemy. I will message him about our partial victory and the need to gather up additional men. Then, David can release his idle militia entrenched at Succoth and reinforce our depleted legions. Finally, I will promise David's satisfaction in his long-awaited retribution due to King Hanun's insult to his ambassadors.

"So, if you can manage here, brother, I will return and write our urgent request immediately." Joab grimaced as he seared a deep wound with a red-hot poker. He spat out the wood he held firmly between his teeth to distract from the pain and keep from screaming. Then, in a steady voice, he declared, "There is booty here in the captured city, but no food, none. I sincerely hope that Malak didn't take any injuries in this foray that would delay his delivery. I will begin immediately to write my petition. It is best to strike while the enemy is still thirsty, burning, and bleeding."

CHAPTER FORTY-NINE
A Crowning Achievement

J oab and Abishai plunged into the dammed-up backwater lake of the wadi Ammon diversion.

The victorious brothers vigorously washed off the dirt, blood, and gore of war. Then, retiring to the command tent, they found pleasure in a fresh change of clean uniforms. Hungrily, the two spent warriors savored a hot meal of steaming porridge, wine, and dried meat. Joab, refreshed from his swim, stirred his sleepy brother Abishai, saying, "Go and see to the men, the living and the dead. Take a headcount and organize burial parties.

"In the meantime, I will compose my thoughts in an urgent plea employing David's insatiable need for recognition. I need to persuade our loving uncle to join us immediately. He is the deciding factor in our plans for total victory. David's ability to recruit men is uncanny. He can provide us the much-needed militia with little or no difficulty. With his help, we will end King Hanun's reign and quash the Ammonite threat forever. Brother, please call up Malak, the messenger. I hear that he fared well, with just a few bumps and bruises, and inform him that I have an urgent dispatch for the king's anxious hearing, needing a speedy delivery."

Abishai, too tired to protest, wearily took his leave to count the quick and the dead.

Joab began crafting his appeal:

David ben Jesse, king of Israel and Judah

To my mother's beloved younger brother, David ben Jesse, hearken unto my words of great joy and pleasant tidings.

I, your dutiful nephew Chief Captain, Joab, petition our great king.

I have this day fought against Rabbah and have taken the City of Waters. The battle, my well-tested warrior uncle, was both fierce and costly. First, we overcame the archers' deadly sting as you had wisely advised, and then we stormed the metropolis and took it. But the mountain bastion that is the crown of the Royal City endures unmolested and remains a formidable challenge, and the secure keep of King Hanun remains unscathed and unchallenged.

I drained the Ammon wadi and gained entry through the gutter, just as I had done in the capture of Jerusalem. Then, my men and I made a breach, opening the gate from inside the city.

I had first believed that a severe thirst from the lack of water would soon subdue King Hanun's castle fortress. But a half-starved informant volunteered the working of the eagle's nest for a crust of bread. As a result, the elevated garrison stands highly prepared with a deep underground cistern and an abundance of rations.

I have ordered the opening of the dam to douse the burning city. It will help to clean the stench of war, slake the people's thirst, and prevent the onset of pestilence. The diseased-laden rats are already feasting on a multitude of burnt corpses.

Therefore, now, gather the rest of the people together, including the militia you have stationed at Succoth.

Come out and encamp with us; together, we will fight against the secure stronghold and defeat it. Then, and please consider, if I take the crown of the royal city, my name will receive acclaim as its conqueror. A title that rightfully and assuredly should be yours to take, my esteemed uncle. I await your learned consideration in the matter.

I remain your obedient servant.

Joab ben Seraiah, Chief Captain.

Joab was pleased with the subtle tone of his plea and considered that his letter was concise and appealing to both a warrior's heart and the vanity of kings.

Malak presented himself, ensuring prompt delivery to Jerusalem and the uneasy king.

"There you are, Malak, and right on time, as usual. I see that you are now a decorated veteran with a head-wrapped blood-stained bandage. With that observation, I need to make the chief captain aware that I have taken a blow to the head in the heat of battle. I am only just now steadying myself from the insult."

Joab, in a rare moment of compassion, suggested, "I can assign another courier if you are not up to the challenge."

Malak looked down and away as if slighted by the suggestion.

"No, Chief Captain, I will rally when I am on the way filling my lungs and stretching my legs. I will, by all accounts, catch my second wind and surpass the time of my previous passage."

"Well said, my stoic messenger, and in that case, I have an urgent dispatch waiting for me only to clasp my seal on your courier's pouch. Would you please inform the king that I await his important answer and that kingdoms and men's lives hang in the sureness of his reply? So make haste; nations rise and fall for want of timely information."

"But, of course, Chief Captain. I am aware, and I always lengthen my stride when lives are on the line."

Malak bowed his respects and departed for the seven hills of Jerusalem.

The king held court, with ambassadors, emissaries, and envoys, all vying for the royal ear: treaties, tributes, and tax levies creating a discord of competing voices. When David caught sight of Malak entering the great hall and was glad for the reprieve, he was acutely anxious for any news from the siege of Rabbah. David dismissed the noisy crowd and bid Malak join him for a private audience. David noticed with dismay the blood-stained bandage caked with dirt and sweat loosely wrapped around Malak's head. David, concerned for his trusted messenger, began in earnest. "I can see plainly from your wound that the battle was fierce. How fare thee, Malak?

"I am well, sire, and healing rapidly—thank you for your concern. To answer your question: Yes, Your Majesty, the struggle was epic, and Israel prevailed, but I am sure there are more specific details in need of the king's approval in Captain Joab's timely dispatch."

David took a breath of relief as Malak handed him the pouch. Then, breaking the seal, he tore into the report. Sitting down,

David read the letter once again, but this time out loud. After spelling out the details, he asked Malak, "You were there and participated firsthand in the conflict, so what do you make of Joab's plea for assistance?"

Malak, honored to give his opinion and advice, spoke up. "If I might be so bold, sire, to reflect beyond my station?"

David curtly scolded, "I would not have asked you if I found no value in your observations."

Malak, reassured, continued, "Joab had lost many men to enemy arrows, both well before and leading up to the final assault. Joab was brilliant and courageous in his gutter ploy, opening the gate from inside the walls. But I believe that without more men and you, my warrior prince, to rally and lead them, the capital fortress of Ammon will remain invincible. Only adding insult to injury and becoming a beckoning beacon to our enemies, signaling that Israel is vulnerable and lacking in its resolve to conquer. I will dare one last remark."

David, so intrigued, agreed. "Speak on."

Malak, uneasy, nevertheless with resolve. "Sire, Chief Captain Joab does not seek acclaim or glory. Instead, he is about winning at all costs, wresting satisfaction from his previous and trying forced retreat. But, devilishly, the enemy trap, so skillfully hatched by the Ammonite and Syrian forces, has left its lasting mark, and Chief Captain Joab still feels the sting of that encounter."

David weighed every word, phrase, and gesture, both in Joab's upbeat plea and Malak's firsthand account. The king of Israel sat still and deep in thought for an unusually long amount of time; Malak stood silent, awaiting the king's pleasure. Finally, David, after a long pause and in a purposeful manner, asked Malak,

"Are you familiar with the ancient writ that counsels, 'That in the mouth of the second witness, the matter shall be established?'"

Malak shook his head, "No, Lord."

David, wise in his own opinion, continued, "You, my loyal messenger, are that second witness, supporting Joab's needful plea. I will comply; besides, I have thirty days before my soon-to-be bride and my eighth wife frees herself from her three-fold religious ritual of mourning. Then, and only then, will she be free to succumb to my loving arms. Keep in mind that the forthcoming wedding has not yet been made public. Not a word of this to anyone, and I do mean anyone. You will get the rest of the story soon enough through the washwomen and gossip mills of Jerusalem.

"For now, I need you to go to Succoth. I have placed a militia garrison there to defend the Jabbok River Water Crossing against Syrian renegades who pirate our merchant caravans traveling between the Euphrates and Egypt. Many former Syrian chieftains chafe under Israeli domination and would like nothing better than to see our ruin.

"My loyal volunteers at Rabbah will soon be required back on their land to plant barley and wheat. If we do not capture the royal city's bastion soon, we will have to wait until next year's harvest. As you can readily agree, that will be too long and too late, leaving us with the shame of an invincible Ammon capital, cursing Israel with future retaliations. King Hanun and his henchmen could easily remain a thorn in our side, threatening us with bloodlust retaliation, as well as harassing future generations.

"As for now, take my message directly to Succoth, bypassing Rabbah. Joab will be too busy licking his wounds and burying his dead to be overly concerned about my delay. At least, for a few days. I will send word of my agreement to join the storming of King Hanun's citadel, along with wagon loads of dark red wine and roasting cattle for him and his battle-weary soldiers to feast on and gain strength. It will take Joab some time to reorganize and reset his borders. My nephew is both creative and quick thinking when facing the abyss of disaster.

"Seek out Captain Etzel, the commander of the Succoth garrison. Give him my sealed letter, and tell him it is by my command. It is a direct order from the king that he is to withdraw from their encampment. It is all explained in the dispatch. Etzel may initially be reluctant because he is under strict instructions not to abandon his position unless ordered by me personally and in my presence. Give him this ring as a token of my fidelity. He had gifted it to me at my coronation, creating an everlasting bond between us. Relay to him that leaving a handful of sentries is needful, making the camp appear fully functional and active. I do not wish to make the outpost look abandoned and invite liars and pirates to attack trade caravans at will and without fear of punishment or reprisal.

"Tell him that he and his troops are to leave on the double-quick for Rabbah and report to Chief Captain Joab. Impart to Etzel that I will be making my way to the City of Waters presently, and I will arrive within a fortnight, time enough to recruit another legion of militia. Gladly assure him that I am looking forward to seeing my old comrade in arms."

David continued, "I am concerned for you, Malak, with the mission I lay before you. You have fought an all-night battle and have suffered a head wound. You have since traveled to Jerusalem with this critical dispatch. What say you, sir? Are you lame or game, and do I need to find another more suited?"

Hurt by David's questioning his fitness, Malak good-naturedly responded, "Sire, it was just a scratch, and it has healed up nicely. I have had a hot meal and a comfortable stretch on a warm bed, and by first light, I will be as sprite as a desert Oryx chasing down an elusive female."

David chuckled at Malak's light-hearted response. "Well said, young man. I'm just making sure, for there is no one else that I trust more for such a critical assignment. In the meantime, I will send out my recruiters to scour the realm for volunteers.

Godspeed, Malak. I will see you next standing next to commander Etzel and ready to enter the gates of the royal city."

With a renewed sense of worth and self-esteem, Malak took his leave and was off to fulfill his bargain with David and destiny.

CHAPTER FIFTY
Militia, Mercenaries, and Malcontents

The king's men searched out every tavern, hostel, and bordello for able-bodied fighters. There were peasant farmers, a few nobles, and a spattering of merchantmen. Some were distressed, a few in debt, and many others were discontents looking for a second chance. The inviting promise of glorious spoil from pillage and plunder from a short shift of battle was hard to ignore. Most men volunteered, though some required extra coaxing, either from the point of a sword or the threat of imprisonment. The necessary levy of men soon filled, and the hastily enlisted mercenary army was now organized and given fighting weapons. Eleven days hence, the freshly formed ranks stood expectant and poised, waiting below and inside the ancient Jerusalem walls. Banners were flying high, heralding the storm of war. The wide-ranging crew of adventurers lured in by the promise of gold and a new life were barely ready for the fight. King David appeared high above, larger than life, with the morning sun's first rays glinting off his polished sword and brightening his simple crown. He addressed his fresh recruits, his voice echoing off the battlements, "My brothers in arms, you well-chosen men and a peculiar people that is Israel. I see no fear in your eyes or hesitation to achieve greatness. Soon the day will come when your courage finds its wings, and you will soar as avenging angels of our almighty God. Forsake your past, break all bonds that tie you down, and release your inner courage to the winds of fate and chance. The time of jackals and flaming arrows will challenge us—for we are on a sacred quest. The shield of God, and the buckler of heaven, will protect us, for we are on His holy mission. We will witness all our enemies routed and their high towers come crashing down upon their heads! We will face a mountain fortress and the last barrier to forming the empire of Israel, three days hence.

"The secure citadel of King Hanun, the scoffer, and scorner, lay before us. His stronghold is our final hurdle; it overflows with gems and gold. The rich spoils will be divided equally among you, my soon-to-be wealthy heroes.

"Ammon's destruction and their brazen pirate lackeys will ensure our free trade all along the king's highway. Once King Hanun's servants no longer plague our caravans, Jerusalem will be a mighty trade center and the envy of the region and the world beyond. Moreover, this certain victory will cement a hedge of protection, enlarging our borders to the Eastern Desert, from Egypt to Damascus.

"By all that you hold as precious and dear, I bid you, stand with me, as we dare the fates, you mighty men of Zion. Wars stand won in the hearts and minds of courageous men well before the first arrow finds its mark.

"We depart for Rabbah, the Royal City of Waters."

David hefted his sword and then lowered it to the horizon, pointing the way to the open gate and fate's and fortune's open road. An uproar erupted and continued without dimming to well beyond the seven hills.

Spirits were high during the march. The men bragged about what they were going to do with their prize money. David, girded with poise and confidence, mixed easily among the ranks. He had a likable, friendly air about him. David swapped stories about his nights in the sheepfold and his harrowing encounters fighting off wolves and lions. At night, while huddled around the warming campfires, David loved the retelling of his battle with Goliath. Especially favored by the men were David's tales of his desperate flight from the clutches of the maddening and murderous King Saul. His men marveled at the many times when the hand of God had guided the outcome.

On the morning of the third day, the first light revealed the royal city nestled once again between two streams of fast-moving waters. The invincible citadel stood overlooking a broken metropolis. Its crowning towers cast foreboding dark shadows in a hopeless challenge to the rising sun.

A cheer went up the moment that King David's royal banner was spotted cresting over the horizon. The three anxious commanders hastily prepared to meet the king, still needing a plan or design to destroy King Hanun's castle stronghold.

As they met, the captains at once struck their chests and bowed in respect. The heart of Israel and the king of the Jews were now in attendance. Breaking protocol, Captain Etzel stepped forward and hugged David. He had chafed at his old friend's extended absence and spoke cheerfully of their reunion, "Sire, let it be my honor to return this ring, proving to me that it was your order to withdraw from Succoth and to meet you here at Rabbah."

David gladly accepted back his regifted token, confirming, "Yes, my valued comrade. I treasure this reminder of our total victory at Helam."

David turned his attention to Malak and praised, "Well done, messenger; all are present as directed."

He then addressed Joab and Abishai, recognizing their triumph. "I could not be more pleased with my two commanding nephews. But before we get carried away with acclaim, for our task is only half-completed, let us retire, find a secure place, and work out a winning stratagem. I need to hear your proposals for securing that unscalable bastion, beheading King Hanun, and causing eternal ruin to his evil realm."

All the valued captains stood silently around the strategy table. Joab, forthright and candid, began. "Sire, all approaches we have examined prove difficult, if not near impossible."

David, with the gravest of interest, spoke up. "My creative nephew, please enlighten us with your valued observations; leave no possibility unexplored, no matter how absurd or impractical," as usual, bolstering Joab's confidence.

Abishai agreed. "If it weren't for your quick thinking, we would have lost the entire army of Israel on our first encounter with this cunning enemy."

"Thank you, my brother, for the confidence and compliment. Know this, that all praise is the meat of vanity. Let us not bask in yesterday's glory while today's fight still lays before us."

Joab slammed the table and chided, "Now that I have your attention, I will waste no more time in idle chatter. Instead, I will get to the heart of the matter. My lord king and fellow captains, we face a stronghold built on a cliff. The only entrance is a narrow bridge that spans a death-defying abyss, and at the far end, a metal gate resistant to fire arrows and battering rams defiantly bars our passage. The fortress ramparts overflow with battle-tested archers. They have a clear view on all sides, and there is no way to launch a surprise attack in daylight. A night battle with ropes and ladders would be dangerous at best, like blind men groping upward in the dark searching for foot- and handholds. Besides, the sentries could cast down rocks at the slightest echo, causing a cascade of broken men.

"We have invested a great deal of time sieging the entire city complex. However, it is valuable to note that an enemy informant has revealed that the fortress remains stockpiled with rations and has access to a limitless water supply. Therefore, our time is limited; we have only until the planting season, and that time will soon be upon us. After that, the continuation of the siege would be fruitless for both them and for us."

Joab winked at his deadly wordplay and continued, "That leaves us with either a ruse of deception or a negotiated settlement. We can inform King Hanun that he can continue as Ammon's monarch and remain among the living if he agrees to a sizable tribute and becomes a vassal state of Israel. As far as faking a subtle ploy, I am at a loss. We have come too far, and the Ammonites are wary of every move and will be expecting some sort of ruse or deception."

David, God's Chosen Crucible

David, Abishai, and Etzel murmured at the suggestion of a bargain. David, sensing the discontent in the room vocalized his concern.

"A conditional surrender only attests to our weakness. Hanun must die. If he remains alive, he could, in time, enlist the help of the warring Aramean [Syrian] tribes. Hanun could rally our enemies into a formidable fighting force, harassing our trade routes and draining our resources. If we leave, all the lives, treasure, and time was all for naught. If we stay, we fight. King Hanun will move mountains, turn rivers, and fill valleys with blood to achieve our ultimate destruction.

"Rabbah reminds me of the siege of Keilah. My brothers and I had attracted four hundred vagabond volunteers possessing, at best, a handful of old and rusted weapons. We faced a trained and well-equipped regular army of Philistine fighters. They were attempting to starve out the people of that iron-barred and high-walled city. Just like here, it looked impossible from the onset. But nothing is impossible for God, for He uses weak things to confound the mighty and the foolish to confound the wise. He does this, so there is no mistaking where the power to overcome derives. Our little band of brothers set out at night to find a weakness in the Philistine defenses. Under the stars, the answer lay before my eyes. Our strength was in their weakness—It was the cattle they had brought with them to roast and eat. The scent of burning flesh wafting over the rampart walls tempted the starving; the now desperate inhabitants were all but ready to surrender. The animals used as a weapon against them were the same animal weapon turned around by God to ensure the Philistine destruction. We stampeded the cattle just before

410

dawn into the sleeping Philistines that lay sleeping in their tents. We gathered up the Keilah army, and together, we routed the pagan invaders.

"After sacrificing some of their captured bullocks in homage to Adonai, the only one and true God, we feasted upon the rest, providing us with the sweet taste of God's omnipotence." The room went silent, for David's exploits were both rousing and inspiring.

King David remained steadfast in his convictions and persisted, "Let us ask for God's will for what he would have us do and to grant us the power to carry it out. I will go and scout the borders of the secure upper city and search out its weakness. You, my faithful nephews, and my old friend Captain Etzel are welcome to join me.

"But, for right now, I need to rest and refresh and time to discover this impregnable citadel's layout and architecture. After that, I would like to set up a cold camp on the far side of the castle and out of range of any errant scouts. I will meet you, gentlemen, at the front gate when the sun reaches its zenith."

CHAPTER FIFTY-ONE

Wolves and Backdoor Explorers

David met his three loyal captains at the appointed time. The sun, in its course, hung high in the noonday sky. The king and each commander had an orderly to carry their sundries, including bedrolls, rations, and water. David was pleased and said so. "Captain Etzel, Joab, and Abishai, thank you for accepting my invitation. Sharp eyes and clear minds will help us to overcome our last barrier to greatness. As we proceed to circle the upper fortress, let us distance ourselves from the soaring arc of deadly arrows. Men, look for possible openings both above and below the cliff walls. Be aware of your surroundings, and apply your powers of observation to the fullest. Please limit your talking to whispers. The noise could carry and alert a tower sentry. Let us focus solely on the task at hand. That goes double for your porters."

David's scouting party was hoping to discover an unprotected opening in the Ammonite defenses. David urged, "Our goal is to find a breakthrough into the belly of the beast." The group cautiously skirted around the killing fields. Joab earlier had gauged the distance covered by the deadly Ammonite marksmen. Abishai, after some travel, pointed out a narrow bridge spanning across a bottomless pit. He warned, "That is the only entrance, and at the end of the walkway is a heavily guarded iron gate."

David spoke his mind. "A battering ram would be useless. The iron portal, even from a distance, appears stout and unyielding. The tight corridor, the accurate archers, and the gorge below are a disaster waiting to happen. No, we need to keep on looking. There must be a weakness. I just know it.

"We will be at the very back of the mountain just before dusk. A small, kindled fire is to our comfort. The damp air is a small price to pay to avoid an open invitation to liars and assassins—no sense signaling our location with glowing embers. I do not doubt that our scouting party is no longer a secret from lookouts on the bastion's high towers. But, until King Hanun is dead, we remain in hostile territory."

The sun nearly down, tickling the horizon and coaxing twilight's last gleaming. The rocky outcropping leading up to the stronghold remained impassable. David and his daring band could not find the slightest crack or path to achieve a secure foothold to the summit.

Signaling his fellow travelers, David quietly announced, "Let us prepare to spend the early hours. I will take the first watch, for this is my favorite time, the twilight of the day. It is also the time when warriors struggle with inner demons and prepare for dawn's upcoming battles."

The curtain of the night fell with a thud, cold and dark, nipping skin and chilling bones. The captains huddled around a small campfire, its dim glow shielded by a boulder. The men contented themselves with warm blankets.

David, God's Chosen Crucible

It was just before the beginning of the second watch when wolves on the prowl began a ferocious back-and-forth howl. David was familiar with the language of the wilderness. He was sure that the pack had found some helpless prey. *Just as well,* he thought, *when they have feasted, they will depart and rest in their sheltered cave.*

In the distance, a human voice shrieked a high-pitched challenge. Its desperate tone made the victim sound more like a child. A youth was somewhere in the nearby forest—the likely target for a voracious pack of man-eaters.

Rousing his sleeping companions, David charged Captain Etzel, "I need you to take the night watch. It requires a strong arm to protect our campsite."

Etzel readily agreed. "Yes, Your Majesty. At my age, I do not relish accidentally finding pitfalls in the dark. Let alone taking part in a pitched battle with ravenous meat-eaters."

David then recruited his nephews. "Joab, you and Abishai will accompany me to the uproar of fangs and claws." David hastily gathered up a firebrand and sparked a makeshift torch. The three unlikely saviors pursued the frightening sounds of yelps and snarls. Then, raising high his handheld fire, David smartly maneuvered through the shadows. His two nephews followed closely, trying to keep up with their fleet and strong-willed uncle.

The bold trio burst into a small clearing, witnessing the last smoking embers of exhausted sticks and twigs. A hungry pack of grays was circling a lone shepherd boy, who was fighting for his life. The youth poked and blocked, escaping capture by furiously wielding a herder's staff. The beasts were snapping and growling, their burning amber eyes slipping in and out of the darkness. The daring predators came closer and closer on each pass, attempting to take a bite out of a tender arm or boney leg. With one hand on his sword and the other on his torch, David took an overhead swipe, caught a wolf in full flight, and split its head from crown to jaw. The beast fell dead at his feet. Joab rushed into the fray. Not to be outdone, Abishai slashed mightily with a broad sword and sliced ruthlessly with a cutting knife. Joab took off an ear and Abishai a tail. The whining, whimpering, and the gurgling of blood stopped the pack's brazen assault. The leader sensed the mounting slaughter and bayed the call to give ground. The man-killers then skulked off into the shadows, bleeding and hungry, and no longer strong for the fight.

"Well done, nephews—you have surely inherited our family's fighting spirit. Beast or man, they do not stand a chance against the offspring of the clan of Jesse," David loudly growled, scattering the last of the wounded animals.

Joab, still catching his breath, questioned, "Uncle, the fire is near dead. If we stay, do we need to add fuel to the embers? Should we wait here to see if the beasts will lick their wounds and return in greater numbers?"

David rekindled his crude torch with the last of the red-hot coals. "No, Joab, the pack might seek a less dangerous game. We need to get back to our lightly defended cold camp before the wolf pack picks up their scent and attacks Etzel and the lightly armed porters."

The shepherd boy knelt in homage to his three strange champions and uttered, "Are you gods that fight like men, or men that fight like gods?"

The would-be heroes looked at each other with both amusement and a sense of accomplishment. David revealed, "We are invading Hebrews at war with King Hanun. What are you doing out here in the wilderness alone in the dark?" The youth, humbled by his near-fatal blunder, said, "I was searching for a lost ewe. The gloom was upon me before I knew it. I was buried deep in the forest and blinded by the darkness. I thought it safer to build a fire than to wander alone in the wilds. I was all but defenseless except for my shepherd's staff. I intended to remain vigilant and on guard until dawn. But, fatigue took hold, and my eyes betrayed me and closed. The chilly mist damped down my fire. I awoke to find myself surrounded by the hungry monsters you fought. The creatures seemed bent on my destruction. I fended off the first two stalkers. One, I slammed over the head. The other I caught under the chin. It yelped and disappeared into the thicket. Three more enormous brutes were getting ready to pounce. I was about to give up and surrender to my grizzly fate when you burst in and saved me from being devoured."

David shared heartfelt compassion, born of his past life clashes. He had experienced the very same challenges as the young shepherd boy's near-fatal encounter. He wistfully described his daring adventures. "I am familiar with your plight, more than you might imagine. I also was entrusted to the sheepfold, just like you. In the night and alone, I fended off lions and wolves. In the day, I faced the menace of hungry bears. My skill with my trusty sling had saved me more than once. I could hit a bird in flight and once took down an eagle. God has chosen me in his fiery crucible. I am now King of Israel and the King of the Jews. What is your name, boy?"

The youth, hesitant by his rescuer's exalted position, stammered, "My name is Baa Batun, Your Majesty. Please, tell me, sire, what stroke of good fortune put you in my desperate path?"

David paused, recalling the moment, "I heard the cries of a life-and-death struggle. The unmistakable howls of hungry wolves carried on the winds of fate. Your shrieks traveled further and truer than natural hearing would permit. The Spirit compelled me to fulfill my great commission and rescue a fellow traveler in trouble. Your yells and shouts led me to your location in the dark and dreary wilderness."

Filled with gratitude, Batum praised, "It surely was a gift from the gods. I owe you my life and will ever be your servant, king of kings and lord of lords."

David gave thanks to God, "Adonai, our great and wonderful God, with heartfelt thanksgiving, we acknowledge Your hand in all things. Come, my courageous nephews. The sun also rises. It is time to journey back to base camp."

After a short while, David inquired, "Batum, how well do you know the mountain stronghold of King Hanun?"

"Well enough, sire. King Hanun is a cruel and grasping monarch. He seized almost all of my father's livestock to sustain the City of Waters. As a result, nearly every creature is gone, taken just before the start of the siege. That is why I was so intent on finding my lost ewe in the dark. We have so very few animals to sustain us through the coming months.

"For many years, our herds have grazed between the two streams at the backside of King Hanun's mountain stronghold. It is a steep sheer drop, so the guards ignore that approach. One day a ram struggled to climb the sheer rock face. The relentless beast, prompted by its instincts, tried and tried until it found a foothold. I chose to pursue—but try as I might, I could not find a stand. I was about to give up and wait out the animal's return. But I took one last jump and stood straight up on a smooth, chiseled blind outcropping. Then I looked to the left and saw another place to step and then another, until a concealed stairway lay before me. I proceeded to climb, but the wily creature kept just out of reach.

"At last, I came to a plateau at the bottom of the fortress wall. I looked over the top to see what appeared to be a door tucked away in the shadows. My curiosity demanded that I try the handle. To my surprise, it creaked open on its rusty hinges—loudly shrieking and threatening me with discovery. I looked up to the battlements, but none peered down, investigating the rusty screeching. Opening the door, I could make out a dark and winding corridor. A cold, foreboding chill blew through. I quickly closed the rusty gate, hoping to stop some unseen evil from escaping.

"I looked around to see if I had been discovered and promptly returned to the ground. But, the fright-struck ram was right behind me and almost knocked me down."

David's eyes flashed at this game-changing information, and he inquired further. "Batum, I need you to take me this hidden path. Can you do this?"

Batum, honor-bound replied, "Indeed, sire—I owe you my very breath. What do you need of me? Consider me your willing servant for life."

CHAPTER FIFTY-TWO

Back Doors and Barricades

David shared this breakthrough knowledge of a backdoor with his two nephews and Captain Etzel. He began, "I believe we may have found the weakness needed to unseat Hanun and capture the Royal City. Our battle with the ferocious wolf pack and the rescue of a shepherd boy has given us an unexpected, God-sent benefit. It appears that the builder of the Ammonite stronghold had foreseen the need for a royal backdoor exit. Batum can guide us to that hidden portal. We are going to need some torches to navigate the inner chamber. Batum described it as, 'A gloomy and foreboding corridor.'"

The group went about ripping rags and soaking them in olive oil; then they wrapped the dripping cloth tightly around each of the four extended staves. Joab scooped up some firebrands and placed them in a clay pitcher. The company set out to the hidden rock ladder and the mysterious rear entrance.

On the backside of the rock face, no sentries were visible. Batum, at first, was having trouble finding the first step. After a while, he became frustrated and complained, "I know it is here. It is a well-formed foothold hidden between the boulders." He jumped harder and higher, but this time he seemed to be suspended in midair. Overjoyed for his rediscovery, he was about to cry out until he looked up and thought better of it. Batun put his finger to his lips and pointed to the castle, indicating that silence was an ally. He then extended a hand to David, pulling him up as he stretched for the next step. Each man, in turn, did the same until all five nimbly scaled skyward. Batum was the first to reach the summit. He hoisted every climber onto the cliff.

He was about to open the door when David tapped him on the shoulder to hold back. David took his oil-soaked rag and rubbed it carefully all over the rusted hinges. Once thoroughly covered, David slowly tugged on the ancient handle.

The liberally applied oil eased open the reluctant joints. A blast of cold air met David at the opening. He remarked, "That stiff breeze can mean only one thing—that there is an open-air inlet on the other side." David directed Joab, saying, "Bring forth the pitcher of embers. It is time to set our torches. Batum, you need to keep a wary eye and alert us if anyone approaches. Keep the door ajar. The course of the cross draft will be our guide."

David took the lead, lighting his torch as he entered the passageway. The three captains followed close behind. The combined light pierced the blackened walkway. Deep within the maze, the path went off in two directions. David puzzled. *One way is to a set of stairs, and that must lead to an upper chamber. The lower walkway that we are on all but vanishes into the darkness.*

Joab questioned the diversion and inquired, "Uncle, what do you make of this divide?"

420

David, always a step ahead, had already made the connection. He mindfully replied, "It is the king's passageway. If the monarch needs to leave his castle unobserved to mingle with his people without fanfare or bother, he will continue on this path leading him to the street. Probably, to a private and little-known back alley. If perchance, the invincible Royal City Falls, and he finds himself cornered in his throne room, he then could take the stairs for an escape, putting himself at the back of the mountain and freedom."

Joab sensed a daring opportunity, "Uncle, what if we take the stairs and catch Hanun unguarded in his private apartments? Could we not grab him by the throat and threaten him with a life-or-death decision—surrender the city to our command or die?"

David, intrigued by the outlandish scheme, whispered, "That would be a legendary turn of events. With that in mind, you and I will climb up those dark stairs and see what else there is to discover. Abishai and Etzel, you two continue this current walkway and explore for a street-level portal. Once uncovered, follow us carefully up the twisting staircase."

The climb was narrow and winding. Suddenly, making a sharp turn, David and Joab stepped onto a small landing. A shaft of sunlight broke through the gloom. The two found an opening to the outer wall. It was the king's secure walkway to the battlements. David took a long, hard look but remained cautious and invisible. He stayed just inside the shadows.

Then, energized by their discovery, David, in a playful tone, suggested, "Let us continue, nephew, and see what other secrets this generous stairwell has to offer." The further up they went, the darkness deepened. The bold scouts scaled the last step and now stood facing a massive oaken escape hatch. The formidable barrier appeared locked and bolted from the inside.

The recess had partially cut beams, and pieces of sawed planks littered the ground. "What do you make of all this fresh debris?" Joab whispered his inquiry to his uncle.

As usual, David, in low tones, voiced the obvious: "Hanun has recently installed a new reinforced security door. Any attempt to enter would mean our ending. But I do see an opportunity here. The barrier follows a design to guard against break-ins, not breakouts."

Bewildered, Joab looked for an understanding of David's puzzling argument. Joab asked, "Sire, what is your meaning? Do you speak in riddles?"

David picked up a hefty beam and wedged it tightly against the oaken door without uttering a word.

At once, Joab understood: if they could not break in, then Hanun could not break out. In due course, he could not escape an unavoidable justice. The two worked tirelessly, hand in glove, until the door was so tightly barricaded that it could not budge until well after judgment. Satisfied with their construction, David signaled to depart.

On their descent, they encountered Etzel and Abishai coming up to the lighted parapet archway. Abishai whispered, "Is it as you said, uncle? The lower course opens to a street-level back alley."

David was tired from the extended effort but had a renewed sense of confidence, as if the battle were already won and just a fond remembrance.

David mused that he was entering the Jerusalem gate, a hero, and his waiting bride Bathsheba dressed in wedding garlands to greet him. He then exclaimed, "We have gained a decisive advantage by the uncovering of the many secret avenues to the enemy's destruction. But like any thoughtful guest, we do not want to overstay our welcome. So we need to depart at once and plan for our return with fury and vengeance."

The group of four was making for the back entrance. Their torches were sputtering and spitting, totally depleted of fuel. One by one, and, in turn, all burnt out. In total blackness, David reassured the temporarily sightless men: "The draft is at our back, so our direction is correct. Put your hand on the shoulder of the man in front of you. Take each step slowly and carefully. Be patient. The stiff breeze means the door is open, and the outside light will soon enough be our beacon to freedom." After several agonizing minutes, a speck of light broke through the solid pitch, and each man unhanded his fellow. They all, in step, hurriedly exited the hollow.

David took a deep breath, shielding his eyes from the brightness. He then expressed his heartfelt gratitude: "Batum, good man. You did as commanded and kept the passageway open. Let us depart before we are spotted. Batum, we will follow you down the rocky incline." Before leaving, David marked the spot with a pile of rocks readily found in the blazing daylight.

Once on the ground, the group hurried for the tree line and cover. "Sire, I have spent these many hours away from my flock. They will be milling about and getting lost without a shepherd to guide them. May I have your leave?" Batum pleaded.

"Your service has been invaluable. You have more than made up the life that you owed me. Now go and see to your lost sheep, and may God go with you."

Batum bowed and vanished over the horizon and back to the sheepfold to ensure his family's survival.

"Gather round," David summoned all present. "We have found the key that unlocks this despot's lair. Our victory is within reach and soon to be in our grasp. I am weary and have not slept in days, and I have been fasting for divine intervention. Praise God for answering my prayers. But, my mind wanders, I have lost my focus, and I need to feast and rest. Joab, let us retire to your city lodgings. There we can discuss our final assault with sharper minds and clearer heads." The group made quick time back to the conquered city.

David, struggling to remain alert, directed Joab, "Feed me, for I starve, and wake me up at sundown. We will then gather at eventide to map out our invasion plans."

CHAPTER FIFTY-THREE

The Deception of Conquest

David feasted and then rested, and was particularly
delighted by the discoveries. His mind stilled, lulled into
the sleep of the just. He was soon refreshed as a newborn calf, as
was his custom to wake up from his nap moments before sunset.

David summoned all the chiefs and lesser captains for a
war council. Every man gathered around a large banquet table
conveniently found in a deserted Ammonite mansion. Wine
and food provided for a beggar's feast, the last desperate morsels
from a starving city. Burning torches and broken furniture surrounded the scarred meeting-hall walls. Finding a handy stave,
David, eager to lay out his plans, pounded the table, calling the
gathering to order. The din tempered, and he began in earnest,
"Men, warriors of Israel and so soldiers of God, our time has
come. The last stronghold defies our conquest, ensuring Israel's
empire and securing the king's highway, our lifeblood's trading
route from the Euphrates to the Egyptian frontier. A buffer to
the Eastern desert's far reaches, our boundaries will have an

added measure of protection from hostile invasion. But most of all, we redress an insult and ridicule enacted against our grieving ambassadors. Were they not sent solely to console King Hanun upon the death of his father? This shameful stain to Israel and me personally continues to fester.

"Men, we need to finish the capture of the royal city before planting season. A further siege is out of the question. If we return with our work only half done, there will be a great forfeit in the future. Hanun will proclaim our weakness and rally all our enemies against us. All our hard-won conquests will count for naught, less than straw. No, now is the time to attack and prevail. Victory will ensure that this scorpion's tail meets destruction, never to rise again.

"I propose a four-pronged attack. First, we have found a secret rear entrance exposing the citadel's inner workings, by God's grace and good luck. Second, deep inside the cavern, there are two pathways into the royal city. One route leads to the street and the other to the lofty ramparts guarding a sealed doorway, which I believe leads to King Hanun's private apartments. Third, I propose that Chief Captain Joab and Co-Commander Abishai take twenty men into the rear mountain passage. You both have explored these dark recesses and, as a result, are best equipped to lead an expedition. Fourth, and most importantly, begin your climb at daybreak, when you hear the shofar horn signaling Captain Etzel's attack on the far eastern slope.

"Do not spark your torches until after you reach the inner sanctum. When entering the void, make your best way possible to the upper and lower gatehouses. Joab will take ten men up the stairs to the parapet walkway when they reach the corridors' junction. Abishai, you take your ten and follow the lower tunnel to the street level back alley. Your mission is to raise the gate at the end of the span that connects the two cities, whatever the cost. I, with the rest of the army lying deep in the shadows, will rise and flood the narrow passageway into the castle and quickly overpower any resistance."

"Captain Etzel, you with your Succoth militia, will gather at dawn, creating a diversion with a chorus of shofar horns. You will attack the east side of the cliff. The slope is shallow enough to storm the walls with ropes and ladders. It is a dangerous venture when facing down a torrent of arrows.

"I need the Ammonite Chief Captain Nemun to take the bait, commit all his forces, and focus away from the gateway overpass.

"This calculated deception could be costly. But it can also give us a much-needed distraction to ensure an opening with little or no resistance at the connecting crossover."

David paused to gauge the mood of the assembled captains. Then, after an uncomfortable silence, he demanded, "I believe my plan is our best option to capture the fortress while suffering the fewest casualties and so minimize our losses. If there are any suggestions or questions, now is the time to voice them."

Jaws dropped, brows were mopped, and fingertips pressed hard against thoughtful lips. The moments passed, each man looking at the other without an opinion or the slightest refinement. Consequently, all thought better of voicing a dissenting challenge without ensuring a better outcome. Reluctantly, Joab laid his doubts on the table.

"Sire, let me begin by saying your plan is brilliant and has every chance of succeeding. But I have doubt—what if we, my brother, and I, are not able to defeat the barrier. Then what?"

David said sadly, "Then I would grieve the loss of my two favorite nephews. I am expecting you to prevail even at the cost of your own lives. But let us say, for argument's sake, that you falter. Then I will reinforce Captain Etzel's Succoth militia, and we will storm the ramparts together with ropes and ladders the best we can."

David continued, with uplifting praise. "Chief Captain Joab and Captain Abishai, you both working together have overcome greater odds than these. I have every confidence in your abilities to make a way or find one. But, Joab, I have some wisdom to impart.. Refrain from focusing on the deadly gulf of failure. See the end from the beginning. You will overcome all obstacles when you envision the summit of success already mounted and standing proud in the sunlight of the spirit."

Joab, enlivened and even excited, put away all his misgivings.

David advised, "Men, we need to concentrate on securing ladders and scaling ropes. Dedicated preparation to details invites luck and lessens any gamble. We will attack three days hence. So go now, and make me proud, my fearless and capable captains of Israel."

The occupied lower city and the outer camp were awash with activity. Ropes were precisely measured and grappling hooks attached. Men practiced swinging the long cords higher and higher until their claws gripped sure onto stone walls. The chopping and splitting of saplings echoed through the forest, providing the production of invasion ladders.

Hours before the dawn of the third day, a final gathering safe-guarded that every captain knew his mission and battle position.

David assembled his well-prepared cadre and began, "Men, loyal soldiers of God, our time is at hand to crush our long-time nemesis, Ammon. Captain Etzel, you will be taking the brunt of the battle. Be assured, my old friends, that the instant the gate stirs upward, I will give a single extended blast from my shofar horn. That is your signal to withdraw and join me in storming the crown of the royal city. I will wait on you both, Joab and Abishai, but for only one turn of the hourglass and not a moment longer. Be advised that, when the last grain of sand drops, the army under my command will withdraw from the shadows and follow you, Etzel, all the way through to the summit. Together we will fight, and we shall prevail. Let us seek the blessings of God early." David prayed for divine intervention.

"Adonai, I praise You with all my heart, mind, and strength. You are my shield and my buckler. I take refuge in Your Hightower. I am not afraid of the dread of night, nor the arrow that flies by day, Lord—You have placed a cover over me and in all my doings. So that in You, I will always remain victorious. I implore You, Lord of hosts, for You are worthy of all my devotion. I call unto You, my Lord, and my God. For I know, the battle is not mine, but it is Yours to decide. Lightning from heaven, cast Your bolts and rout my enemies.

"Into your hands, I place my fate and the fate of Israel. ah-MAIN."

CHAPTER FIFTY-FOUR
A Battle of Crushing Bricks and Death-Defying Arrows

Brothers in arms Joab and Abishai, the two co-commanders, departed hastily with their twenty-man raiding party. The benefit of a full moon was God-sent. The silvery glow prevented pitfalls and the need for torches. The back-door invaders patiently waited just inside the wood-line shadows for the uprising trumpet call. The stealthy raiders needed enough sunlight to maneuver up the treacherous rock face and into the hidden cavern without being spotted.

Captain Etzel's entire Succoth militia, despite all odds, stood determined to scale the rocky heights. They waited eagerly for the gray light of dawn and the sound of the shofar horn inviting them into the turmoil.

Poised at the rally point, with an hourglass in hand, David assured his anxious men, hidden in the trees and shadows, that the crossover iron gate would open as if by magic. If not, he would wait for the last grain of sand to plummet, announcing their rally into the hillside vortex of spears and arrows.

The morning chill now filled with chattering teeth and the anxious sweat of coming death. Then suddenly, the sunlight burst through the darkness. A shofar horn sounded, and in the distance, a lone enemy alarm responded. The fight was on.

Chief Captain Nemun woke with a start, at the shofar's staccato wail and at the heavy pounding on his chamber door. An orderly rushed in, not waiting for an invitation. Then, catching his breath, he sputtered, "Chief Captain, Israel is attacking our Eastern slope with force and vigor. At this very moment, a swarm of warriors covers the rise, climbing upward, dragging their siege ladders, and carrying scaling ropes. What are your orders?"

Nemun, gaining his senses, swallowed hard and shouted, "Go and rouse my captains. I want every archer and all available men to secure the eastern battlements."

Every available Ammonite warrior rushed to the eastern wall. Parapets overflowed with archers. Long forked poles made ready to push off enemy ladders. The remainder of fighting men stood prepared down below as reinforcements to ward off the coming onslaught.

Captain Nemun gave standing orders to his men held in reserve below the battlements. "Men, be prepared at a moment's notice to replace our fallen comrades." He then rushed up the stairs to the center of the conflict. His bowmen were effectively repelling the bloody climb of the Succoth militia. The captain of the archers pushed his way through the heightening chaos and clamor.

Reaching the newly arrived chief captain, he reported, "Lord, we have been able to slow the upward climb of the storming invaders with swarms of arrows and spears. But the long siege and the relentless enemy attacks have depleted our stores of barbs and shafts. Without that defense, our stronghold will collapse, and King Hanun, I fear, will be humiliated and slaughtered."

Nemun paused, for he knew defeat was inevitable without his marksmen to hold back the enemy upsurge on his eastern border. Then in a moment of inspiration, Nemun blurted out, "Bricks!"

The lesser commander, puzzled, repeated, "Bricks? Please, Chief Captain, what is your meaning by this?"

Nemun, feeling inspired, continued, "Bricks may very well save the day. I will bring up the reserves equipped with hammers, chisels, and levering bars. We will start breaking out the bricks in the wall—and with that, a torrent of crushing blocks shall commence." Nemun commanded, "Hurl them down ruthlessly upon the enemy's head. The unrelenting pounding might even begin a rockslide, sweeping off these trespassers and smashing all their hope for success."

At the same time, at the very back of the fortress, twenty-two intruders swiftly scaled the cliff and employed its hidden footpaths. Reaching the inset doorway, they ignited their torches with a pitcher of red-hot embers. The covert band then entered the recesses of the inner sanctum. The junction of corridors eerily appeared, outlined by the flickering light of sparking torches. Their timing was critical for the successful completion of their mission. Joab and his ten men took the stairs to the battlements. Abishai took his ten and headed for the back-alley entrance into the city.

A Battle of Crushing Bricks and Death-Defying Arrows

As David had expected, it was a garrison city, and all soldiers were immediately ordered to the eastern wall to repel invaders. The early-morning streets remained deserted. Abishai's squad made good time getting to the gatehouse. Abishai faced a few Ammonite sentries. He held back, waiting for his brother to reach the upper battlements and release the locking levers.

Joab and his men encountered an unexpected pocket of enemy resistance. Both groups were equally surprised at the meeting. But Joab fought bravely through to the overhead tower despite heavy losses, and before the guards below could aid their upper overwhelmed comrades, Abishai made short work of all opposition. Lastly, Joab called down to his brother, "Abishai, the gate is free—hoist the pulley ropes and invite in the army of David. Today we fulfill the destiny of the empire of Israel."

The last grain of sand in David's hourglass dropped; time had run out, and still, the gate remained shut and locked. David knew that Captain Etzel and his Succoth volunteers were taking a pounding. He dare not hesitate, for any delay could cost the lives of many courageous men on the far side of the citadel. David stood up and took a deep breath to shout out the command to redeploy to the eastern slope and reinforce the Succoth militia's desperate ascent to the well-defended ramparts. At that moment, the rusted iron gate screeched, giving up a sliver of daylight and a slice of hope. The door slowly hiked up and up until finally exposing the inner city. David discarded his sandglass in favor of his shofar horn. He blew three mighty blasts, loud enough to wake the dead. Etzel's army had indeed been severely stung, pierced with arrows through the heart and lungs. Some heads suffered the crush from falling blocks. Upon hearing the

433

trumpeted withdrawal, all the Succoth militia speedily retreated from the hillside slaughter.

The army of Israel funneled into the city over the abyss on the narrow land bridge. Their advance was so swift that they flooded the entrance and suffered little resistance.

Abishai met his vengeful uncle at the entrance to the royal city. David, at once, directed him to take his men and attack the remaining Ammonite army cornered in the eastern quarter. He then ordered two companies of men to ascend to the level above and aid Joab in crushing the remaining lethal archers.

Suddenly the savaged Succoth militia appeared in their midst like men possessed as they entered the enemy stronghold. They chose to be in for the kill instead of sitting it out and licking their grievous wounds.

Captain Etzel—bloodied from the battle, his eyes burning with hatred—asked, "My king, what are your orders? Where would you have us to wreak the greatest havoc?"

David was troubled at the condition of his brutalized comrade. He sought to console his friend with the promise of retribution. "You have done a man's work today, challenging this impregnable mountain stronghold. I want you and your men to accompany me to the castle keep and invade King Hanun's throne room. I am confident that he awaits my presence. It is impolite to leave a king wondering and waiting. If we encounter opposition, you and your men will have the pleasure of crushing any token resistance. Take no thought for Captain Nemun and his Ammonite army. My two nephews have taken the rest of the men and will finish off the cornered holdouts in due course."

CHAPTER FIFTY-FIVE

A Fierce Reprisal and Punishment by Example

David and Etzel's vengeful warriors hastily crossed the isolated city. They mounted the stairs leading into the palace and immediately engaged a band of lethal suicide bodyguards protecting the entrance. These zealous fanatics had pledged their very lives in defense of the king and fiercely challenged the unwelcomed intruders. The sentinels made a courageous stand for themselves, buying some time by slowing David's entrance into the heart of the mansion. But, savagely, Etzel's Succoth warriors' pent-up fury made short work of the doomed defenders.

David's furious punishers were freed from all opposition and sped down the dimly lit corridor, stopping at a massive, locked doorway barring their invasion. The entryway is the last barrier of protection that shields the king's throne room from intrusion. Calling out, David directed, "Men, lift that long oaken bench, and we will use it as a battering ram." With all their might, ten big men slammed the heavy bench into the concrete beams. A curious second bang came from behind the unyielding entry. The thick planks cracked and splintered, but the great gate refused to give way.

On the third strike and with the bench about to crumble, the door flung open. To David's surprise, a wall tapestry hung to one side, revealing King Hanun and his entourage of nobles. They, too, were desperately ramming a hidden passageway that held fast, refusing to budge even the slightest. The king's emergency escape hatch appeared to be hopelessly jammed—the same exit that David had earlier wedged shut with foresight, timbers, and a little luck.

King Hanun turned to face the crash, only to witness a crush of soldiers entering the hall. He grew pale as if he had seen the ghost of retribution. The Ammonite nobles hastily drew their swords but then were encircled by dirty and blood-stained warriors just as quickly. The tattered and torn crowd appeared as dead men freshly risen from the grave. The smell of rotting fruit, cabbage, eggs, and garlic, the unmistakable scent of death hung over their heads. The outnumbered nobles dropped their swords that clattered noisily to the floor and cautiously moved against the wall. David's ire at a boil, he yelled, "Hanun, you have mocked me, and you have evaded justice. The time of reckoning is at hand. You have insulted my emissaries with ridicule, disdain, and embarrassment. As you have done to them, you have done it also unto me." Hanun knew his time had come and made a last desperate plea with a troubled apology, saying, "Great king, I was misguided by my royal advisers. They had convinced me that your ambassadors came to spy out my strengths and weaknesses." He pointed toward his pack of quaking counselors huddled in the corners. "My ministers said that yours was 'a contrived kindness'—that it was a ploy using the grief of my father's death to determine our strengths and readiness for battle."

Even though the truth often hides behind the cunning mask of anger, David would have none of it. This Ammonite thorn in Israel's side would fester no longer—and, proving his intent, he said, "A king feigning ignorance is like a harlot claiming virginity. Do not prolong your charade. Draw out your jewel-encrusted blade. We will fight man to man and king to king. If you prevail, you win your life. My men will spoil the city but leave you breathing. If you refuse to engage, I will run you through where you stand. So, defend yourself as a man, or suffer slaughter as a coward!"

Hanun, enraged at the slight, frantically lunged. David deflected, and sparks spit as their sharpened iron swords clashed. Hanun, much younger, had stamina and agility. David knew it had to be a quick kill, using years of practice and honed skills before Hanun could wear him down, using an abundance of energy, his youthful benefit. After several well-placed cuts, Hanun mounted a whistling sweep, trying to slice David in half. David saw it coming and stepped out of the way, leaving Hanun off balance. David took advantage and stepped in with a reverse spin and severed Hanun's head at the neck. The torso slumped in a heap to the ground.

Hanun's severed skull took flight until it thudded to the floor, one eye half-closed in a perpetual stare. King Hanun's exquisite gold crown found rest at David's feet. Etzel picked up the emblem of royal power, amply studded with precious gems. It indeed must have had the value of a talent of gold.

The Ammonite nobles groveled, placing their foreheads on the floor and exposing their necks in the ultimate act of submission. Their last but futile attempt to remain alive, seeking mercy and David's good graces.

With words that seemed to echo beyond the grave, Etzel placed the ornate trophy on the kneeling David's head, saying, "May God crown you with a crest of glory, king of virtue, and a monarch of majesty—King of Israel, and the King of the Jews. May your house, kingdom, and throne be established forever." David bowed his head at Etzel's worthy blessing. The weighty icon of power almost slid off his head at the bending.

The Succoth avengers seemed to have moved further away and remained eerily silent. Eager to show his royal prize and quell any further conflict, David commanded, "You Ammonite ministers, you faulty and cowardly advisers, follow me to the palace entrance, and bring forth the head of the king bound in his royal apron.

"Etzel, my dear friend, you and your spirited warriors are to guard against any escape attempts through windows, side doors, or darkened passageway." Therefore, the crowd treaded cautiously through the scattered corpses at the castle's raised entranceway.

David stepped into the bright sunlight, shielding his eyes from the glare. Joab came hastily bounding up the stairs, gushing, "Great king, you have adorned yourself with the sterling Ammonite crown, which befits your station. You have outdone yourself killing the king and have captured a pack of Ammonite nobles all by yourself. A magnificent accomplishment, Your Majesty!"

David readily disagreed. "No, no, nephew, not alone. Captain Etzel and his intrepid crew made this capture possible." David turned his head, calling out, "Etzel, come forth." But there were only his governing Ammonite prisoners and a long, empty corridor. David was puzzled; there were no echoing footsteps or sounds of any kind.

Joab questioned, "Uncle, that is quite impossible. Chief Captain Etzel and all his men, every last one, died in the climb. Their bodies corrupt in the sun, where they fell dead on the mountainside, struck through or crushed. I witnessed their horrific end from high atop the watchtower."

The short hairs on the back of David's neck stood up, and a chilling shiver ran down the length of his back. David was now thoroughly confounded from the recounting of his unfathomable ghostly encounter. He could neither explain nor comprehend his sojourn into the dark ethereal realm.

King David looked up and saw clouds forming a stairway to the sun. He thanked God for the needed help, and, in a faint whisper, he uttered, "God's will, not mine, be done." David then turned and demanded of Joab, "Now you swear to me on all that you hold holy that you will tell no one, and we will never speak of this strange happening again!"

Joab countered, "I do so swear by my head."

David questioned, "Nephew, what news of our invasion have you come to report?" Joab took a moment, still trying to digest the supernatural tale that challenged his sense of order.

Joab choked down his unsettled curiosity and thought best to move on, saying, "Sire, the Ammonite army defies our advances.

We have them surrounded in the eastern quarter of the city. They have no room to evade or maneuver. A few have fled by scaling down the high battlements in a desperate attempt to escape death or surrender. But, alas, Your Majesty, many Ammonite soldiers still stubbornly withstand the forces of Abishai, my brother. It is the enemy's last futile attempt to break free, and many prefer a warrior's death to cowardly humiliation."

David anxiously inquired, "What of our losses, and did you effect the arrest of Chief Captain Nemun?"

Looking down and away, Joab replied, "No, my lord. Nemun is the glue that binds the last threads of resistance, and our losses are mounting."

David snatched the blood-stained bundle of bone, brain, and contorted face of the slaughtered monarch and motioned for Joab to follow him up to the rampart stairs, saying, "Let us hurry. I will display Hanun's solid gold crown and his bloody head, so all will know that their king is dead."

David and Joab climbed high above the fray, the western sun glinting off the polished gold crown and sparkling reflective gemstones. Joab hefted his shofar horn and gave three mighty blasts; all eyes looked up, and for the moment, the fighting stopped. David lifted the Ammonite crown from off his brow and held it high in his right hand. In his left hand, he grabbed a hunk of matted hair and thrust the severed head skyward, forcing all to concede the downfall of their beloved sovereign.

David, without uttering a word, caused all Israel to begin an uproar of victory. The Ammonites, deflated and forlorn, cast away their weapons of war, ending their hopeless defense. The very sight of the mutilated head of their beloved monarch had crushed their will to fight.

Turning to Joab, David declared, "Go now and round up the nobles, gentry, and the captains of hundreds. Bind them, but keep our more esteemed captives separate; I don't want them organizing and starting any trouble. Ammon has been a thorn in our side longer than memory can recall. We need to break their will to fight, so they menace us no longer. I will fill their hearts with trouble and let them know to fear Israel as they dread the night. I need you to bring forth the people so they might witness savage acts of vengeance where there is no mercy, pardon, or concession. We need to instill fear from balls to bones that their loyalty is to Israel and Israel alone, surpassing all other troubles and concerns."

All the survivors of both the upper and lower City of Waters became needed witnesses. Next, David outlined specific punishments to make unforgettable examples of what to expect for slackers, loafers, and rebels. Then, the population remained in the open field beyond the city walls. David then used the governors and high-ranking officials as stark reminders for the penalty of disobedience.

He ordered, "All farmers who do not meet their yearly tribute can expect a painful end under the iron spikes of harrows."

In such a way, Chief Captain Nemun met his piercing death in full view of all the people. Next, David called forth the builders and carpenters of wood, saying, "If you lack your required tribute, we will saw you in two with a dull blade." Next, a high-ranking minister laid across a makeshift table let loose harrowing screams as the teeth bit into his flesh, letting out an ear-piercing howl that curdled the blood of even the most hardened stoic. The woodsmen, so, too, were threatened for falling production; a noble came forward and was brutally hacked to death with an iron ax instilling their ominous warning. David left the gruesome highlight for last. The Ammonite prime minister ruthlessly passed through the brick kiln that roasted him alive, a stern warning to the masons to dismantle the city's walls and its crowned fortress. They were also to come to Israel as a tribute when summoned or suffer the same agonizing inferno.

The overwhelmed populace cringed with horror at the brutal and ongoing object lessons. Pleased with the crowd's reaction, David called forth his right-hand man and ever-loyal Chief Captain Joab, stating, "Nephew, this harsh lever of submission requires a broader extension to all the greater and lesser cities of Ammon. I have realized that the removal of the Ammonite governing class will prevent any future rebellions and ensure long-lasting obedience to our will."

"We will go 'ahead' with Hanun's severed head, and with the remnants of his defeated army, we will freely pillage, and none will dare challenge." David wryly smiled at his wordplay. "We will leave only enough provisions for the people to survive on until next harvest season.

"I have drained my treasury in this endless Ammonite siege and need every shekel to continue the ongoing costs of governing Israel. So let us take the army and refill our coffers."

David spoiled Ammon towns and cities, and, with a caravan of carts overflowing with treasure, he crossed over the Beth-barah to Jerusalem and matrimony.

CHAPTER FIFTY-SIX
A Mourning Borne for a Marriage to Endure

All across the seven hills of Jerusalem, glad tidings rang out. King David was now the conqueror of Ammon and the bringer of spoil and riches untold. He would soon pass through Zion's Golden gate and into legend.

The glorious news swept through every quarter of the city. The seemingly constant wars with Edom, Moab, Arameans (Syria), and lastly, Ammon, had finally ended, assuring prosperity from free trade and peace from the security of buffer states reaching as far as the Eastern Desert.

Before entering Jerusalem, David called forth his armor-bearer to retrieve King Hanun's decaying head. He reached in, grabbed it by its matted hair, and shook off buzzing flies; it seemed alive with maggots. Then, raising it the length of his outstretched arm, he marveled at its lightness compared to Goliath's massive skull. For dramatic effect, David also placed Hanun's golden crown upon his crimson locks of hair.

Garlands dangled from the rooftops. Jerusalem was in a joyous mood, and many took to singing and dancing in the streets. David, flanked by the heroes Abishai and Joab, proudly paraded through the streets to the sound of cheering crowds. Finally, the triumphant three mounted the mansion steps, the king's household all in attendance.

Abiathar, David's friend and loyal high priest, rushed in to greet the gallant trio, spouting praises and thanksgiving.

"Thank our mighty God; He has seen fit to return our beloved sovereign unharmed. My eyes stream with tears of joy at the sight of the king's well-being. Sire, we have planned a banquet in your honor this very night. All I need is your approval. It would mean so very much to all the people."

David turned to Joab. "The stench from this rotting trophy at once needs a fitting burial. Take the dammed thing, nephew—my arm aches, and my hand grows weary. Bury it outside the walls at Golgotha [or the place of the skull] and give Goliath some needed company."

Joab took the gruesome artifact and placed it in a handy sack. Then, fighting off the buzzing flies, he gingerly stepped aside and departed.

Relieved of his burden, David replied to Abiathar's request for a gala. "We need to speak in private as to my plans for this evening's festivities. I require your delicate discretion, high priest, and you, too, Ebed, my faithful body servant. Come with me to more private confines and away from prying eyes and errant ears."

The trio made their way to David's apartments. At once, David turned and produced a notched stick illustrating the passage of time. He recounted, "The thirty days of Bathsheba's grieving has concluded. She has completed her observance of our venerated rituals and is now available by law to remarry. Is that not so, Abiathar?"

Abiathar knowingly approved. "Yes, sire, that is so. By the laws of Israel, you are now free to marry the widow Bathsheba bat Eliam. What then would you have of me to assist in your joyous nuptials?"

David had long anticipated embracing his soulmate and delighting in her charms as man and wife in the eyes of God. In the back of David's mind, he pondered. *Will our secret be shamefully exposed in Bathsheba's ill-timed and pregnant blossoming?* He needed to get her undercover and out of the public eye, avoiding the inevitable.

His longing and patience were long since exhausted. David lamented, "I suffer the press from many quarters; time is not my ally. I need a holy man to perform my wedding ceremony under the canopy, straight away. What say you, Abiathar ben Ahimelech?"

"I am pleased by the honor," Abiathar joyfully agreed. "I would be delighted, sire. When were you planning on this sacred ritual taking place?"

"Why, this very evening will do nicely. Besides, it is my favorite time of day. The twilight often promises hidden treasures of carnal pleasures that often flee from the light of day."

David again stressed his need for haste. Then, sensing the king's urgency, Abiathar, troubled by the lack of notice, saying, "I will make do as best I can, and as the king commands. It will have to be a small gathering, Sire—just the most intimate of friends and family, I take it."

"Yes, my good priest. You do understand that it will be an unrehearsed and private affair. I will see to the summoning of the guests. It would be best for you to prepare the place and the necessary ritual trappings. How hard can it be? This ceremony invites my eighth wife to my bed; you could provide the chupah [or wedding canopy] you should by now be able to do it in your sleep."

Abiathar agreed. "By your leave, Majesty, there is much to prepare to see to all the details." Abiathar collected his thoughts about the arrangements; he was about to rush off obedient to the king's need for speed and discretion.

"Where are you, Ebed? You were right here a moment ago," David called out, looking around for his vanishing manservant. "Here I am, sire—right behind you. What would you have of me, Your Majesty?"

David turned around, attempting to calm himself from his pre-marital jitters, saying, "Oh, there you are, blending in as usual. I need a change of fresh clothing and for you to gather up some reliable and discreet porters. But, first, I need you to put the wedding plans in motion. As soon as you have finished giving the other servants their assigned tasks, we need to leave for the lady Bathsheba's residence. I will fetch her to be my wife, and we need to be as subtle as possible.

"Ebed, you are the master of back-alley navigation that can accomplish our travel with little or no notice.

"As soon as I arrive, the lady will know that I am whisking her away to be my bride. Like any woman, when leaving her nest, she will have a longing to retain familiar keepsakes. While she is so engaged in collecting her keepsakes, I will set about making a list of likely participants.

"The holy ritual will require ten righteous men, a minyan by tradition, to make it valid in the eyes of God."

Ebed voiced his concern. "Your Majesty, I must confess that, in this late hour of preparation, that might be too great a challenge to gather that many honest men. Does it have to be ten, and why ten? Perhaps we can make do with fewer because of our time constraints."

David was becoming impatient, but he took the time to explain. "Our rituals are ancient and sacred, and we seek to align with the mind of God. Therefore, with unbridled passion, we put Him to remembrance, and by doing so, we can gather in a multitude of blessings.

"The required ten men go back to the time of Father Abraham's rescue mission. Father Abraham sought out his brother Lot in the wicked twin cities of Sodom and Gomorrah. Spewing from those twin ghettos of evil, the stench of wickedness, corruption, and abominations rose to the heavens. Nevertheless, with significant risk to his person, Abram started for the sake of fifty. Still, he persisted in his negotiations with God several times, risking Adonai's anger to spare the perverted populace.

"Finally, Abraham asked for the sake of ten righteous men. Would God hold back his hand? But, of course, even ten honorable men representing a community of honor went wanting, and God departed. The fire of the sun descended, not leaving one brick upon another."

Ebed thoughtfully responded, "Thank you, sire. I can now see why ten is the number of virtue and is required to uphold God's holy order."

David persisted. "I have an insight for you, Ebed. When Abraham and the two angels entered Lot's home, Lot instructed his wife Ado, and by custom, to entertain each angel with a portion of salt. Salt is the element that turns corruption into incorruption and so would recognize them as eternal beings. But, Ado had none, not a pinch. So, she went to her neighbors with the intent to borrow—and yet, try as she might, not a grain was forthcoming.

"The two heavenly messengers took Abraham, Lot, and Ado, Lot's wife, and their two daughters by the hand and hurriedly vacated the city. The two angels gave a stern warning not to look back, saying, "Do not turn your eyes back upon the face of evil, for evil will pursue you until it consumes you. The town and the plain that we are rushing upon will soon be utterly destroyed with fire and brimstone. The scurrying group tucked their skirts into their girdles, and so girding their loins, for a misguided step could mean a death sentence. So, with all due haste, the fleeing band sought refuge in the surrounding high mountain passes. Ado, Lot's wife, hearing the uproar, paused and gazed back to witness God's vengeance, all but ignoring the deadly warning not to do so. The sight so penetrated Ado's mind and soul that she instantly turned into a pillar of salt, forever locked in her dominant thought—her unfulfilled search for the salt of salvation."

Humbled by David's depth of understanding and insight, Ebed quietly uttered, "Sire, you have been gifted by God much beyond common understanding."

David confessed, "Intelligence is the glory of God, and He has enlightened my mind many times. I am merely a receptacle.

He is the source of all righteousness, intelligence, knowledge, wisdom, compassion, justice, and power."

"I stray from our task at hand. I have the list of guests and witnesses, Ahithophel, her grandfather, Eliam, her father, my nephews, commanders Joab and Abishai, Zeruiah and Abigail, my two sisters. But, of course, the guest list would not be complete without my brothers, Eliab and Abinadab, Shammah, Nethanel, Raddai, Ozem. I am aware that some might be unavailable on such short notice. Give the list to Abiathar. The priest will make sure that we have ten good men to make the marriage legal and acceptable by the laws of Israel and in the mind of God. If we do this correctly, the union will be fruitful, and our heirs will prosper. Let us now go at once to the lady Bathsheba's house and ask if she has some personages she wishes to attend. You will need some help to gather in the guests, so recruit some discreet and fleet messengers in the king's name to deliver my urgent invitations."

Ebed cleared his throat to help steady his backbone. "Lord King, if I may be so bold."

"Speak on—time is precious, and I grow anxious."

"Well, sire, should an invitation to your wives and consorts be extended?"

Looking down and violently shaking his head, David growled, "No, absolutely not. The last time they were all invited to one of my weddings, it ended in a catfight. So I cannot invite one or even some. It has to be all or none. The alliances of the wives, like politics, shift. Sometimes best of friends and sometimes best of enemies. The marriage to another woman is just the right spark that can burn down the house. Of course, they will eventually meet Bathsheba, but on their terms individually and alone, and in time, the power sway will change. But not tonight—too great a risk to fuel a bonfire of vanities."

"Yes, lord, I understand—and I might say, the wisest of decisions."

"As for you, Ebed, I need you to direct your cooks and scullery maids to prepare a wedding feast for my small family gathering. It will be at twilight. I wish the hall to be well lighted. Have your stewards prepare extra torches. Let us be off. I brim with anticipation and excitement."

David was navigating the side streets and avoiding heavily trafficked thoroughfares. The heavily hooded king and his entourage of baggage handlers evaded observation, appearing as common merchantmen.

Eventually, David arrived at Bathsheba's doorstep, eager and well-prepared. He was more than ready to fetch his lady love, making her his eighth wife, restoring his peace of mind and the lady's honor, by elevating Bathsheba's stature to consort, affording her protection and privilege and status beyond reproach.

The disguised monarch boldly burst in, casting aside all polite conventions. His first and only sight was Bathsheba. His jaw dropped, and his breath caught with an all-encompassing vision of her loveliness. The two lovers, too long denied, rushed each other—touching, kissing, and hugging, re-kindling smoldering embers of passion's unquenchable fire. They, both straining, their hearts entwined, longing to take their solemn vows and elevate their love as man and wife, never divided or separated again.

"Bathsheba, my beloved daughter of the vow, your name fits you like a crown," David, utterly smitten, whispered into her ear. "I have come to fetch you and bring you back to my home and wed you this very evening. All the necessary preparations are in progress. After this night, you will have no reason to return to this house. You can bury your unpleasant memories in the past and leave them far behind you. Bathsheba, you have a new life both in your belly and from this night forward ahead of you with me, your new husband, at your side.

"I have made a list of possible guests. Look and tell me if there is anyone you wish to add as essential or to dismiss as troublesome."

Bathsheba studied the names and agreed, "Other than my closest friend and handmaiden Almah, and all seems to be in order. Oh, Fiona, a woman of noble birth and a closed-mouthed friend. She prefers to remain in the shadows; even though she will not attend, an acknowledgment of my love and respect requires an invitation."

"Very well, my love—then consider it done."

Calling upon Ebed, David confidently advised, "All is well, Ebed. I recollect our winding approach and can easily maneuver our back-alley transit. You have your orders; execute them as if your life depended on the outcome."

Ebed bowed. He secretly enjoyed the ongoing familiarity afforded by the king's good-natured chiding. Although sometimes, he could not tell if the king was joking or in earnest. He nodded and, not wishing to take any chances, vanished out of sight as if the specter of unfulfilled responsibilities were haunting him through the open doorway.

The porters and their wheeled carriages soon overflowed with Bathsheba's sundries. Then, finally, the lovers' strange caravan, cloaked in hoods and veils, wound their way to the king's mansion.

451

The star-crossed lovers and Bathsheba's cherished treasures found a new home in the royal apartments.

The carters, maids, and servants were offhandedly dismissed, quieting the din of activity. Bathsheba then called out, "Not you, Almah. I must shed these drab widow's weeds and don a gay and festive sheath, something to match my soaring spirits."

Almah giggled as one girl to another and cheerily replied, "Quite so, madam—my thoughts entirely. I know just the stunning frock that will enhance your beauty and grace. But it has been packed away too long and needs some loving touch-up. So, I must see to the pressing, and I will return when, once again, it appears elegant. I wait upon your summons."

Almah bowed and departed, leaving the loving couple finally alone and to their own devices.

"I thought this day would never come, my love," Bathsheba exhaled with a sense of relief. David paused briefly in wonder, his eyes fixed upon Bathsheba as if seeing her for the first time.

Uneasy at his penetrating stare, she questioned, "David, my love, you seem distracted. What is the matter?"

David, as if coming out of a fleeting dream, spoke up. "I have pined for you during endless nights and stress-filled days. You have been in my vivid dreams and my first thinking upon awakening, and now you are soon to be mine for all time. A single moment has not passed without the thought of us entwined in a heated embrace. My love for you flourishes like a garden of heavenly delights. Every time I think I have reached the summit of ecstasy, the vision of you takes me to greater heights."

Overwhelmed with David's ardent longing, Bathsheba nearly swooned, her knees unsure and her feet slipping. Rushing over,

David caught her before she fainted, placing her gently on the bed. With the weakest of protests, Bathsheba whispered, "My love, we will be man and wife soon enough, and I need time to prepare. Dearest David, can you not bide your time and quell your ardor for even the briefest of moments?"

Being so inflamed, David ignored her feeble pleadings. Instead, he tore away her stays and, in a heated rush, labored to unite as one with his lady love. Their lovemaking, both potent and sublime, energized with desire too long denied. Dreamily, the euphoric couple, oblivious to coming events, collapsed drenched in sweat from love's impulsive, unbridled passion.

A harsh and harried knock on the chamber door startled the slumbering couple. The sound was so rousing it might as well have been Gabriel's trumpet call to judgment. David, angered by the intrusion, growled, "Who dares insult the king's door with that wretched relentless pounding? Who else but my tardy time-reminder, protocol captain, and master of my wardrobe, Ebed—what say you?"

A muffled whimper escaped from unsure lips, "Yes, It is I, sire." Ebed pleaded, "Kind king, a thousand pardons for my frantic hammering. My light tapping seemed hollow, and I received no reply. The sun is about to set, and the great hall is well lighted. The marriage canopy has been hung and lies covered in garlands. All preparations are complete as you had commanded—even to say, mindfully surpassed. The festivity only awaits the groom and bride's well-anticipated presence. The fatted calf is steaming and dripping gravy. Your guests salivate at the aroma and begin to chafe from your absence. The high priest stands at the ready to perform the sealing ceremony."

"Very well, Ebed. I am awake and aware," David assured. "Be at peace, my faithful servant. You have not provoked me to punishment. Instead, I commend your devotion and service. It is time to make Uriah's orphaned widow legally my wife and to rest any malicious gossip. I need you to bring forth two basins of water and summon Almah, Lady Bathsheba's maidservant, without delay to these quarters. After that, I will retire to my adjoining closet and freshen up there. I need you to assure my guests and the high priest that I will be along presently." David, with a wry smile, tried to explain away his absence. "Tell them that I have recently consummated a delicate and most urgent affair of state."

CHAPTER FIFTY-SEVEN
Vows Pure and Profane

Freshly perfumed and adorned in his most stylish finery, David was wearing his simple gold crown that spoke of a complicated and powerful man. He confidently strode into the reception hall to "Ooohs" and "Aaahs" and a standing ovation.

David bowed, taking the praise in stride, from both sides of the marriage aisle. They all wished to congratulate the victorious homecoming hero and happily accept Bathsheba as the royal family's newest member. David gave the proper respect to his future in-laws: Ahithophel, his valued minister, and Eliam, his prospective father-in-law, saying, "Uriah the Hittite was a brave and mighty man of valor. But lest we forget, the sword of war devours one as well as another. He died in the service of God and Israel. A courageous and befitting ending for such a brave warrior."

After hugging his brothers and kissing his sisters, David spoke a heartfelt welcome: "Most honored guests, family, and friends, thank you for honoring my hasty and impulsive invitation. I can only confess that when love bites, and it leaves its mark, you have no choice but to follow your heart wherever it may take you.

"Thank you for sanctifying this joyous occasion, my dearest friend, Levite, and High Priest, Abiathar ben Ahimelech. Abiathar and I have known each other since the massacre at Nob. I will never forget his near-fatal escape with the Ephod of gold and finding me at Keilah right after the winning stampede of cattle. There is a special bond between the two of us, for we are more like brothers than the closest of friends. Lest in my excitement I am remiss, my esteemed father-in-law Eliam, the son of Ahithophel the Gilonite, one of my bodyguard Mighties. He has been with me since the fate-filled days at the cave of Adullam. Even most recently, at the victory at Rabbah, a man you can always count on in a fight, and his father, Ahithophel, my neighbor, and prime minister. Talking to Ahithophel is like talking to an oracle of God. Welcome—and welcome all."

David, pleased with his performance, continued, "We now have all the necessary elements to complete the marriage ritual, the chupah, or to say, the wedding canopy, and the kiddushin, or to say, the sanctification of a dedicated priest, and the minyan of ten righteous men. The only thing missing is the prospective bride. Some would say that she is the only essential part of the entire ceremony."

As the last chuckle faded from the amused audience, a vision of loveliness stood poised at the grand hall entrance. Bathsheba, her face aglow with health and vitality, the only evidence of her yet secret pregnancy. Her dress had a concealing and simple, understated elegance. Bathsheba's presence signaled for all to find their proper places in the holy observance. Eliam, her father, gallantly walked over to his daughter and escorted her to the wedding canopy. He remained at her side until traditionally giving the bride away to her new husband. David was flanked by his oldest brothers, Eliab, and Abinadab, fulfilling the required two witnesses. David then put on his Kitel, a shawl in remembrance of the mortality of his body. He then placed a cover over Bathsheba in memory of Isaac's chosen wife, Rebecca. The covering represents modesty and that the soul and character are more important than physical beauty, and a commitment from the groom to clothe and shelter his bride.

Abiathar, in his hand a goblet filled with red wine, began, "Blessed are You, our God, ruler of the world, Creator of the fruit of the vine.

"Blessed are You, Lord our God, Master of the Universe, Who has sanctified us with His commandments, and commanded us regarding forbidden unions, and Who forbad betrothed women to us, and permitted to us those married to us by canopy and sanctification. So praised are You, Lord, Who sanctifies His people Israel with the chupah and Kiddushin, or wedding."

David, well-practiced, as it was his eighth time under the huppah canopy, turned to Bathsheba and spoke, "Behold, you are consecrated to me with this ring according to the laws of Moses and Israel."

"With this ring, you are made holy to me, for I love you as my soul. You are now my wife." David placed it on her finger. It was now Bathsheba's turn in voicing her promise: "With this ring, you are made holy to me, for I love you as my soul. You are now my husband. The beloved is mine, and I am the beloved's."

Abiathar, standing beside David and Bathsheba, with a second goblet filled with wine, began the seven blessings of matrimony.

"Blessed are You, LORD, our God, sovereign of the universe, Creator of the vine-fruit.

"Blessed are You, LORD, our God, sovereign of the universe, who created everything for His Glory.

"Blessed are You, LORD, our God, sovereign of the universe, Creator of man.

"Blessed are You, LORD, our God, sovereign of the universe, Who created man in your image, fashioning perpetuated life. Blessed are You, LORD, Creator of man.

"The barrenness will indeed rejoice and be glad to gather in her children to herself joyfully (in haste). Blessed are You, LORD, Gladdener of Zion by way of her children.

"Loving companions will surely gladden as you gladdened your creations in the Garden of Eden in the east. Blessed are You, LORD, Gladdener of groom and bride.

"Blessed are You, LORD, our God, sovereign of the universe, Who created joy and gladness, groom and bride, mirth, song, delight and rejoicing, love and harmony and peace and companionship. Quickly, LORD our God, there should be heard in Judah's cities and the courtyards of Jerusalem the voice of joy, the voice of gladness, the voice of the groom, and the voice of the bride. The jubilant voices of grooms from the bridal canopy and young people from the feast of their singing. Blessed are You, LORD, Gladdener of the groom with the bride.

"That concludes the rite; who now stands before me is the one flesh of man and wife. I congratulate the groom, King of Israel, and the King of the Jews, and my very best wishes to the bride, the king's beloved consort, Bathsheba bat Eliam," Abiathar declared with heartfelt passion.

David turned and kissed his bride in an unseemly long and sensual embrace. Unable to contain himself, David announced to all present, "It is time for you, my honored guests, to partake of the fatted calf and for my new wife and me to depart and enjoy each other's company with some quiet time and knowing conversation. Enjoy the meal and the wine, and thank you for your prompt attendance that helped to make this night a memorable and holy occasion."

Without further ado, the love-hungry couple feverishly withdrew behind closed doors.

CHAPTER FIFTY-EIGHT
The Double-Edged Sword of a Prophet's Tongue

Nathan, chosen by God, gave all his heart and soul to the Lord's greater glory. Nathan had mentored under the guidance of the prophet Samuel.

As the fathering mouthpiece of God on earth, he is called upon when the still, small voice cannot penetrate the heart of the remorseless and unrepentant. A prophet's piercing words are needed to tingle the ears of the sinful.

It was the passing of a glorious time. David sat upon a throne that ruled over a vast dominion, the empire of Israel. He was married to his soulmate, who had just given birth to their love child, and just as the oracles had correctly predicted, a man child.

The King's Highway flowed with trade goods like a river of gold. Jerusalem flourished, becoming the center of all regional commerce, growing in stature and power.

Nathan flowed when he walked as if he carried the wind in his hair. In his hand, an imposing rod that was just the right length and girth to correct Israel's disobedient children. The prophet appeared bent from the weight of the world that rested on his broad shoulders. The mantle of righteousness is never an easy burden to carry.

Nathan entered the great hall, unannounced and unchallenged. No one in Israel dared to obstruct the progress of a prophet. Thoroughfares gave way, and crowds hastily parted at his unrelenting approach. The room brightened, and all went silent when Nathan crossed over the threshold.

In a festive mood and regaling in his banquet room, David celebrated another male heir that helped to ensure a long-lasting dynasty.

David directed his attention to Nathan. He warmly declared, "You honor us by your presence, mighty man of God. What brings you here, on this joyous occasion? Have you come to bless our newborn child?"

Nathan shook his head "No" and insisted, "There is a more pressing matter at hand. I have an urgent question that only you, the king, can answer."

David, intrigued, agreed. "Speak on, holy man."

Nathan lowered his voice and deepened his tone. "This is a private and delicate matter, sire, and for your notice only."

David announced to the celebrating court his obliged obedience to God's mouthpiece.

"It is needful for me to take my leave from these festivities and commune with Nathan in a private audience. So, the rest of the court, friends, family, and honored guests, please continue celebrating the glorious birth of our newest son. I will rejoin you in short order once the prophet has revealed his thoughts. You can expect my return to the merriment in due course."

David led Nathan to a private alcove at the end of a darkened corridor. He posted guards to secure the doors against spying eyes and pressing ears.

"We are quite alone, and we will not be disturbed; whenever you are ready, holy man," David uttered anxiously, his curiosity aroused.

Nathan took a deep breath and gathered in his wits, for the judgment of God—like Pharaoh's decree—would slip from the prince's own condemning lips.

"I require your ruling of judgment on a recent and troubling event that only you, David, king of Israel and the Jews, can lawfully pronounce."

Nathan set a trap for the self-conviction of words and deeds.

Nathan began, "There were two men in a bustling Israeli city; one rich and the other poor. The rich man had many flocks and herds, but the poor man had nothing, save one little ewe lamb, which he had bought with all the money he had. He nourished it and cared for it like it was one of his children. It grew up together with him and with his family. It ate his food, and drank of his cup, and lay on his heart, and was unto him as like a daughter. There came a traveler visiting the rich man, and by the law, he needed to entertain the stranger, for some have entertained angels unawares. Were we not guests of God in the desert and remain to this very day guests of God in the wilderness of life?"

David readily agreed, "Yes, yes—go on."

"Selfishly, the rich man did not take from his flocks or herds to feed the visitor in his charge. But instead, he cruelly took the poor man's one ewe lamb and prepared it for the foreigner to feast upon."

David's fury thundered against the rich man, and he said so to Nathan. "As the Lord lives, the man who has done this thing shall surely die for this outrage."

David then numbered the punishments that the rich man was to suffer to satisfy the cause of justice, saying, "He shall restore the lamb fourfold, because he did this thing, and because he had no pity."

Nathan, his eyes aflame, piercing to the very soul, announced, in no uncertain terms, "You are that man. So says the Lord God of Israel, "I anointed you king over Israel, and I delivered you out of the hand of Saul. I gave you your master's house and your master's wives into your heart and hand. I gave you the houses of Israel and Judah. If that had been too little, I would have given you more, even any such things that you needed or wanted. But instead, you have despised the commandment of the Lord, to do evil in His sight? You have killed Uriah the Hittite with treachery and have taken his wife for your own. You have slain him with the sword of the children of Ammon. You have thought to fool the children of men with cunning deceit, and you have thought to circumvent the judgment of God with your deception.

"Furthermore, the sword shall never depart from your house, and this is because you have loathed me and have taken the wife of Uriah the Hittite to be your wife. I will raise evil against you out of your own house. I will take your wives before your eyes and give them to your neighbor. He shall lie with your wives in the sight of the sun. I will do this thing before all Israel and in full daylight for what you did in secret shadows."

David, caught in the snare of his own making, sought mercy, saying, "I have sinned against the Lord."

Nathan relieved his morbid concern. "The Lord has put away your sin. You shalt not die.

"Through this deed, you have given great occasion to the enemies of the Lord to blaspheme—because of this child that is born to you this day, it shall surely die."

David, heartbroken and sullen, had no words left to say in his defense.

Nathan, having completed the Lord's bidding, departed back to his place.

The Lord then struck down the child that Uriah's wife bore unto David, and it was very sick.

Searching both high and low, Ebed finally located the grieving monarch on his knees and, ill at ease, seeking comfort in the shadows. Ebed pleaded, "Sire, the man-child born to you this day seems to be on the brink of destruction. The physicians have been alerted and are at the baby's side. Bathsheba has no ill effects, but she is beside herself at the baby's sudden illness."

David looked up from his misery and uttered, "Go, Ebed—dismiss the guests, and tell them that the baby is sick unto death; request their heartfelt prayers of intervention."

David sincerely begged God for the life of the child, saying, "Lord God, I have sinned a grievous evil in the taking of the life of Uriah the Hittite. I sought a man's life through conspiracy and deceit and then married his pregnant wife with my child in her belly. I have shamefully hidden the act with deception from man, and I believed even from You, my most omnipotent and all-knowing God, Adonai. For this, I am heartily sorry for offending thee. I beg for the life of an innocent if it is your will; I will accept your judgment."

David rent his garment and said, "Like Joshua, I will lay upon the earth and put dust in my hair, for I am lower than the dust, for even the dust will move by Your command."

Fasting, David went to the garden and fell to the earth on his face until evening.

The sunset was vivid, and the sundown meal was lavishly prepared, but David was noticeably absent. So finally, in desperation, the Elders of his house went to the garden and attempted to raise him from the rocky and unforgiving ground. They invited him to bread and get under cover, warning him of the desert night's raw blanketing cold. But he would have none of it and scolded, "Leave me alone, and do not interfere again with my act of contrition."

That first bone-chilling night, David's spirit was overflowing with menacing ghosts and stealthy goblins of regret. The king's sleep was erratic, and his rest evasive. The morning burst forth with warmth, and the reprieve from his misery was like a hug from a welcomed friend. Then, by midday, the sun turned into a punishing, scorching enemy. David's ruddy complexion blistered from the unrelenting desert heat. Elders and servants came forward with bread and water. They went so far as to scold the monarch for jeopardizing his health and, consequently, the health of the nation. David, clutching the dirt with his face pressed firmly to the earth, growled at any attempted rescue. He pleaded, "I have sinned a great sin against the Lord. I dedicate my pain and my penance to sway God's favor and spare my innocent newborn child. Be off with you before I scourge you."

David lay unmoving, sometimes crying and sometimes praying, dozing off in spurts and bouts. Scorpions, snakes, frogs, and ravens would occasionally investigate the strange warm-bodied creature anchored to their hunting ground.

The days slowly passed, and there was no rain to quench or soothe neither parched body nor lips. Instead, David's stiffness and pain increased, reaching a crescendo on the seventh day. A whole week of voluntary suffering had passed, and his endurance was at the breaking point, but had God heard his tormented plea?

CHAPTER FIFTY-NINE

Aftermath and Answers

The Lord answered David on that seventh day, through the lips of his servants, and one day before the child would have been named and circumcised.

All the servants of David feared to tell him of the child's passing.

They murmured, saying, "While the child was alive, he would not listen to our pleadings for his well-being. How now will he torture himself if we tell him that the child is dead?"

David could feel something was amiss. He confirmed his uneasiness when he sensed distraught servants whispering among themselves. He perceived that the child's fragile life had ended. To test the denial of his petition and his sickly, sinking feeling, David called out, demanding to know, "Is the child dead?" Sadly and, in a still, small voice, the lowliest servant acknowledged what was already felt, "Yes, lord, the child is no more."

Nodding in acceptance of God's will, the king arose from the earth, washed off the grime and grit of his ordeal, and changed his soil-encrusted robes. David anointed himself with the oil of gladness and came into the Lord's house and worshipped, saying,

"Have mercy upon me, O God, according to thy lovingkindness: according to the multitude of thy tender mercies blot out my transgressions. Wash me thoroughly from mine iniquity, and cleanse me from my sin. For I acknowledge my transgressions: and my sin is ever before me. Against You, and only You, have I sinned, and done this evil in thy sight: that You might be justified when You speak and be clear when You judge. Behold, I was shaped in iniquity, and in sin did my mother conceive me. Behold, you desire the truth in the inward parts—and in the hidden parts of the heart, You will make me know wisdom. Purge me with hyssop, and I shall be clean: wash me, and I shall be whiter than snow. Make me hear joy and happiness; that the bones which You have broken may rejoin and rejoice. Hide Your face from my sins and blot out all mine iniquities. Create in me a clean heart, O God, and renew a right spirit within me. Cast me not away from Your presence and take not Your holy spirit from me. Restore unto me the joy of Your salvation and uphold me with Your free spirit. Then will I teach transgressors your ways, and sinners shall convert unto You. Deliver me from bloodguiltiness, O God, the God of my salvation: and my tongue shall sing aloud of Your righteousness. O Lord, open my lips, and my mouth shall show forth Your praise. You desire not to sacrifice; else would I give it: You delight not in burnt offering.

"The sacrifices of God are a broken spirit: a broken and a contrite heart, O God, You will not despise. Do good in Your good pleasure unto Zion: build You the walls of Jerusalem. Then shall You be pleased with the sacrifices of righteousness, with burnt offering and whole burnt offering: then shall they offer bullocks upon thine altar."

Finishing his oblations, David filled with the spirit of God. But the natural man hungered for the life-sustaining staff of life. So, David returned to his house to the relief of all his ministers, elders, and servants.

Ebed, seeing the king, at once hurried to his side, fawning and bowing his sincere and unwavering adoration. Then, wasting not a moment, David demanded, "I starve; bring forth victuals, hot or cold, with bread and butter; raid the kitchen and empty the lauder."

A stream of food quickly appeared. David started to salivate before the first morsel passed his lips.

Unable to rein in his curiosity, Ebed dared to question a pressing puzzlement. He screwed up his courage and begged, "Sire—a thousand pardons, but I am confounded; I cannot find a reason for your odd conduct."

David, spiritually uplifted, and his hunger satisfied, pleasured himself with a satisfying burp and agreed to his manservant's inquiry. "Speak on, Ebed, if this will settle your restless mind."

"Sire, it is your behavior. First, you were unapproachable in that you fasted and wept and called upon God mightily while the child was still alive. But as soon as the child died, you rose from the ground and did eat. It seemed like you mourned when the child was breathing and, as a matter of course, accepted the child's death in passing."

David, a bit agitated, looked up and scolded, "If it were anyone else but you, Ebed, who would question the king in such a personal and private matter, the punishment for such disrespect would be severe. But the Lord has gifted me with discernment, and its value lies in the broadcast of His glory.

"While the child was alive, I will explain that I fasted and wept, for who can tell whether God will abide by my suffering and be gracious unto me and allow the child to live? But now that he is dead, for what reason should I fast? Can I bring him back again? At the appointed time, I shall go to him, but he shall not return to me."

Bathsheba's lament raced across David's head. Yet, all this time, was he so tediously involved with his selfish plea for mercy and too busy with a self-imposed penance to consider Bathsheba's dilemma.

David pondered: Was he an absentee landlord or a self-involved juvenile? Had he not felt Bathsheba's pain and suffering from the bone-crushing loss of a newborn child as well?

David rushed to her side to render aid and comfort as best he could muster.

A week had passed, and her delivery, thank God, was without incident or accident. Bathsheba's body was on the mend, but her soul had a lasting scar that she would carry forever.

David quietly entered their love nest and found Bathsheba seated by a window and staring out over a scenic landscape, deep in her thoughts of her adulterous affair and the aftermath of God's severe judgment. Would she ever be able to have a child or, hereafter, become useless and barren?

David cleared his throat as he quietly approached so as not to startle her soul-searching reflections. In her closeness, he rested his hand on her shoulders and said nothing but just reveled in the moment, the view, and her nearness. David mused for a strongman; she held the keys to paradise for a weak one, the gateway to Hades, but he loved her more than life itself.

After a time, she crooked her neck, touching his hand with her cheek, delighting in the comfort of his presence. Only then, and in the gentlest of tones, did David attempt a pale consolation.

"My dear wife, our trial is but a little while, and most often, people mistake God as cruel. But He is compelled by His own words to mete out divine justice. His way is to balance all of creation, for mercy cannot rob justice.

"We have felt the sting of the Master's judgment, and we are better for the experience. Thus, we perceive a curse, but it is often a blessing when seen through the eyes of eternity.

"Are we not better off for our suffering and seek God's glory with a greater conviction and diligence? Even darkly through a veil of tears, we mold ever so slightly in His likeness and image.

"Are we not gladdened to suffer guilt or innocence here and now in a life that is but the briefest of dreams? Or to endure the abandonment of an all-knowing God through the endless torment of the eternities?"

She rose, her soul touched and her exquisite pain ebbed to a dull ache. A calm, welcoming breeze drifted through the open window, soothing her troubled mind. A refreshing breath filled her chest, helping hope to expel despair.

David slid his hand behind her head and slowly pressed her face into his chest in an overwhelmingly manly embrace. They entwined, becoming as one and delightfully transported on the wings of love to their secret paradise. He gently placed her on a down-filled pillow and caressed her tender, milk-swollen breasts. Their lips refused to part even for a moment. Then, with fingers as light as feathers, he stroked her until chills brought on a shiver to her spine.

Their lovemaking was slow, caring, and tender; it was not like their usual heated and passion-filled romp. Instead, it was lovemaking as if it were for the very first time. The night's tender embraces turned into the cock's crow of a new day dawning. The lovers' eyes blinked open long before a sound was uttered, neither wanting to break the spell of their extended enchantment.

Bathsheba held herself tight against David's side and whispered, "I heard a still, small voice in the night—real or imagined, I know not. It said, 'I was with child, and it was a man child, and he would be beloved of the Lord, and a friend of God.'"

David sat up in a bolt and confirmed, "I heard the very same thing but thought I was dreaming.

"God's time is not our time, and God's thoughts are not our thoughts. He will reveal His secrets at the perfect time and not a moment before. We will have to wait upon God's next episode, chapter, and verse."

The end of the middle.

ABOUT THE AUTHOR

J oseph Ganci was born
in Beth-Israel Hospital
in Brooklyn, New York. He is
the firstborn so dedicated to
God by the laws of Israel. The
son of Joseph and RoseMary.
He is a Levite and an ordained
Highpriest. But remains a
passionate Italian. Joseph is a
Vietnam combat veteran and
an Honors society member. He currently resides in Houston,
Texas. He has fathered five daughters and has five grandchildren.

Request for Reviews Template

As you know, reviews are critical to book-publishing success, but you must ask for them! You may want to consider adding some variation of the text below to the back matter of your book:

I hope you enjoyed this book. Would you do me a favor?

Like all authors, I rely on online reviews to encourage future sales. Your opinion is invaluable. Would you take a few moments now to share your assessment of my book at the review site of your choice? Your opinion will help the book marketplace become more transparent and useful to all.

Thank you very much!

Joseph

Made in the USA
Coppell, TX
10 April 2024

31127540R00284